A Charlton Standard Catalogue

# BESWICK COLLECTABLES

## Ninth Edition

By
**John and Diana Callow**

and
**Frank Corley**

**W. K. Cross**
**Publisher**

*The Charlton Press*

**TORONTO, ONTARIO • PALM HARBOR, FLORIDA**

### Library and Archives Canada Cataloguing in Publication

Beswick collectables : a Charlton standard catalogue

Annual.
9th ed. -
Continues in part: Storybook figurines, Royal Doulton, Royal Albert, Beswick
ISSN 1714-8707
ISBN 0-88968-298-4 (9th ed.)

1. Beswick (Firm)--Catalogs.  2. Porcelain figures--Catalogs

NK4660.B47          738.8'2'029          C2005-901582-9

**Printed in Canada
in the Province of Ontario**

## EDITORIAL

Editor                              Jean Dale

Graphic Technician          Davina Rowan

## ACKNOWLEDGEMENTS

The Charlton Press wishes to thank those who have helped with the ninth edition of *Beswick Collectables, (A Charlton Standard Catalogue)*. The previous book, 8th edition *Storybook Figurines* was divided into two parts, with the Beswick items moving to this edition.

### Contributors to the Ninth Edition

The publisher would also like to thank the following individuals and companies who graciously supplied photographs or information or allowed us access to their collections for photographic purposes: **Ted Crooks**, Swansea, U.K.; **Ann Davidson**, Cupertino, Ca.; **Judy Tollefson**, Argyle, Texas, U.S.A.

## A SPECIAL NOTE TO COLLECTORS

We welcome and appreciate any comments or suggestions in regard to *Beswick Collectables*. If any errors or omissions come to your attention, please write to us, or if you would like to participate in pricing or supply previously unavailable data or information, please contact Jean Dale at (416) 488-1418, or e-mail us at chpress@charltonpress.com.

## DISCLAIMER

## The Charlton Press

**Editorial Office**
**P.O. Box 820, Station Willowdale B**
**North York, Ontario, M2K 2R1 Canada**
**Telephone (416) 488-1418 Fax: (416) 488-4656**
**Telephone (800) 442-6042 Fax: (800) 442-1542**
**www.charltonpress.com  e-mail: chpress@charltonpress.com**

# HOW TO USE THIS PRICE GUIDE

## THE PURPOSE

The ninth edition of what used to be *Storybook Figurines* is now *Beswick Collectables*. A book solely devoted to the products of the John Beswick Studio. In 2005 the Beswick brand was sold by Royal Doulton.

As with the other catalogues in Charlton's Beswick reference and pricing library, this publication has been designed to serve two specific purposes. First, to furnish the collector with accurate and detailed listings that provide the essential information needed to build a rewarding collection. Second, to provide collectors and dealers with current market prices for Beswick collectable figures.

## STYLES AND VERSIONS

**STYLES:** A change in style occurs when a major element of the design is altered or modified as a result of a deliberate mould change. An example of this is *The Duchess With Flowers* (style one) and *The Duchess With a Pie* (style two).

**VERSIONS:** Versions are modifications in a minor style element, such as the long ears becoming short ears on *Mr. Benjamin Bunny*.

**VARIATIONS:** A change in colour is a variation; for example, *Mr. Jeremy Fisher's* change in colourways from spotted to striped leggings.

## THE LISTINGS

The Beatrix Potter figures are arranged alphabetically, other models are numerical sequence. At the beginning of the Beatrix Potter listings are seven pages graphically outlining backstamp variations. Backstamps are illustrated for eleven major varieties covering over fifty years of production. In the Beatrix Potter pricing charts, the reader will see Beswick and Royal Albert model numbers, backstamp numbers and market prices.

All of the above listings include the modeller, where known, the name of the animal figure, designer, height, colour, date of issue, varieties and series.

# TABLE OF CONTENTS

# INTRODUCTION

The Company which was founded in 1894 by James Wright Beswick, and later after his death in 1920, traded as John Beswick, grew in an amazingly short space of time from a small acorn into a sturdy oak tree.

## The Acorn took root ...

J. W. Beswick

James Wright Beswick rapidly established his company after he acquired a lease on the Baltimore Works in Albion Street, Longton, Stoke-on-Trent in 1894. By 1898 two more premises were in operation, the Britannia Works in High Street, and the Works in Gold Street, both in Longton. After only four years, in March 1898, the firm J. W. Beswick was exhibiting at "The Furnishing Trades Exhibition and Market" at the Agricultural Hall, Islington, London. Fancy goods included vases, pots, figures, cheese stands and covers, and bread trays.

The figures mentioned above were probably the Staffordshire type mantle-piece ornaments in the shape of generals, gardeners, milkmaids, dogs etc., which had been popular fifty years before, and surprisingly for which there was still a demand.

Unfortunately, such items of early manufacture do not carry a backstamp or marking by which they could be recognized.

When James Wright Beswick died in 1920, at the age of seventy-five, the firm was taken over by his son John Beswick.

## The oak tree grows ...

As the 1930's approached the prices for wares from the Gold Street Factory in Longton continued to be aimed at a level to sell readily in the cheaper markets, while at the same time the quality of products was maintained or even improved. New designs and decorations were shown at the British Industries Fairs. These were less prosperous times and John Beswick turned his attention away from ornamental wares and increasingly to tableware.

By 1933, due to the many successful new lines being introduced, the Company was approached by G. Hardy and Co., of Nottingham, a firm of pottery distributors, who negotiated with John Beswick to have items produced to their own designs. These were originally marketed under the name

of "Trentham Art Ware", but later many pieces remained in production to be sold under the Beswick name.

Sadly John Beswick did not live to see the great growth of his father's Company and after a long illness died in October 1934. His son, John Ewart Beswick, or Mr Ewart as he was known, then became Chairman and Managing Director. Gilbert Beswick (Ewart's uncle) became sales director.

John Beswick

## The oak tree flourishes...

The years that followed were ones of great activity. The outbreak of war in 1939 coincided with what, at first sight, would seem to be a surprising and dramatic expansion in, and a change in the nature of, the products from the Beswick factory. The stimulus for all this activity was the need for Britain at that time to export in order to survive, and in the period to the end of 1945, around three hundred new shapes were added.

War-time controls imposed on the home market by the Board Trade, restricted domestic sales to everyday articles. With the European companies being prevented from exporting, Beswick seized their chance to expand their markets overseas.

Items which continued to be produced for export included novelties in the blue decoration No. 8700, and animal subjects. The first of the horses and foals for which Beswick was later to become world famous, also appeared during this time. By April 1941 it was reported that eighty per cent of their output was accounted for by export orders, The trade in novelties was extended to comical pieces, wild animals, dogs, cats etc. which replaced, in overseas markets, the type of wares previously available from German, Czech and Italian sources.

Twelve child figures were introduced in 1942 as the "Kindergarten series". The similarity of these to the corresponding Hummel figures is obvious. It appears that the man in charge of production of the Hummel figures in Germany had escaped to England just before the outbreak of war, and had approached Beswick with the idea of continuing production of some of the figures. Maybe we are biased, but we find the Beswick versions more appealing. After the war when production was resumed in Germany, these figures were withdrawn by Beswick, but possibly it was as late as 1952, since they appear in a catalogue for 1951.

The idea of introducing Beatrix Potter figures came from Mrs. Lucy Beswick, wife of Ewart Beswick, following a visit to the Lake District, where Beatrix Potter had written and illustrated her stories, and it was in 1947 that the first of the Beatrix Potter series, Jemima Puddleduck was modeled. Permission was sought from the publishers, Frederick Warne and Company, to reproduce Jemima and other characters, and by the end of the year a total of ten models had been produced, all modeled by Arthur Gredington.

John Ewart Beswick and Gilbert Beswick

In complete contrast, were the models based on an entirely new series of cartoon animal characters introduced under the direction of David Hand (formerly with Walt Disney), for the J. Arthur Rank Organisation. Eight of these were modeled in 1949 by Arthur Gredington, and were destined initially for the export market. The series was entitled "David Hand's Animaland", the first to be modelled being No. 1151 "Felia Cat". These delightful characters all appeared on film, and we expect many of you will remember seeing them at your local cinema.

Beswick had accepted submissions from four freelance lady modelers between 1935 and 1947, but their contribution formed only a small part of the models produced during this period. However in 1951 a young trainee modeller, Jan Granowska, arrived to work at Beswick from Eastern Europe. She designed models of figures and animals of a novel type which were quite a departure from the usual Beswick production at that time. Many people consider these models to be amongst the finest figures ever to have been produced, by Beswick. In her relatively short stay between 1951 and 1954 a surprising number of pieces were produced; young girls in national costume, fun animal pieces and Disney cartoon characters. Her name will be remembered along with the great modellers who contributed so much to the success of the company.

In addition to Arthur Gredington who was appointed the first full time modeller for Beswick in 1939, during the 1950s and 1960s Colin Melbourne, Graham Orwell and Graham Tongue (subsequently to become head modeller and later, Design Manager) were resident modellers. Albert Hallam,

who began at Beswick in 1926 as an apprentice mouldmaker, became responsible for development of new shapes and eventually worked in the modelling department.

### It was a busy time.

### The first blow to our sturdy oak...

Things changed dramatically when in 1969 Ewart Beswick wished to retire. He had no son, so there was not another generation to continue the family business and the company was sold to Royal Doulton. Though many of the staff remained to continue the traditions, in 1972 the first blow was struck when ornamental and table-ware were progressively discontinued and production of these items ceased by the end of 1973.

Various animal models and novelties continued to survive, but the soul began to disappear from this once family business.

The quality of goods later produced was never of the same high standard – just compare the attention to detail and the quality of painting between the early models and the later ones.

### The oak's declining years...

There was a last surge of new series produced in the 1990s e.g. English Country Folk, Little Loveables, Beswick Bears and the Pig Promenade.

Together with these series were the commissioned and limited edition series such as Top Cap, Footballing Felines and Sporting Characters from Sinclair's and The Flintstones, Tom, Jerry and Droopy plus Felix the Cat from U.K. International ceramics.

Despite these attempts the company was dying.

In 1989 even the name began to disappear when Beatrix Potter figures were transferred to the Royal Albert backstamp. This was later seen to have been a mistake, and models again appeared with a Beswick backstamp.

### Goodbye to our once sturdy and proud oak...

In 2002 the factory closed its doors for the last time and in 2003 the site was sold.

The World of Beswick was gone forever.

### 1894 – 2002
### ON A PERSONAL NOTE....

In 1985 when we founded The Beswick Collector's Circle we had no idea of the impact of our action and how dramatic the result would be in a relatively short time, less than ten years!

We found out that the world was full of collectors who shared our love of the products produced by John Beswick. The Circle was the first club to be formed and in the years that we were the Co-ordinators the membership grew and grew and reached as far as the U.S.A, Canada and Australia.

Our aim has always been to make people aware of the quality of the products. Good modelling and attention to detail in the painting produced quality models, which were and still are worthy of collecting – if you can find that elusive piece?

When we retired in 1995 a new Beswick Collector's Club was formed and is still in being today.

We continue to keep an eye on all things Beswick and recently were very saddened to learn that the models in the Beswick Museum had been sent to auction – surely it would have been a gesture of goodwill had Royal Doulton allowed them to be transferred to the Hanley Museum to form part of a permanent display of the area's history?

**Diana and John Callow.**

## BACKSTAMPS

Backstamp 1 Is the earliest printed stamp found.

1. Script Beswick Ware Made In England

2. Circular BESWICK ENGLAND

3. Oval BESWICK ENGLAND

4. Semi- circular BESWICK ENGLAND
impressed mark

5. BESWICK CREST ENGLAND

## SEALS

In addition to the first small gummed seal, green with gold lettering, an alternative oval style with gold lettering on a green background was used. The small green seal was replaced by the oval style.

1. Small gummed seal
(first style) green with gold lettering

2. Small gummed seal
(Second style) green with gold lettering

**Note:** Beswick backstamps give no indication of the year in which a model was issued.

The ones shown on this page were in common use over the years. Some series had their own special backstamps — most of them are shown in this book.

The smallest Beswick models, due to lack of space have no backstamp and some have just the word "England", in upper case letters.

# SECTION ONE

## STORYBOOK CHARACTERS

Alice, Style One, Model No. 2476

# ALICE IN WONDERLAND

**2476**
**ALICE™**
**Style One**

| | |
|---|---|
| Designer: | Albert Hallam and Graham Tongue |
| Height: | 4 ¾", 12.1 cm |
| Colour: | Dark blue dress, white apron with red trim |
| Finish: | Gloss |
| Issued: | 1973 - 1983 |
| Series: | Alice |

| Beswick Number | U.K. £ | U.S. $ | Price Can. $ | Aust. $ |
|---|---|---|---|---|
| 2476 | 135. | 250. | 315. | 335. |

**2477**
**WHITE RABBIT™**

| | |
|---|---|
| Designer: | Graham Tongue |
| Height: | 4 ¾", 12.1 cm |
| Colour: | White rabbit wearing a brown coat and yellow waistcoat |
| Finish: | Gloss |
| Issued: | 1973 - 1983 |
| Series: | Alice |

| Beswick Number | U.K. £ | U.S. $ | Price Can. $ | Aust. $ |
|---|---|---|---|---|
| 2477 | 150. | 275. | 350. | 375. |

### 2478
### MOCK TURTLE™

Designer: Graham Tongue
Height: 4 ¼", 10.8 cm
Colour: Browns and grey
Finish: Gloss
Issued: 1973 - 1983
Series: Alice

| Beswick Number | U.K. £ | U.S. $ | Price Can. $ | Aust. $ |
|---|---|---|---|---|
| 2478 | 125. | 225. | 275. | 300. |

### 2479
### MAD HATTER™

Designer: Albert Hallam
Height: 4 ¼", 10.8 cm
Colour: Burgundy coat, yellow and blue check trousers, yellow and red bow tie, grey hat
Finish: Gloss
Issued: 1973 - 1983
Series: Alice

| Beswick Number | U.K. £ | U.S. $ | Price Can. $ | Aust. $ |
|---|---|---|---|---|
| 2479 | 135. | 250. | 315. | 335. |

### 2480
### CHESHIRE CAT™
### Style One

Designer: Albert Hallam and Graham Tongue
Height: 1 ½", 3.8 cm
Colour: Tabby cat
Finish: Gloss
Issued: 1973 - 1982
Series: Alice

| Beswick Number | U.K. £ | U.S. $ | Price Can. $ | Aust. $ |
|---|---|---|---|---|
| 2480 | 185. | 335. | 425. | 450. |

**2485**
**GRYPHON**™

| | |
|---|---|
| Designer: | Albert Hallam |
| Height: | 3 ¼", 8.3 cm |
| Colour: | Browns and greens |
| Finish: | Gloss |
| Issued: | 1973 - 1983 |
| Series: | Alice |

| Beswick Number | U.K. £ | U.S. $ | Price Can. $ | Aust. $ |
|---|---|---|---|---|
| 2485 | 100. | 175. | 225. | 250. |

**2489**
**KING OF HEARTS**™

| | |
|---|---|
| Designer: | Graham Tongue |
| Height: | 3 ¾", 9.5 cm |
| Colour: | Burgundy, yellow, white, blue and green |
| Finish: | Gloss |
| Issued: | 1973 - 1983 |
| Series: | Alice |

| Beswick Number | U.K. £ | U.S. $ | Price Can. $ | Aust. $ |
|---|---|---|---|---|
| 2489 | 50. | 100. | 125. | 135. |

**2490**
**QUEEN OF HEARTS**™
**Style One**

| | |
|---|---|
| Designer: | Graham Tongue |
| Height: | 4", 10.1 cm |
| Colour: | Blue, green, yellow, white and burgundy |
| Finish: | Gloss |
| Issued: | 1973 - 1983 |
| Series: | Alice |

| Beswick Number | U.K. £ | U.S. $ | Price Can. $ | Aust. $ |
|---|---|---|---|---|
| 2490 | 50. | 100. | 125. | 135. |

### 2545
### DODO™

| | |
|---|---|
| Designer: | David Lyttleton |
| Height: | 4", 10.1 cm |
| Colour: | Browns and greens |
| Finish: | Gloss |
| Issued: | 1975 - 1983 |
| Series: | Alice |

| Beswick Number | U.K. £ | U.S. $ | Price Can. $ | Aust. $ |
|---|---|---|---|---|
| 2545 | 150. | 275. | 350. | 375. |

ALICE SERIES
"Dodo"
BESWICK
MADE IN ENGLAND
© ROYAL DOULTON TABLEWARE LTD 1975
REGISTRATION APPLIED FOR

### 2546
### FISH FOOTMAN™

| | |
|---|---|
| Designer: | David Lyttleton |
| Height: | 4 ¾", 14.6 cm |
| Colour: | Blue, gold, white and brown |
| Finish: | Gloss |
| Issued: | 1975 - 1983 |
| Series: | Alice |

| Beswick Number | U.K. £ | U.S. $ | Price Can. $ | Aust. $ |
|---|---|---|---|---|
| 2546 | 225. | 400. | 500. | 550. |

ALICE SERIES
"Fish Footman"
BESWICK
MADE IN ENGLAND
© ROYAL DOULTON TABLEWARE LTD 1975
REGISTRATION APPLIED FOR

### 2547
### FROG FOOTMAN™

| | |
|---|---|
| Designer: | David Lyttleton |
| Height: | 4 ¼", 10.8 cm |
| Colour: | Maroon jacket with yellow trim, blue trousers |
| Finish: | Gloss |
| Issued: | 1975 - 1983 |
| Series: | Alice |

| Beswick Number | U.K. £ | U.S. $ | Price Can. $ | Aust. $ |
|---|---|---|---|---|
| 2547 | 225. | 400. | 500. | 550. |

ALICE SERIES
"Frog Footman"
BESWICK
MADE IN ENGLAND
© ROYAL DOULTON TABLEWARE LTD 1975
REGISTRATION APPLIED FOR

**LC 1 (3859)**
**THE MAD HATTER'S TEA PARTY™**

| | |
|---|---|
| Modeller: | Martyn Alcock |
| Size: | 5" x 8 ½", 12.7 x 21.6 cm |
| Colour: | Green, yellow, red and blue |
| Issued: | 1998 in a limited edition of 1,998 |
| Finish: | Gloss |
| Series: | Alice's Adventures |
| Comm. by: | Lawleys by Post |

| Beswick Number | U.K. £ | U.S. $ | Price Can. $ | Aust. $ |
|---|---|---|---|---|
| LC 1 (3859) | 115. | 200. | 250. | 275. |

**LC 2 (3952)**
**ALICE™**
**Style Two**

| | |
|---|---|
| Modeller: | Martyn Alcock |
| Height: | 4 ½", 11.9 cm |
| Colour: | Pink and white |
| Finish: | Gloss |
| Issued: | 1999 in a limited edition of 2,500 |
| Series: | Alice's Adventures |
| Comm. by: | Lawleys by Post |

| Beswick Number | U.K. £ | U.S. $ | Price Can. $ | Aust. $ |
|---|---|---|---|---|
| LC 2 (3952) | 35. | 65. | 80. | 90. |

**Note:** Issued, numbered and sold as a pair with the Cheshire Cat.

**LC 3 (3953)**
**CHESHIRE CAT™**
**Style Two**

| | |
|---|---|
| Modeller: | Martyn Alcock |
| Height: | 3 ½", 8.9 cm |
| Colour: | Ginger striped cat |
| Finish: | Gloss |
| Issued: | 1999 in a limited edition of 2,500 |
| Series: | Alice's Adventures |
| Comm. by: | Lawleys by Post |

| Beswick Number | U.K. £ | U.S. $ | Price Can. $ | Aust. $ |
|---|---|---|---|---|
| LC 3 (3953) | 25. | 45. | 55. | 60. |

**Note:** Issued, numbered and sold as a pair with Alice.

## LC 4 (4007)
## Queen of Hearts™
## Style Two

| | |
|---|---|
| Modeller: | Martyn Alcock |
| Height: | 5 ¼", 13.3 cm |
| Colour: | Red, dark blue, yellow and pink |
| Finish: | Gloss |
| Issued: | 2000 in a limited edition of 2,500 |
| Series: | Alice's Adventures |
| Comm. by: | Lawleys by Post |

| Beswick Number | U.K. £ | U.S. $ | Price Can. $ | Aust. $ |
|---|---|---|---|---|
| LC 4 (4007) | 45. | 80. | 100. | 110. |

# BEATRIX POTTER FIGURINES
## NOTES ON COLLECTING BESWICK BEATRIX POTTER FIGURES

Collecting Beswick Beatrix Potter figures appeals to many collectors simply because the figurines are tangible representations of creatures previously known only through the exquisite illustrations that accompany the *Beatrix Potter Tales,* tales known the world over. But, for the passionate collector in pursuit of arcana, what adds to this appeal is Beswick-Royal Doulton's penchant for backstamp modifications, design and colour changes, and early discontinuations.

While presumably these steps improved production efficiency, quality control and the marketing process the unintended consequences were a large number of visible differences in the products as well as in their backstamps. Differences which are huge in the eyes of the collectors.

The first events involved modifications to the Beswick-England logo, a key feature of the original backstamp.

**Background:** The backstamps of the original ten Beswick Beatrix Potter figures, introduced in 1948, used gold lettering, a cursive script and a round Beswick-England logo, now known as the BP-1a, or, gold circle backstamp. This was followed in 1949 by the introduction of a gold parallel lines logo, the BP-1b, and in 1951 by a gold oval logo, the BP-2a. In retrospect, the reasons for the changes are easy to understand: the original gold circle was simply too large to fit on small base figures — first Tailor of Gloucester in 1949 and then Mrs. Rabbit in 1951. And, while the gold parallel lines modification might have been a suitable one-time exception for the Tailor of Gloucester only it was probably considered an unattractive choice for broader use. Hence, when Mrs. Rabbit came along only two years later and initial attempts to use the gold circle didn't work out Beswick acted to create the gold oval logo.

**Notes:**

* Tailor of Gloucester: an unknown, but very tiny quantity of pre-production prototypes were produced with the BP-1a gold circle backstamp before the BP-1b parallel lines replaced it; they are extremely rare.

* use of the BP-1b gold parallel lines backstamp was discontinued in 1951 after the BP-2a gold oval was created for Mrs. Rabbit.

* very small quantities of the BP-1b gold parallel lines backstamp were used on the original ten 1948 figures, probably in 1949, before the error was caught.

* Mrs. Rabbit: as in the case of Tailor of Gloucester, an unknown but small quantity first were produced with BP-1a gold circle backstamp; they are rare.

* in 1954, a third small base figure, Johnny Town-Mouse, was introduced using the BP-2a gold oval backstamp. A very tiny quantity of pre-production prototypes were produced with the BP-1a gold circle backstamp; they are extremely rare.

* the relative scarcity of BP-1a gold circle backstamps for the other three 1954 figures — Miss Moppet, Flopsy Mopsy & Cottontail and Foxy Whiskered Gentleman — suggests that the BP-2a gold oval also was used on some of them somewhat earlier than 1955.

* general use of the BP-2a gold oval for all standard range figures began in 1955.

* pre-production prototypes of the three figures introduced in 1955 — Tommy Brock, Duchess and Pigling Bland — have the BP-1a gold circle backstamp; they are extremely rare.

The next major event involved a series of design, colour and backstamp changes starting in 1969 and extending into 1975.

**Background:** When Beswick was acquired by Royal Doulton in 1969 it appears that the new owners did so with a plan of action in mind, a plan which had as much to do with contrasting corporate cultures, management styles and proclivities as with production line problems. This led to an extended transition period lasting until 1975 during which multiple changes to the various products took place. Although the version and variation changes were little noticed by customers and collectors at the time in later years they have had the effect of shifting the emphasis of serious Beswick Beatrix Potter collecting to versions and variations and away from the original figures. While it is probable that the versions, variations and associated backstamps of many of those thirty-seven original figures were consequences of well-intentioned management steps to improve the production side of things at the Beswick plant we don't have an insider's account of the rationales underlying those initiatives. However, the evidence that came off the production line in that period strongly suggests that major management decisions were made in several areas. though unevenly implemented:

Decision 1: do something about the untidy plethora of gold oval backstamps:

* it appears that Beswick had no standards applicable to backstamp format. The lettering was a hodge-podge of styles — large script, small script, large block letters, hand-made block letters, reverse slant script and two more styles of smaller size block letters. Moreover, the lettering styles were unique to the figures newly introduced in a particular year rather than to the whole range of production. Perhaps the most unusual examples involve the crude hand-made block lettering on the three 1955 figures, including Duchess (flowers).

* starting in 1973 a new, standardized brown-lettered backstamp was introduced. The initial version, the BP-3a, like all its gold predecessors, did not carry a copyright date.

* copyright dates were added to backstamps in 1975, a decision probably driven by legal considerations.

Decision 2: improve production efficiency for certain figures by simplifying their moulds:

* at the expense of a loss in aesthetic appeal Benjamin Bunny's shoes, Mrs. Rabbit's umbrella and Mr. Benjamin Bunny's pipe were moulded to their bodies to reduce susceptibility to damage in the production process and to improve yields; also, for similar reasons, the loop of Tommy Brock's spade handle was eliminated and a minor change made to the tip of the bottle in Appley Dapply's basket.

Decision 3: simplify the decoration process and "improve" the eye-appeal of certain figures by lightening colours and standardizing hand-painting:

* the colours of Squirrel Nutkin's coat and nut were lightened.

* Little Pig Robinson's striped tunic was replaced with a textured one.

* Pigling Bland's and Mr. Benjamin Bunny's dark maroon coats were changed to lilac.

* the top of Tabitha Twitchit's striped dress and the patterned dress of Goody Tiptoes became plain.

* Mr. Jackson's skin became brown instead of green.

* Timmy Tiptoes red jacket was changed to pink.

* the pattern of Mrs. Tiggy-Winkle's dress was changed from diagonals to squares.

* Mr. Jeremy Fisher's spotted legs became striped.

* Miss Moppet's mottled fur (sometimes subtly striped) became bold striped.

* a number of less obvious colour standardization changes were made to address long-time variations not much noticed by the collecting world until recent years:

* Timmy Tiptoes brown and grey fur variations became grey only;

* Other changes: Mrs. Rabbit (dress colours). Goody Tiptoes (dress colour, pattern and a longer base), Old Mr. Brown (colour of squirrel), Amiable Guinea Pig (jacket colour), Aunt Pettitoes (dress colour), Pig-Wig (skin and dress colours), and, Sir Isaac Newton (jacket colour, scarf pattern).

* in addition to the foregoing colour standardization changes, but several years later, the dark blues of the following figures were changed to a light blue: Peter Rabbit, Tom Kitten, The Old Woman Who Lived in a Shoe, Anna Maria, Cecily Parsley, and, Mrs. Flopsy Bunny. The reason for this is not clear but it has been suggested that it was done out of paint formulae considerations. But, curiously, the dark blue of Mrs. Rabbit and the Bunnies was not changed. Distressingly, all these light blues evolved into sickly pale blues during the Royal Albert period.

Decision 4: Special cases: Tommy Brock:

* for the fifteen or so years prior to the 1969-1975 transition period the size of TB's eye patches varied within fairly small limits — mainly half-way between the two now familiar extremes, and always curling inward towards the centre of his forehead. The patches had a somewhat feathery appearance and the background was an off-white; they all had open spade handles and carried the BP-2a gold oval backstamp.

* differences in eye patch size would probably have gone unnoticed except that very early during the transition, circa 1970, an initial decision was made to use a crisp, very small eye patch against a much whiter background

usually oriented in a straight line towards the ears in striking contrast to the original appearance. The new small eye patch and the open spade handle continued until the new BP-3a backstamp was introduced in 1973.

* backstamps were BP-2a gold oval until 1973 when the BP-3a brown backstamp was introduced.

* towards the end of the transition period, circa 1975, the present large eye patch was introduced. The two styles are readily recognizable by their exaggerated sizes — one small, one large — crisp rather than fuzzy appearance and the fact that they generally point in a straight line towards the ears — the large eye patches touch the ears — rather than curling inward towards the centre of the forehead.

* circa 1974 the closed spade handle was introduced. Initially, Tommy's gloved hand is on top, <u>covering the top of the handle</u>. This was later modified to the current version, which has the gloved hand grasping the shaft of the handle. The eye patches continued to be small and the backstamps were BP-3a and BP-3b.

* circa 1975, the dramatically large eye patch was introduced with the BP-3b backstamp.

* during the transition many of the changes in eye patch size, spade handle or backstamp overlapped. The result is multiple combinations of eye patch styles, spade handle configurations and backstamps.

Benjamin Bunny. In a similar manner to Tommy Brock, the metamorphoses of Benjamin Bunny are of particular collector interest:

* version 2: circa 1973 Benjamin's shoes were moulded to his body.

* version 3: circa 1975 the tips of Benjamin's ears were shortened to the edge of his tam.

* leaving aside the shoe and ear mould changes, the jacket colours of version 1 varied between light green and tan, but not brown.

* version 2 started out the same as version 1, but with the BP-3b backstamp the jacket became brown and the orange pompon with red stripes became a solid orange.

* the version 3 jacket started out brown and remained that colour until sometime in the Royal Albert period it became cream.

* In sum, three mould versions, three backstamp possibilities, two pompom colour schemes, and, three jacket colours all overlapping and occurring within a span of about three years! Are there exceptions to the above? Of course, that's what hand painting is all about!

**Overall comment:** It would appear that undertaking to tune-up the entire range of Beatrix Potter production, while probably successful from the Royal Doulton management point of view, resulted in some figures being produced in multiple versions, variations and backstamps before things settled down. In particular, for figures undergoing both a mould change and a decorating change synchronization of the two changes was not in the cards, The result is a collector's dream: multiple mould, colour, pattern and design changes with up to three backstamp possibilities — BP-2, BP-3a and BP-3b.

Other transition period changes:

* Mrs. Tiggy-Winkle: while there are dress pattern differences in the early years they seem minor and insufficient to justify a v1/v2 distinction.

* Timmy Willie: the multicoloured base on some of the early figures — mainly BP-1's — is very attractive and is an example of desirable decorator discretion. The multicoloured base variation is a must for the serious collector!

* Sally Henny Penny: some of the BP-3a's and early BP-3b's have red hearts rather than red checks on the breast feathers, and a tiny red tongue in an open mouth. Note: the open mouth appears to be a matter of whether the mould used was new and clean or clogged from repeated use; in any event, there are definitely open mouth versions.

* Louise Irvine B1 and B3 backstamps: when brown backstamps were introduced in 1973 the Beswick designers of the five latest figures at that time — Appley Dapply, Pickles, Pig-Wig, Mr. Alderman Ptolemy and Sir Isaac Newton — had apparently anticipated the change over and had produced slightly different variations of the new brown backstamp design. Backstamps for the first three figures were similar to the new design in all respects except that the figure names are all in capital letters; this anomaly, Irvine's B1 category, applies to all of the no copyright date figures (BP-3a's) as well as some copyright date figures (BP-3b's). The last two figures also used the new brown lettering format except the the words "Made in England" are used vice the single word "England"; this is Irvine's B3 category and again the anomaly applies to both no copyright date and copyright date versions. The B1/B3 anomalies disappeared sometime after 1975.

**Discontinuations:**      Nine of the original 73 Beswick figures were discontinued prior to the 1989 shift to the Royal Albert backstamp and three more shortly thereafter. Presumably marketing reasons were the main factor.

* Duchess (flowers), 1955-1967; the first figure discontinued is rare and hard to come by.

* from 1982 to 1984 an additional eight figures were discontinued after varying periods of production. Although some are scarce none of the eight are rare: Anna Maria 1963-1983; Amiable Guinea Pig 1967-1983; Pickles 1971-1982; Pig-Wig 1972-1982; Sir Isaac Newton 1973-1984; Simpkin 1975-1983; Ginger 1976-1982; Duchess (pie) 1978-1982.

* three additional figures — Thomasina Tittlemouse 1981-1989, Susan 1983- 1989 and Old Mr. Pricklepin 1983-1989 — apparently were scheduled to be discontinued prior to the Royal Albert backstamp change-over. However, small quantities still in production instead received the BP-6a Royal Albert backstamp. All are rare, with Susan being more so.

# SCARCEST BESWICK/ROYAL ALBERT
# BEATRIX POTTER FIGURES AND BACKSTAMPS

## Relative Scarcity Lists of Beswick and Royal Albert Beatrix Potter Figures, Versions, Variations and Backstamps

In the absence of actual production data scarcity rankings are based on years of production only. But, actual production depended on sales, some figures were more susceptible to damage than others and over time older figures simply tended to disappear beyond the reach of collectors.

To arrive at a comfortable perspective on scarcity and value of Beswick/Royal Albert Beatrix Potter figures a collector needs to have a feel for the relative numbers of each figure, version, variation and backstamps produced. In general, this means how long each was in production — years in the case of most figures, versions and variations but for backstamps sometimes only days or months.

The lists which follow list years-in-production broken down not only by figure, version and variation but also by backstamp. Caveat: Years-in-production does not mean that the same length of time in production for different figures resulted in equal numbers of figures produced — some were much more popular than others (which is why others were discontinued early).

Until eBay, collectors searching for items in various secondary markets saw scarcity as a reflection of what appeared in those markets they favoured, with the number of a particular figure likely to appear at a particular time related, in a broad sense, to the actual number originally produced. Now, eBay and other internet auction sites have vastly increased the number and variety of figures available on the secondary market by matching up the relatively limited pool of collectors with a vastly increased quantity of available figures, figures that have been pulled out of attics, basements, closets, shoe boxes, etc., figures that otherwise would have remained unavailable to collectors. Moreover, assuming willing-buyer, willing-seller transactions are the final arbiter of true value, tracking internet auctions can provide a good indication of a figure's current value.

Other considerations:

Different collectors collect different parts of the Beswick figure/version/variation/backstamp spectrum. That is, many Beswick Beatrix Potter collectors collect only a portion of the figures available, or, ignore the different versions, variations and backstamps.

Overlapping collector communities distort availability of certain type figures. For example, cat collectors search out Ginger and Simpkin, mouse collectors search out Anna Maria and rabbit collectors collect Peter, Benjamin etc. — all to the exclusion of the full range of Beatrix Potter figures.

Version/variation scarcity:

The appeal and collectability of individual versions or variations of multiple version/variation figures is related to unique discernable differences — something that can be seen by a viewer. Thus, for example, a version two or version three Benjamin Bunny is collectable in its own right because the differences can be seen.

Backstamp scarcity:

Since different backstamps can be detected only through handling, the appeal of a figure having a short run with a particular backstamp tends to be esoteric and limited to a much smaller segment of the collector community. Nonetheless, backstamps, particularly the first backstamp used on a figure/version/variation, are highly collectable. In particular, the super-rare backstamps are in a class by themselves when it comes to value, although, there are fewer collectors willing to pay the price their pure scarcity might otherwise command.

## Category I: Rare figures (and versions/variations)

There are only four truly scarce figures, or, versions/variations thereof: Tommy Brock, handle out, large eye patch; Tommy Brock, hidden handle, small eye patch; Duchess (flowers); and, Mr. Benjamin Bunny, pipe out, lilac jacket. Generally, figures produced for a year or more are not truly scarce, While some may appear to be scarce at a particular time — and often rather pricey — they usually are available on eBay on a fairly regular basis, given a bit of patience.

### Original Beswick figures:

| Figure | Version/Variation | | Years in production |
|---|---|---|---|
| Mr. Benjamin Bunny | v 1b | pipe out, lilac jacket | extremely rare |
| Tommy Brock | Ver 1, var 3 | handle out, large eye | rare |
| Tommy Brock | Ver 2, var 2 | hidden handle, small eye | scarce |
| Duchess (flowers) | | | scarce |
| Mr. Jackson | v 1 | green frog | 1 |
| Mr. Benjamin Bunny | v 2a | pipe in, maroon jacket | 2 |
| Benjamin Bunny | v 2 | shoes in, ears out | 2 |
| Tommy Brock | Ver 3, var 2 | handle in, small eye | 2 |
| Duchess (pie) | | | 4 |

### Original new Beswick (BP-10 and BP-11) figures:

| Figure | Version/Variation | | Years in Production | |
|---|---|---|---|---|
| Jeremy Fisher Catches a Fish | v 1 | (full vee cut out) | >0 | |
| Two Gentlemen Rabbits | | | 1 | |
| Mrs. Tiggy-Winkle Buys Provisions | | | 1 | |
| Head Gardener | | | 1 | |
| Peter Rabbit Gardening | | | >1 | |
| Hunca Munca with Pan | | | 2 | |
| Peter Rabbit Digging | | | 2 | |
| Little Pig Robinson | P5104 v2 | (textured) | >2 | months* |
| Rebeccah Puddle-Duck | P5584 | | >2 | months* |
| Mr. Benjamin Bunny | P5647 v2b | (pipe in, lilac jacket) | >2 | months* |
| Hunca Munca Sweeping | P5940 | | >2 | months* |

\* Technically new figures but in fact simply 2002 reissues of old figures with new "P" numbers and BP-11a backstamps:

## Category II: Rare backstamps

There are a number of exceptionally scarce backstamps:

### BP-1a (gold circle) backstamps:

| Figure | Version/Variation | | Years in Production | |
|---|---|---|---|---|
| Tailor of Gloucester | | | * | handful |
| Johnny Town-Mouse | | | * | handful |
| Duchess (with flowers) | | | | handful |
| Tommy Brock | V 1 and V 2 | | | handful |
| Pigling Bland | V 1 | | | handful |
| Mrs. Rabbit | V 1 | | * | rare |
| Miss Moppet | V 1 and V 2 | | 1 | very scarce |
| Flopsy, Mopsy & Cottontail | | | 1 | very scarce |
| Foxy Whiskered Gentleman | | | 1 | very scarce |

* Difficulties with fitting the gold circle on small base figures first surfaced in 1949 with Tailor of Gloucester and led to the ultra small-type BP-1b gold parallel lines backstamp. A similar problem arose in 1951 with the introduction of Mrs. Rabbit, which led to the so-called "flattened circle" (oval) modification of the gold circle. In 1955 this special oval backstamp, the BP-2 became standard. Another small base figure, Johnny Town-Mouse, apparently began using the gold oval soon after its introduction in 1954; its gold circle is very rare.

## BP-1b (gold parallel lines) backstamps:

| Figure | Version/Variation | Years in Production | |
|---|---|---|---|
| Jemima Puddle-Duck | | * | rare |
| Peter Rabbit | V 1 | * | rare |
| Tom Kitten | V 1 | * | rare |
| Timmy Tiptoes | V 1 | * | rare |
| Little Pig Robinson | V 1 | * | rare |
| Benjamin Bunny | V 1 | * | rare |
| Samuel Whiskers | | * | rare |
| Tailor of Gloucester | | 2 | scarce |

* The BP-1b backstamp, intended only for the small base Tailor of Gloucester, was used briefly in error in early 1949 on most of the ten original figures.

## BP-2a (gold oval) backstamps:

| Figure | Version/Variation | Years in Production |
|---|---|---|
| Pig-Wig | | handful |
| Benjamin Bunny | V 2 | very rare |

## BP-2b (gold-brown transition) backstamps:

| Figure | Version/Variation | | Years in Production |
|---|---|---|---|
| Peter Rabbit | V 1 | BP-2b | scarce |
| Timmy Tiptoes | V 1 | BP-2b | scarce |
| Squirrel Nutkin | V 1 | BP-2b | scarce |
| Mrs. Tittlemouse | V 1 | BP-2b | scarce |
| Flopsy, Mopsy and Cottontail | | BP-2b | scarce |
| Mr. Benjamin Bunny | Version 2, variation 2 | BP-2b | scarce |

## BP-3a (brown Beswick, no copyright date) backstamps:

| Figure | Version/Variation | Years in Production |
|---|---|---|
| Mr. Benjamin Bunny | Version 2, variation 2 | may not exist |
| Sally Henny Penny | | 1 |

## BP-3c (no 's after Beatrix Potter) backstamps:

| Figure | Version/Variation | Years in Production |
|---|---|---|
| Johnny Town-Mouse with Bag | | may not exist |

## BP-4 (John Beswick signature) backstamps:

| Figure | Version/Variation | Years in Production | |
|---|---|---|---|
| Samuel Whiskers | | | handful |
| Little Black Rabbit | | | handful |
| Mr. Jeremy Fisher Digging | | 1 | scarce |
| Mr. Tod | | 1 | scarce |
| Johnny Town-Mouse with Bag | | 1 | scarce |

## BP-5 (gold backstamp Royal Albert) backstamps:

| Figure | Version/Variation | Years in Production | |
|---|---|---|---|
| Jemima Puddle-Duck | | 1 | scarce |
| Peter Rabbit | V 2 | 1 | scarce |
| Benjamin Bunny | V 3 | 1 | scarce |
| Hunca Munca | | 1 | scarce |
| Flopsy, Mopsy and Cottontail | | 1 | scarce |
| Mrs. Rabbit and Bunnies | | 1 | scarce |

## BP-6a (brown Royal Albert) backstamps:

| Figure | Version/Variation | Years Produced |
|---|---|---|
| Susan | | handful |
| Thomasina Tittlemouse | | rare |
| Old Mr. Pricklepin | | rare |

## BP-8a (Beswick Ware) backstamps:

| Figure | Version/Variation | Years in Production |
|---|---|---|
| Jemima and Her Ducklings | | handful |
| Mrs. Tiggy-Winkle Washing | | scarce ~ 1700 |

## BP-10 series (new Beswick) backstamps (originally old Beswick or Royal Albert):

| Figure | Version/Variation | | Years in Production | |
|---|---|---|---|---|
| Peter Ate a Radish | | BP-10b | >0 | may not exist |
| Mrs. Flopsy Bunny | | BP-10b | 1 | |
| Pigling Bland | V 2 | BP-10c | 1 | |
| And This Pig Had None | | BP-10a | 6 | |
| Benjamin Ate a Lettuce Leaf | | BP-10a | 6 | |
| Peter and the Red Pocket Handkerchief | | BP-10a | 8 | |
| Mrs. Rabbit Cooking | | BP-10b | 8 | |
| Tom Kitten | V 2 | BP-10c | 12 | |
| Old Mr. Brown | | BP-10a | 12 | |
| Jemima Puddle-Duck & Foxy Whiskered Gentleman | | BP-10a | 12 | |
| Peter with Daffodils | | BP-10b | 12 | |

# PRICE RANGES OF THE SUPER RARE

## Category I: Super Rare Figures

| Figure | Version/ Variation | Back Stamp | Years Produced | Price Range |
|---|---|---|---|---|
| Mr. Benjamin Bunny | Version 1, Variation 2 | BP-3a | extremely rare | $3500-5000 |
| Duchess (flowers) | | BP-2a | 13 - scarce | $2500-3500 |
| Tommy Brock | Version 1, Variation 3 | BP-2a/BP-3a | rare | $1500-2,500 |
| Tommy Brock | Version 2, Variation 2 | BP-3a | rare | $1000-1500 |

## Category II: Super Rare Backstamps

| Figure | Version/ Variation | Back Stamp | Years Produced | Price Range |
|---|---|---|---|---|
| Tailor of Gloucester | | BP-1a | <1* (handful) | $5000 and up |
| Johnny Town-Mouse | | BP-1a | <1* (handful) | $5000 and up |
| Duchess (flowers) | | BP-1a | <1 (handful) | $6500-9500 |
| Pigling Bland | V 1 | Bp-1a | <1 (handful) | $5000-7000 |
| Tommy Brock | V 1 | BP-1a | <1 (handful) | $5000-7000 |
| Mrs. Rabbit | V 1 | BP-1a | <1* (rare) | $1500-2500 |
| Miss Moppet | V 1/V 2 | BP-1a | 1 (very scarce) | $600-1000 |
| Flopsy, Mopsy & Cottontail | | BP-1a | 1 (very scarce) | $600-1000 |
| Foxy Whiskered Gentleman | | BP-1a | 1 (very scarce) | $600-1000 |

* Difficulties with fitting the BP-1a gold circle on small base figures first surfaced in 1949 with Tailor of Gloucester and led to the BP-1b gold parallel lines design. A similar problem in 1951 with Mrs. Rabbit led to the BP-2a gold oval modification; at the same time, use of the BP-1b on Tailor of Gloucester was discontinued in favour of the new design. In 1954 another new small base figure, Johnny Town-Mouse, began using the new oval design very soon after being introduced with the gold circle; in 1955 the oval BP-2 became standard for all figures.

| Figure | Version/ Variation | Back Stamp | Years Produced | Price Range |
|---|---|---|---|---|
| Tailor of Gloucester | | BP-1b | 2 (scarce) | $650-800 |
| Jemima Puddle-Duck | | BP-1b | * (rare) | $1500-2500 |
| Peter Rabbit | V 1 | BP-1b | * (rare) | $1500-2500 |
| Tom Kitten | V 1 | BP-1b | * (rare) | $1500-2500 |
| Timmy Tiptoes | V 1 | BP-1b | * (rare) | $1500-2500 |
| Little Pig Robinson | V 1 | BP-1b | * (rare) | $1500-2500 |
| Benjamin Bunny | V 1 | BP-1b | * (rare) | $1500-2500 |
| Samuel Whiskers | | BP-1b | * (rare) | $1500-2500 |

*very small number used in error, probably in 1949; there may be several other figures.

| Figure | Version/ Variation | Back Stamp | Years Produced | Price Range |
|---|---|---|---|---|
| Pig-Wig | | BP-2a | <1 (handful) | $5000-7000 |
| Benjamin Bunny | V 2 | BP-2a | <1 (very rare) | $2500-3500 |

## Super Rare Backstamps — continued

| Figures | Version/ Variation | Back Stamp | Years Produced | Price Range |
|---|---|---|---|---|
| Peter Rabbit | V 1 | BP-2b | handful | $1000-1500 |
| Timmy Tiptoes | V 1 | BP-2b | handful | $1000-1500 |
| Squirrel Nutkin | V 1 | BP-2b | handful | $1000-1500 |
| Mrs. Tittlemouse | V 1 | BP-2b | handful | $1000-1500 |
| Flopsy, Mopsy & Cottontail | | BP-2b | handful | $1000-1500 |
| Mr. Benjamin Bunny | Vers 2, Var 2 | BP-2b | handful | $1000-1500 |
| Mr. Benjamin Bunny | Ver 2, Var 2 | BP-3a | may not exist | $ 750-1500 |
| Johnny Town-Mouse with Bag | | BP-3c | may not exist | $3500-5000 |
| Samuel Whiskers | | BP-4 | handful | $1500-2000 |
| Little Black Rabbit | | BP-4 | handful | $1500-2000 |
| Susan | | BP-6a | handful | $3500-5000 |
| Thomasina Tittlemouse | | BP-6a | rare | $1000-1500 |
| Old Mr. Pricklepin | | BP-6a | rare | $1500-2500 |
| Jemima and Her Ducklings | | BP-8a | handful | $1500-2500 |
| Peter Ate a Radish | | BP-10b | *may not exist | $2500-3000 |
| Mrs. Flopsy Bunny | | BP-10b | 1 month | $300-500 |
| Pigling Bland | V 2 | BP-10c | 1 month | $300-500 |

*While Beswick reported a BP-10b backstamp of Peter Ate a Radish in 1998 (and released a photograph), it is unclear if any figures with this backstamp were released.

# RELATIVE SCARCITY INDEX FOR BESWICK BEATRIX POTTER FIGURES (1948-1988)

This index is based on the approximate number of production years of each figure by backstamp, and by variety where applicable.

In the real world, actual scarcity is a simple reflection of what is appearing in various markets at a particular time. However, the numbers of a particular figure likely to appear in a particular secondary market is related, in a broad sense, to the actual numbers produced, and, the geographical distribution when initially marketed. Of course, the reality is that none of this information is available. Also, figures which have been discontinued, probably were discontinued because they were not successful in the marketplace - meaning that a years worth of production of Duchess with Flowers is probably not comparable to a years production of, say, Peter Rabbit. Nonetheless, the intent of this index is to use the estimated years of production as a rough measure of the number of a particular figure/variety that exist - in a global sense.

| Name of Figure | Beswick Number | Gold Circle BP-1a | Parallel Lines BP-1b | Gold Oval BP-2a | Trans-ition BP-2b | Brown Line | | | Sig'n BP-4 | Total Beswick |
|---|---|---|---|---|---|---|---|---|---|---|
| | | | | | | BP-3a | 3b | 3c | | |
| **1948** | | | | | | | | | | |
| Jemima Puddle-Duck | P1092 | 7 | * | 18 | | 2 | 11 | 2 | 1 | 41 |
| Peter Rabbit | P1098/1 | 7 | * | 18 | <1 | 2 | 5 | | | 32 |
| | P1098/2 | | | | | | 6 | 2 | 1 | 9 |
| Tom Kitten | P1100/1 | 7 | * | 18 | | 2 | 5 | | | 32 |
| | P1100/2 | | | | | | 6 | 2 | 1 | 9 |
| Timmy Tiptoes | P1101-1 | 7 | * | 18 | <1 | 2 | 5 | | | 32 |
| | P1101/2 | | | | | | 6 | 3 | | 9 |
| Squirrel Nutkin | P1102/1 | 7 | | 18 | <1 | 2 | 5 | | | 32 |
| | P1102/2 | | | | | | 6 | 3 | | 9 |
| Mrs. Tittlemouse | P1103 | 7 | * | 18 | <1 | 2 | 11 | 3 | | 41 |
| Little Pig Robinson | P1104/1 | 7 | * | 18 | | 2 | 1 | | | 28 |
| | P1104/2 | | | | | | 11 | 3 | | 14 |
| Benjamin Bunny | P1105/1 | 7 | * | 18 | | 2 | 1 | | | 28 |
| | P1105/2 | | | 1 | | 2 | 1 | | | 4 |
| | P1105/3 | | | | | | 11 | 2 | 1 | 14 |
| Samuel Whiskers | P1106 | 7 | * | 18 | | 2 | 11 | 2 | 1 | 41 |
| Mrs. Tiggy-Winkle | P1107/1 | 7 | * | 18 | | 2 | | | | 27 |
| | P1107/2 | | | 1 | | 2 | 11 | 2 | 1 | 17 |

* When the BP-1b was introduced in 1949 for Tailor of Gloucester an apparent production line error resulted in use of the new BP-1b backstamp being used on miniscule quantities of these figures before the error was corrected; the error may have involved all ten of the 1948 figures plus Timmy Willie (1949).

| Name of Figure | Beswick Number | Gold Circle BP-1a | Parallel Lines BP-1b | Gold Oval BP-2a | Transition BP-2b | Brown Line BP-3a | - 3b | - 3c | Sig'n BP-4 | Total Beswick |
|---|---|---|---|---|---|---|---|---|---|---|
| **1949** | | | | | | | | | | |
| Tailor of Gloucester | P1108 | * | >2 | 22 | | 2 | 11 | 2 | 1 | 40 |
| Timmy Willie | P1109 | 6 | | 18 | | 2 | 11 | 2 | 1 | 40 |
| **1950** | | | | | | | | | | |
| Mr. Jeremy Fisher | P1157/1 | 5 | | 18 | | 2 | | | | 25 |
| | P1157/2 | 1 | | | | | 11 | 3 | | 15 |
| Lady Mouse | P1183 | 5 | | 18 | | 2 | 11 | 3 | | |
| **1951** | | | | | | | | | | |
| Hunca Munca | P1198 | 4 | | 18 | | 2 | 11 | 2 | 1 | 38 |
| Ribby | P1199 | 4 | | 18 | | 2 | 11 | 3 | | 38 |
| Mrs. Rabbit | P1200/1 | * | | 21 | | 2 | | | | 24 |
| | P1200/2 | | | | | | 11 | 2 | 1 | 14 |
| **1954** | | | | | | | | | | |
| Flopsy, Mopsy and Cottontail | P1274 | 1 | | 18 | <1 | 2 | 11 | 2 | 1 | 35 |
| Miss Moppet | P1275/1 | 1 | | 18 | | 22 | 4 | | | 25 |
| | P1275/2 | | | | | | 8 | 2 | | 11 |
| Johnny Town-Mouse | P1276 | * | | 18 | | 2 | 11 | 3 | | 35 |
| Foxy Whiskered Gentleman | P1277 | 1 | | 18 | | 2 | 11 | 2 | 1 | 35 |
| **1955** | | | | | | | | | | |
| Tommy Brock | P1348/1 (1-1) | ** | | 18 | | 1 | | | | 19 |
| | P1348/2 (1-2) | | | 2 | | 2 | | | | 4 |
| | P1348/3 (1-3) | | | | | 1 | 1 | | | 2 |
| | P1348/4 (2-2) | | | | | 1 | | | | 1 |
| | P1348/5 (3-2) | | | | | 1 | 2 | | | 3 |
| | P1348/6 (3-3) | | | | | | 11 | 2 | 1 | 14 |
| Duchess (With Flowers) | P1355 | ** | | 13 | | | | | | 13 |
| Pigling Bland | P1365/1 | ** | | 18 | | 2 | 1 | | | 21 |
| | P1365/2 | | | | | | 11 | 3 | | 14 |

* Note 1: Minuscule pre-production quantities. Tailor of Gloucester was shifted to the BP-1b on introduction and in 1951 to the BP-2a; both Mrs. Rabbit and Johnny Town-Mouse were shifted to the BP-2a backstamp shortly after introduction — each due to their small bases.

** Note 2: Minuscule quantities; all three figures had small pre-production quantities produced with the BP-1a gold circle backstamp in 1954 but were introduced with the new BP-2a gold oval backstamp when regular production began in 1955.

| Name of Figure | Beswick Number | Gold Circle BP-1a | Parallel Lines BP-1b | Gold Oval BP-2a | Trans-ition BP-2b | Brown Line BP-3a - 3b - 3c | | | Sig'n BP-4 | Total Beswick |
|---|---|---|---|---|---|---|---|---|---|---|
| **1959** | | | | | | | | | | |
| The Old Woman Who Lived in a Shoe | P1545 dk bl | | | 14 | | 2 | | | | **16** |
| | P1545 lt bl | | | | | | 11 | 3 | | **14** |
| **1961** | | | | | | | | | | |
| Goody Tiptoes | P1675 | | | 12 | | 2 | 11 | 3 | | **28** |
| Tabitha Twitchit | P1676/1 | | | 12 | | 2 | | | | **14** |
| | P1676/2 | | | | | | 11 | 3 | | **14** |
| **1963** | | | | | | | | | | |
| Old Mr. Brown | P1796 | | | 10 | | 2 | 11 | 3 | | **26** |
| Anna Maria | P1851 | | | 10 | | 2 | 9 | | | **21** |
| **1965** | | | | | | | | | | |
| Mr. Benjamin Bunny | P1940/1 | | | 8 | <1 | 1 | | | | **9** |
| | P1940/2 | dark jacket | | | | 1 | 1 | | | **2** |
| | | light jacket | | | <1 | <1 | 11 | 2 | 1 | **14** |
| Cecily Parsley | P1941/1 | | | 8 | | 2 | 11 | | | **21** |
| | P1941/2 | | | | | | | 3 | | **3** |
| Mrs. Flopsy Bunny | P1942 | dark blue | | 8 | | 2 | | | | **10** |
| | P1942 | light blue | | | | | 11 | 2 | 1 | **14** |
| **1967** | | | | | | | | | | |
| Amiable Guinea Pig | P2061 | | | 6 | | 2 | 9 | | | **17** |
| **1970** | | | | | | | | | | |
| Aunt Pettitoes | P2276 | | | 3 | | 2 | 11 | 3 | | **19** |
| Cousin Ribby | P2284 | | | 3 | | 2 | 11 | 3 | | **19** |
| **1971** | | | | | | | | | | |
| Appley Dapply | P2333/1 | | | 2 | | 2 | 1 | | | **5** |
| | P2333/2 | | | | | <1 | 11 | 3 | | **14** |
| Pickles | P2334 | | | 2 | | 2 | 8 | | | **12** |
| **1972** | | | | | | | | | | |
| Pig-Wig | P2381 | | | * | | 2 | 8 | | | **<10** |

* Note: Minuscule quantity; a small pre-production quantity was produced with the BP-2a gold oval backstamp in 1972; when regular production began in 1973 the BP-3a brown (no date) backstamp was used.

| Name of Figure | Beswick Number | Gold Circle BP-1a | Parallel Lines BP-1b | Gold Oval BP-2a | Transition BP-2b | Brown Line BP-3a - 3b - 3c | | | Sig'n BP-4 | Total Beswick |
|---|---|---|---|---|---|---|---|---|---|---|
| **1973** | | | | | | | | | | |
| Mr. Alderman Ptolemy | P2424 | | | | | 2 | 11 | 3 | | **16** |
| Sir Isaac Newton | P2425 | | | | | 2 | 10 | | | **12** |
| **1974** | | | | | | | | | | |
| Sally Henny Penny | P2452 | | | | | 1 | 11 | 3 | | **15** |
| Mr. Jackson | P2453/1 | | | | | 1 | | | | **1** |
| | P2453/2 | | | | | | 11 | 3 | | **14** |
| **1975** | | | | | | | | | | |
| Simpkin | P2508 | | | | | | 9 | | | **9** |
| Mr. Benjamin Bunny and Peter Rabbit | P2509 | | | | | | 11 | 2 | 1 | **14** |
| **1976** | | | | | | | | | | |
| Mrs. Rabbit and Bunnies | P2543 | | | | | | 10 | 2 | 1 | **13** |
| Tabitha Twitchit and Miss Moppet | P2544 | | | | | | 10 | 2 | 1 | **13** |
| Ginger | P2559 | | | | | | 7 | | | **7** |
| Poorly Peter Rabbit | P2560 | | | | | | 10 | 2 | 1 | **13** |
| **1977** | | | | | | | | | | |
| Hunca Munca Sweeping | P2584 | | | | | | 9 | 2 | 1 | **12** |
| Little Black Rabbit | P2585 | | | | | | 9 | 2 | 1 | **12** |
| Fierce Bad Rabbit | P2586/1 | | | | | | 4 | | | **4** |
| | P2586/2 | | | | | | 6 | 2 | 1 | **9** |
| **1979** | | | | | | | | | | |
| Duchess (Holding a Pie) | P2601 | | | | | | 4 | | | **4** |
| Chippy Hackee | P2627 | | | | | | 7 | 3 | | **10** |
| Mr. Drake Puddle-Duck | P2628 | | | | | | 7 | 2 | 1 | **10** |
| **1981** | | | | | | | | | | |
| Rebecca Puddle-Duck | P2647 | | | | | | 5 | 2 | 1 | **8** |
| Thomasina Tittlemouse | P2668 | | | | | | 5 | 3 | | **8** |

| Name of Figure | Beswick Number | Gold Circle BP-1a | Parallel Lines BP-1b | Gold Oval BP-2a | Transition BP-2b | Brown Line BP-3a - 3b - 3c | | | Sig'n BP-4 | Total Beswick |
|---|---|---|---|---|---|---|---|---|---|---|
| **1982** | | | | | | | | | | |
| Diggory Diggory Delvet | P2713 | | | | | 4 | 3 | | | 7 |
| **1983** | | | | | | | | | | |
| Susan | P2716 | | | | | 3 | 3 | | | 6 |
| Old Mr. Pricklepin | P2767 | | | | | 3 | 3 | | | 6 |
| Benjamin Bunny Sat on a Bank | P2803/1 P2803/2 | | | | | 3 | 3 | | | 3 3 |
| The Old Woman Who Lived in a Shoe Knitting | P2804 | | | | | 3 | 3 | | | 6 |
| Jemima Puddle-Duck Made a Feather Nest | P2823 | | | | | 3 | 2 | | 1 | 6 |
| **1985** | | | | | | | | | | |
| Mrs. Tiggy Winkle Takes Tea | P2877 | | | | | 1 | 2 | | 1 | 4 |
| Cottontail | P2878 | | | | | 1 | 3 | | | 4 |
| **1986** | | | | | | | | | | |
| Old Mr. Bouncer | P2956 | | | | | | 3 | | | 3 |
| Goody/Timmy Tiptoes | P2957 | | | | | | 3 | | | 3 |
| Timmy Willie Sleeping | P2996 | | | | | | 3 | | | 3 |
| **1987** | | | | | | | | | | |
| Tom Thumb | P2989 | | | | | | 2 | | | 2 |
| Tom Kitten and Butterfly | P3030 | | | | | | 2 | | | 2 |
| Little Pig Robinson Spying | P3031 | | | | | | 2 | | | 2 |
| **1988** | | | | | | | | | | |
| Mr. Jeremy Fisher Digging | P3090 | | | | | | | | 1 | 1 |
| Mr. Todd | P3091 | | | | | | | | 1 | 1 |
| Johnny Town-Mouse with Bag | P3094 | | | | | | | | 1 | 1 |

# RELATIVE SCARCITY INDEX
# FOR
# ROYAL ALBERT BEATRIX POTTER FIGURES: 1989-1998

| Year Figure Introduced/<br>Name of figure | Doulton<br>Number | Gold<br>BP 5 | Brown<br>BP-6a |
|---|---|---|---|
| **1948** | | | |
| 1. Peter Rabbit | P1098/2 | 1 | 10 |
| 2. Jemima Puddle-Duck | P1092 | 1 | 10 |
| 3. Tom Kitten | P1100/2 | | 10 |
| 4. Timmy Tiptoes | P1101/2 | | 9 |
| 5. Squirrel Nutkin | P1102/2 | | 10 |
| 6. Mrs. Tittlemouse | P1103 | | 5 |
| 7. Little Pig Robinson | P1104/2 | | 10 |
| 8. Benjamin Bunny | P1105/3 | 1 | 10 |
| 9. Samuel Whiskers | P1106 | | 7 |
| 10. Mrs. Tiggy-Winkle | P1107/2 | | 10 |
| **1949** | | | |
| 11. Tailor of Gloucester | P1108 | | 10 |
| 12. Timmy Willie | P1109 | | 5 |
| **1950** | | | |
| 13. Mr. Jeremy Fisher | P1157/2 | | 10 |
| 14. Lady Mouse | P1183 | | 10 |
| **1951** | | | |
| 15. Hunca Munca | P1198 | 1 | 10 |
| 16. Ribby | P1199 | | 10 |
| 17. Mrs. Rabbit | P1200/2 | | 10 |
| **1954** | | | |
| 18. Flopsy, Mopsy & Cottontail | P1274 | 1 | 9 |
| 19. Miss Moppet | P1275/B | | 10 |
| 20. Johnny Town-Mouse | P1276 | | 5 |
| 21. Foxy Whiskered Gentleman | P1277 | | 10 |
| **1955** | | | |
| 22. Tommy Brock | P1348/4 | | 10 |
| 24. Pigling Bland | P1365/2 | | 10 |
| **1959** | | | |
| 25. The Old Woman Who Lived<br>a shoe | P1545/2 light blue | | 9 |
| **1961** | | | |
| 26. Goody Tiptoes | P1675 | | 9 |
| 27. Tabitha Twitchit | P1676/2 | | 7 |

| Year Figure Introduced/ Name of figure | Doulton Number | Gold BP 5 | Brown BP-6a |
|---|---|---|---|
| **1963** | | | |
| 28. Old Mr. Brown | P1796 | | 10 |
| **1965** | | | |
| 30. Mr. Benjamin Bunny | P1940/2 | | 10 |
| 31. Cecily Parsley | 1941/2 | | 5 |
| 32 Mrs. Flopsy Bunny | P1942/2 light blue | | 10 |
| **1970** | | | |
| 34. Aunt Pettitoes | P2276 | | 5 |
| 35. Cousin Ribby | P2284 | | 5 |
| **1971** | | | |
| 36. Appley Dapply | P2333/2 | | 10 |
| **1973** | | | |
| 39. Mr. Alderman Ptolemy | P2324 | | 9 |
| **1974** | | | |
| 41. Sally Henny Penny | P2452 | | 5 |
| 42 Mr. Jackson | P2453/2 | | 9 |
| **1975** | | | |
| 44. Mr. Benjamin Bunny and Peter Rabbit | P2509 | | 7 |
| **1976** | | | |
| 45. Mrs. Rabbit and Bunnies | P2543 | 1 | 9 |
| 46. Tabitha Twitchit/Miss Moppet | P2544 | | 5 |
| 48. Poorly Peter Rabbit | P2560 | | 9 |
| **1977** | | | |
| 49. Hunca Munca Sweeping | P2584 | | 10 |
| 50. Little Black Rabbit | P2585 | | 9 |
| 51. Fierce Bad Rabbit | P2586/2 | | 9 |
| **1979** | | | |
| 53. Chippy Hackee | P2627 | | 5 |
| 54. Mr. Drake Puddle-Duck | P2628 | | 10 |
| **1981** | | | |
| 55. Rebecca Puddle-Duck | P2647 | | 10 |
| 56. Thomasina Tittlemouse | P2668 | | <1 see note |
| **1982** | | | |
| 57. Diggory Diggory Delvet | P2713 | | 9 |

**Note:** A very small quantity was produced with the BP-6a backstamp prior to being discontinued in 1989.

| Year Figure Introduced/<br>Name of figure | Doulton<br>Number | Gold<br>BP 5 | Brown<br>BP-6a |
|---|---|---|---|
| **1983** | | | |
| 58. Susan | P2716 | | <1 see note |
| 59. Old Mr. Pricklepin | P2767 | | <1 see note |
| 60. Benjamin Bunny Sat on a Bank | P2803/2 | | 9 |
| 61. The Old Woman Who Lived in a Shoe Knitting | P2804 | | 10 |
| 62. Jemima Puddle-Duck made a Feather Nest | P2823 | | 9 |

**Note:** Very small quantities were produced with the BP-6a backstamp prior to being discontinued in 1989.

| | | | |
|---|---|---|---|
| **1985** | | | |
| 63. Mrs. Tiggy Winkle Takes Tea | P2877 | | 10 |
| 64. Cottontail (at Lunchtime) | P2878 | | 8 |
| **1986** | | | |
| 65. Old Mr. Bouncer | P2956 | | 7 |
| 66. Goody and Timmy Tiptoes | P2957 | | 8 |
| 67. Timmy Willie Sleeping | P2996 | | 8 |
| **1987** | | | |
| 68. Tom Thumb | P2989 | | 9 |
| 69. Tom Kitten and Butterfly | P3030 | | 5 |
| 70. Little Pig Robinson Spying | P3031 | | 5 |
| **1988** | | | |
| 71. Mr. Jeremy Fisher Digging | P3090 | | 6 |
| 72. Mr. Todd | P3091 | | 5 |
| 73. Johnny Town-Mouse with Bag | P3094 | | 6 |
| **1989** | | | |
| 74. Mother Ladybird | P2966 | | 8* |
| 75. Babbity Bumble | P2971 | | 5* |
| 76. Peter in the Gooseberry Net | P3157 | | 7* |
| **1990** | | | |
| 77. John Joiner | P2965 | | 8* |
| 78. Jemima Puddle-Duck and Foxy Whiskered Gentleman | P3193 | | 9 |
| 79. Mittens and Moppet | P3197 | | 5* |
| 80. Gentleman Mouse Made a Bow | P3200 | | 7* |
| 81. Foxy Reading the Country News | P3217 | | 8* |
| 82. Lady Mouse Made a Curtsey | P3220 | | 8* |
| **1991** | | | |
| 83. Benjamin Wakes Up | P3234 | | 7* |
| 84. Peter and the Red Pocket Handkerchief | P3242 | | 8 |
| 85. Miss Dormouse | P3251 | | 5* |
| 86. Pigling Eats Porridge | P3252 | | 4* |
| 87. Christmas Stocking | P3257 | | 4* |

| Year Figure Introduced/ Name of figure | Doulton Number | Gold BP 5 | Brown BP-6a |
|---|---|---|---|
| **1992** | | | |
| 88. Mrs. Rabbit Cooking | P3278 | | 7 |
| 89. Ribby and the Patty Pan | P3280 | | 7* |
| 90. Hunca Munca Spills the Beans | P3288 | | 5* |
| 91. Benjamin Ate a Lettuce Leaf | P3317 | | 7* |
| 92. And This Pig Had None | P3319 | | 7* |
| 93. No More Twist | P3325 | | 6* |
| **1995** | | | |
| 94. Peter in Bed | P3473 | | 4 |
| 95. Mr. McGregor | P3506 | | 4 |
| 96. Peter Ate a Raddish | P3533 | | 4** |
| **1996** | | | |
| 97. Peter with Postbag | P3591 | | 3 |
| 98. Peter with Daffodils | P3597 | | 3 |
| **1997** | | | |
| 99. Mrs. Rabbit and Peter | P3646 | | 2 |

| Large Figures | | Number | Year | BP-6b | BP-7 | BP-9a |
|---|---|---|---|---|---|---|
| 1. | Peter Rabbit | P3356 | 1993 | 5 | 1 | |
| 2. | Jemima Puddle-Duck | P3373 | 1993 | 5 | | 1 |
| 3. | Tom Kitten | P3405 | 1994 | 4 | | |
| 4. | Benjamin Bunny | P3403 | 1994 | 4 | | |
| 5. | Mrs. Tiggy-Winkle | P3437 | 1997 | 1 | | |
| 6. | The Tailor of Gloucester | P3449 | 1995 | 3 | | |
| 7. | Mr. Jeremy Fisher | P3372 | 1994 | 4 | | |
| 8. | Mrs. Rabbit | P3398 | 1994 | 4 | | |
| 9. | Foxy Whiskered Gentleman | P3450 | 1995 | 3 | | |
| 10. | Peter and the Red Pocket Handkerchief | P3592 | 1996 | 2 | | |

## Notes on Royal Albert backstamp figures:

Of the twenty-six new figures introduced during the Royal Albert backstamp period, the seventeen identified with asterisks were not produced with the Beswick BP-10 backstamp; in addition, only a handful of Peter Ate a Radish (double asterisk) were produced with the new backstamp — apparently in error

1. The following nine Beswick figures were not produced as Royal Albert or new Beswick figures:
   — Duchess (flowers)
   — Anna Maria
   — Amiable Guinea Pig
   — Pickles
   — Pigwig
   — Sir Isaac Newton
   — Simpkin
   — Ginger
   — Duchess (holding pie)

## RELATIVE SCARCITY INDEX
## OF
## NEW BESWICK BEATRIX POTTER FIGURES: 1998 - 2002

| Year Figure Introduced/ Name of figure | Doulton Number | BP 10a/b/c/ | | BP-11a |
|---|---|---|---|---|

### 1948

| | | | | |
|---|---|---|---|---|
| 1. Jemima Puddle-Duck | P1092 | 2 | a | 2 |
| | PS1092 | | | 1 |
| 2. Peter Rabbit | P1098/2 | 2 | b | 2 |
| | PS1098/2 | | | 1 |
| 3. Tom Kitten | P1100/2 | <1 | c | |
| 5. Squirrel Nutkin | P1102/2 | <2 | a | |
| 7. Little Pig Robinson | P1104/2 | 1 | c | |
| 8. Benjamin Bunny | P1108/3 | <2 | c | |
| | PS1105/3 | | | 1 |
| 10. Mrs. Tiggy-Winkle | P1107/2 | <2 | c | |
| | PS1107/2 | | | 1 |

### 1949

| | | | | |
|---|---|---|---|---|
| 11. Tailor of Gloucester | P1108 | 2 | c | 2 |

### 1950

| | | | | |
|---|---|---|---|---|
| 13. Mr. Jeremy Fisher | P1157/2 | 2 | a | |
| | PS1157/2 | | | 1 |
| 14. Lady Mouse | P1183 | <2 | a | |

### 1951

| | | | | |
|---|---|---|---|---|
| 15. Hunca Munca | P1198 | <2 | b | |
| 16. Ribby | P1199 | <2 | c | |
| 17. Mrs. Rabbit | P1200/2 | 2 | c | 2 |

### 1954

| | | | | |
|---|---|---|---|---|
| 19. Miss Moppet | P1275/B | 2 | b | 2 |
| 21. Foxy Whiskered Gentleman | P1277 | 2 | a | 2 |
| | PS1277 | | | 1 |

### 1955

| | | | | |
|---|---|---|---|---|
| 22. Tommy Brock | P1348/4 | 2 | a | 2 |
| 24. Pigling Bland | P1365/2 | <1 | c | |

### 1963

| | | | | |
|---|---|---|---|---|
| 28. Old Mr. Brown | P1796 | <1 | a | |

### 1965

| | | | | |
|---|---|---|---|---|
| 30. Mr. Benjamin Bunny | P1940/2 | <2 | b | |
| 32. Mrs. Flopsy Bunny | P1942/2 | <1 | b | |

### 1971

| | | | | |
|---|---|---|---|---|
| 36. Appley Dapply | P2333/2 | 2 | a | 2 |

## NEW BESWICK BEATRIX POTTER FIGURES: 1998 - 2002 (cont.)

| Year Figure Introduced/ Name of figure | Doulton Number | BP 10a/b/c/ | | BP-11a |
|---|---|---|---|---|
| **1977** | | | | |
| 49. Hunca Munca Sweeping | P2584 | 2 | a | |
| **1979** | | | | |
| 54. Mr. Drake Puddle-Duck | P2628 | <2 | b | |
| **1981** | | | | |
| 55. Rebeccah Puddle-Duck | P2647 | <2 | b | |
| **1983** | | | | |
| 61. The Old Woman Who Lived in a Shoe Knitting | P2804 | 2 | a | 2 |
| **1985** | | | | |
| 63. Mrs. Tiggy-Winkle Takes Tea | P2877 | 2 | a | 2 |
| **1990** | | | | |
| 78. Jemima Puddle-Duck and Foxy Whiskered Gentleman | P3193 | <1 | a | |
| **1991** | | | | |
| 84. Peter and the Red Pocket Handkerchief | P3242 | <1 | a | |
| **1992** | | | | |
| 88. Mrs. Rabbit Cooking | P3278 | <1 | b | |
| 91. Benjamin Ate a Lettuce Leaf | P3317 | <1 | a | |
| 92. And This Pig Had None | P3319 | <1 | a | |
| **1995** | | | | |
| 94. Peter in Bed | P3473 | 1 | a | 2 |
| 95. Mr. McGregor | P3506 | 1 | b | 2 |
| 96. Peter Ate a Raddish | P3533 | >0 | b | |
| **1996** | | | | |
| 97. Peter with Postbag | P3591 | 2 | b | 2 |
| 98. Peter with Daffodils | P3597 | <1 | b | |
| **1997** | | | | |
| 99. Mrs. Rabbit and Peter | P3646 | 2 | b | 2 |

## NEW BESWICK BEATRIX POTTER FIGURES: 1998-2002 (cont.)

| Year Figure Introduced/ Name of figure | Doulton Number | BP 10a | BP-11a | BP-8a |
|---|---|---|---|---|
| **1998** | | | | |
| 100. Tom Kitten in the Rockery | P4976 | 3 | | |
| 101 Peter Rabbit Gardening | P4977 | >1 | | |
| 102. Jemima and her Ducklings | P3786 | 3 | 2 | >0* |
| *BP-8a backstamp used in error on a very small number of figures | | | | |
| 103. Mrs. Tiggy-Winkle Washing | P3789 | >2 | | >0* |
| *BP-8a backstamp used in error on approximately 1800 figures | | | | |
| **1999** | | | | |
| 104. Jeremy Fisher Catches a Fish | P3919/1 | >1 | | |
| | P3919/2 | 2 | 2 | |
| 105. Peter in the Watering Can | P3940 | 2 | 2 | |
| **2000** | | | | |
| 106. Johnny Town-Mouse ... Corn | P3931 | 1 | 2 | |
| 107. Yock-Yock in the Tub | P3946 | 1 | 2 | |
| 108. Timmy Willie Fetching Milk | P3976 | 1 | 2 | |
| 109. Farmer Potatoes | P4014 | 1 | 2 | |
| 110. Mrs. Tittlemouse II | P4015 | 1 | 2 | |
| 111. Amiable Guinea Pig | P4031 | 1 | 2 | |
| **2001** | | | | |
| 112. Hunca Munca with Pan | P4074 | | 2 | |
| 113. Peter Rabbit Digging | P4075 | | 2 | |
| **2002** | | | | |
| 114. Two Gentlemen Rabbits | P4210 | | <1 | |
| 115. Mrs. Tiggy-Winkle Buys Provisions | P4234 | | <1 | |
| 116. Head Gardener | P4236 | | <1 | |
| 117. Little Pig Robinson II | P5104 | | <1 | (~ 3 months) |
| 118. Hunca Munca Sweeping II | P5584 | | <1 | (~ 3 months) |
| 119. Rebeccah Puddle-Duck II | P5647 | | <1 | (~ 3 months) |
| 120. Mr. Benjamin Bunny II | P5940 | | <1 | (~ 3 months) |

# THE CORLEY X-CHART

## Check-off List for Beswick/Royal Albert Beatrix Potter Figures: 1948-2002

| Year | Name of Figure | Doulton Number | Beswick Circle BP-1 | Gold Oval BP-2 | Beswick Brown Straight Line BP-3a | BP-3b | BP-3c | Sig'n BP-4 | Black BP-10/11 | Royal Albert Gold BP-5 | Royal Albert Brown BP-6a |
|------|----------------|----------------|------|------|------|------|------|------|------|------|------|
| **1948** | | | | | | | | | | | |
| 1. | Jemima Puddle-Duck | P1092 | 1a/b | 2a | X | X | X | X | 10a/11a | X | X |
| 2. | Peter Rabbit | | | | | | | | | | |
| | short base dark blue | P1098/1 | 1a/b | 1a/b | X | X | | | | | |
| | short base light blue | P1098/2 | | | X | X | | | | | |
| | long base light blue | P1098/2 | | | X | | X | X | 10B/11A | X | X |
| 3. | Tom Kitten | | | | | | | | | | |
| | dark blue | P1100/1 | 1a/b | 2a | X | X | | | | | |
| | light blue | P1100/2 | | | | X | X | X | 10c | | X |
| 4. | Timmy Tiptoes | Red jacket | | | | | | | | | |
| | Brown squirrel | P1101/1 | 1a/b | 2a | X | X | | | | | |
| | Grey squirrel | P1101/1 | 1a/b | 2a | X | X | | | | | |
| | Timmy Tiptoes | Pink jacket | | | | | | | | | |
| | Brown squirrel | P1101/2 | | 2a/b | X | X | | | | | |
| | Grey squirrel | P1101/2 | | 2a | X | X | X | | | | X |
| 5. | Squirrel Nutkin | P1102/1 | 1a/b | 2a | X | X | | | | | |
| | | P1102/2 | | 2a/b | | X | X | | 10a | | X |
| 6. | Mrs. Tittlemouse | P1103 | 1a/b | 2a/b | X | X | X | | | | X |
| 7. | Little Pig Robinson | P1104/1 | 1a/b | 2a | X | X | | | | | |
| | | P1104/2 | | | | x | x | | 10c | | X |
| 8. | Benjamin Bunny | | | | | | | | | | |
| | Green | P1105/1 | 1a/b | 2a | X | | | | | | |
| | Green | P1105/2 | | 2a | X | | | | | | |
| | Brown | P1105/2 | | | | X | | | | | |
| | Brown | P1105/3 | | | | X | X | X | | X | X |
| | Cream | P1105/3 | | | | | | | 10c | | X |
| 9. | Samuel Whiskers | P1106 | 1a/b | 2a | X | X | X | X | | | X |
| 10. | Mrs. Tiggy-Winkle | P1107/1 | 1a/b | 2a | X | | | | | | |
| | | P1107/2 | | 2a | X | X | X | X | 10c | | X |
| **1949** | | | | | | | | | | | |
| 11. | Tailor of Gloucester | P1108 | 1a/b | 2a | X | X | X | X | 10c/11a | | X |
| 12 | Timmy Willie | P1109 | 1a/b | 2a | X | X | X | X | | | X |
| **1950** | | | | | | | | | | | |
| 13. | Mr. Jeremy Fisher | P1157/1 | 1a | 2a | X | X | | | | | |
| | | P1157/2 | 1a | ? | ? | X | X | | 10a | | X |
| 14. | Lady Mouse | P1183 | 1a | 2a | X | X | X | | 10a | | X |

## Check-off List for Beswick/Royal Albert Beatrix Potter Figures: 1948-2002 (cont.)

| Year | Name of Figure | Doulton Number | Beswick Circle BP-1 | Gold Oval BP-2 | Beswick Brown Straight Line BP-3a | BP-3b | BP-3c | Sig'n BP-4 | Black BP-10/11 | Royal Albert Gold BP-5 | Royal Albert Brown BP-6a |
|---|---|---|---|---|---|---|---|---|---|---|---|
| **1951** | | | | | | | | | | | |
| 15. | Hunca Munca | P1198 | 1a | 2a | X | X | X | X | 10b | X | X |
| 16. | Ribby | P1199 | 1a | 2a | X | X | X | | 10c | | X |
| 17. | Mrs. Rabbit | P1200/1 | 1a | 2a | X | X | | | | | |
| | | P1200/2 | | | | X | X | X | 10c/11a | | X |
| **1954** | | | | | | | | | | | |
| 18. | Flopsy, Mopsy and Cottontail | P1274 | 1a | 2a/b | X | X | X | X | | X | X |
| 19. | Miss Moppet | P1275/1 | 1a | 2a | X | X | | | | | |
| | | P1275/2 | 1a | 2a | X | X | X | | 10b/11a | | X |
| 20. | Johnny Town-mouse | P1276 | 1a | 2a | X | X | X | | | | X |
| 21. | Foxy Whiskered Gentleman | P1277 | 1a | 2a | X | X | X | X | 10a/11a | | X |
| **1955** | | | | | | | | | | | |
| 22. | Tommy Brock | P1348/1-1 | 1a | 2a | | (Until 1973 a mid-range eye patch was the norm) | | | | | |
| | | P3148/1-2 | | 2a | X | | | | (circa 1972-74) | | |
| | | P1348/1-3 | | 2a | X | | | | (circa 1972-74) | | |
| | | P1348/2-2 | | | X | | | | (circa 1974) | | |
| | | P1348/3-2 | | | | X | X | | (circa 1974-75) | | |
| | | P1348/3-3 | | | | X | X | X | 10a/11a | | X |
| 23 | Duchess (with flowers) | P1355 | 1a | 2a | | | | | | | |
| 24. | Pigling Bland | P1365/1 | 1a | 2a | X | X | | | | | |
| | | P1365/2 | | | | X | X | | 10c | | X |
| **1959** | | | | | | | | | | | |
| 25. | The Old Woman Who Lived in a Shoe | P1545 | | | | | | | | | |
| | dark blue | | | 2a | X | X | | | | | |
| | light blue | | | | | X | X | | | | X |
| **1961** | | | | | | | | | | | |
| 26. | Goody Tiptoes | P1675 | | | | | | | | | |
| | Light pink, pattern | | | 2a | X | X | | | | | |
| | Dark pink, no pattern | | | | | X | | | | | |
| | Dark pink, no pattern, long base | | | | | X | X | | | | X |
| 27. | Tabitha Twitchit | P1676/1 | | | | | | | | | |
| | Striped dress | | | 2a | X | X | | | | | |
| | | P1676/2 | | | | | | | | | |
| | Plain dress, white face | | | | | X | | | | | |
| | Plain dress, ugly face | | | | | X | X | | | | X |
| **1963** | | | | | | | | | | | |
| 28. | Old Mr. Brown | P1796 | | | | | | | | | |
| | Brown squirrel | | 2a | X | X | | | | | | |
| | Orange squirrel | | | | X | X | | | 10a | | X |
| 29. | Anna Maria | P1851 | | | | | | | | | |
| | Dark blue | | 2a | X | X | | | | | | |
| | Light blue | | | | X | X | | | | | |

# BEATRIX POTTER

AMIABLE GUINEA-PIG
Style One

AMIABLE GUINEA-PIG
Style Two

AND THIS PIG HAD NONE

ANNA MARIA

APPLEY DAPPLY
Bottle Out

APPLEY DAPPLY
Bottle In

AUNT PETTITOES

BABBITTY BUMBLE

BENJAMIN ATE A
LETTUCE LEAF

BENJAMIN BUNNY
Small Size
Ears Out, Shoes Out

BENJAMIN BUNNY
Small Size
Ears Out, Shoes In

BENJAMIN BUNNY
Small Size
Ears In, Shoes In, Brown Shoes

# BEATRIX POTTER

**BENJAMIN BUNNY**
Small Size, Ears In, Shoes In
Gold Shoes

**BENJAMIN BUNNY**
Small Size, Satin Finish

**BENJAMIN BUNNY**
Large Size, Brown Shoes

**BENJAMIN BUNNY
SAT ON A BANK**
Head Looks Down

**BENJAMIN BUNNY
SAT ON A BANK**
Head Looks Up

**BENJAMIN WAKES UP**

**CECILY PARSLEY**
Head Down, Bright Blue Dress

**CECILY PARSLEY**
Head Up, Pale Blue Dress

**CHIPPY HACKEE**

**CHRISTMAS STOCKING**

**COTTONTAIL**

**COUSIN RIBBY**

# BEATRIX POTTER

DIGGORY DIGGORY DELVET

DUCHESS
Style One (Holding Flowers)

DUCHESS
Style Two (Holding a Pie)

FARMER POTATOES

FIERCE BAD RABBIT
Feet Out

FIERCE BAD RABBIT
Feet In

FLOPSY, MOPSY AND
COTTONTAIL, Style One

FOXY READING
COUNTRY NEWS

FOXY WHISKERED
GENTLEMAN
Small Size, Gloss Finish

FOXY WHISKERED
GENTLEMAN
Small Size, Satin Finish

FOXY WHISKERED
GENTLEMAN
Large Size, Green buttons

GENTLEMAN MOUSE
MADE A BOW

# BEATRIX POTTER

GINGER

GOODY AND TIMMY TIPTOES

GOODY TIPTOES

HEAD GARDENER

HUNCA MUNCA
Style One

HUNCA MUNCA
Style Two

HUNCA MUNCA
SPILLS THE BEADS

HUNCA MUNCA SWEEPING
Small Size, Brown Dustpan

HUNCA MUNCA SWEEPING
Small Size, Gold Dustpan

HUNCA MUNCA SWEEPING
Large Size, Gold Dustpan
and Broom Handle

JEMIMA AND HER DUCKLINGS

JEMIMA PUDDLE-DUCK
Small Size, Yellow Scarf Clip

# BEATRIX POTTER

**JEMIMA PUDDLE-DUCK**
Small Size, Gold Scarf Clip

**JEMIMA PUDDLE-DUCK**
Small Size, Satin Finish

**JEMIMA PUDDLE-DUCK**
Large Size, Yellow Scarf Clip

**JEMIMA PUDDLE-DUCK**
MADE A FEATHER NEST

**JEMIMA PUDDLE-DUCK WITH**
**FOXY WHISKERED GENTLEMAN**

**JEREMY FISHER**
**CATCHES A FISH**

**JOHN JOINER**

**JOHNNY TOWN-MOUSE**

**JOHNNY TOWN-MOUSE**
**EATING CORN**

**JOHNNY TOWN-MOUSE**
**WITH BAG**

**LADY MOUSE**

**LADY MOUSE MADE**
**A CURTSY**

# BEATRIX POTTER

LITTLE BLACK RABBIT

LITTLE PIG ROBINSON
Blue Striped Dress

LITTLE PIG ROBINSON
Blue Checked Dress

LITTLE PIG
ROBINSON SPYING

MISS DORMOUSE

MISS MOPPET
Mottled Brown Cat

MISS MOPPET
Brown Striped Cat

MITTENS AND MOPPET

MOTHER LADYBIRD

MR. ALDERMAN PTOLEMY

MR. BENJAMIN BUNNY
Pipe Out, Dark Maroon Jacket

MR. BENJAMIN BUNNY
Pipe In, Lilac Jacket

# BEATRIX POTTER

MR. BENJAMIN BUNNY
AND PETER RABBIT

MR. DRAKE PUDDLE-DUCK

MR. JACKSON
Green Toad

MR. JACKSON
Brown Toad

MR. JEREMY FISHER
Small Size, Spotted Legs

MR. JEREMY FISHER
Small Size, Striped Legs

MR. JEREMY FISHER
Large Size, Lilac Buttons

MR. JEREMY FISHER
DIGGING

MR. McGREGOR

MR. TOD

MRS. FLOPSY BUNNY

MRS. RABBIT
Small Size, Umbrella Out

# BEATRIX POTTER

**MRS. RABBIT**
Small Size
Umbrella Moulded To Dress

**MRS. RABBIT**
Large Size
Gold Umbrella Point and Handle

**MRS. RABBIT**
**AND BUNNIES**

**MRS. RABBIT AND PETER**
Large Size

**MRS. RABBIT COOKING**

**MRS. TIGGY-WINKLE**
Small Size, Diagonal Striped Dress

**MRS. TIGGY-WINKLE**
Small Size, Plaid Dress

**MRS. TIGGY-WINKLE**
Small Size, Platinum Iron

**MRS. TIGGY-WINKLE**
Small Size, Satin Finish

**MRS. TIGGY-WINKLE**
Large Size
Creamy-brown Iron

**MRS. TIGGY-WINKLE**
Large Size, Platinum Iron

**MRS. TIGGY-WINKLE**
**BUYS PROVISIONS**

## Check-off List for Beswick/Royal Albert Beatrix Potter Figures: 1948-2002 (cont.)

| Year | Name of Figure | Doulton Number | Beswick Circle BP-1 | Gold Oval BP-2 | Beswick Brown Straight Line | | | Sig'n BP-4 | Black BP-10/11 | Royal Albert Gold BP-5 | Royal Albert Brown BP-6a |
|---|---|---|---|---|---|---|---|---|---|---|---|
| | | | | | BP-3a | BP-3b | BP-3c | | | | |
| **1965** | | | | | | | | | | | |
| 30. | Mr. Benjamin Bunny | P1940/1a | | | | | | | | | |
| | Maroon jacket pipe out | | | 2a | X | | | | | | |
| | | P1940/1b | | | | | | | | | |
| | Lilac jacket pipe out | | | | X | | | | | | |
| | | P1940/2a | | | | | | | | | |
| | Maroon jacket pipe in | | | | X | X | | | | | |
| | | P1940/2b | | | | | | | | | |
| | Lilac jacket pipe in | | | 2b | X | X | X | X | 10b | | X |
| 31. | Cecily Parsley | P1941/1 | | | | | | | | | |
| | Dark blue | | | 2a | X | X | | | | | |
| | Light Blue | | | | X | X | X | | | | |
| | | P1941/2 | | | | | | | | | |
| | Light blue | | | | | | X | | | | X |
| 32. | Mrs. Flopsy Bunny | P1942 | | | | | | | | | |
| | Dark blue | | | 2a | X | X | | | | | |
| | Light blue | | | | | X | X | X | 10b | | X |
| **1967** | | | | | | | | | | | |
| 33. | Amiable Guinea Pig | P2061 | | | | | | | | | |
| | Brown jacket | | | 2a | X | | | | | | |
| | Tan jacket | | | | X | X | | | | | |
| **1970** | | | | | | | | | | | |
| 34. | Aunt Pettitoes | P2276 | | | | | | | | | |
| | Light blue pattern | | | 2a | X | | | | | | |
| | Bright blue pattern | | | | ? | X | X | | | | X |
| 35. | Cousin Ribby | P2284 | | 2a | X | X | X | | | | X |
| **1971** | | | | | | | | | | | |
| 36. | Appley Dapply | P2333/1 | | 2a | X | X | | | | | |
| | | P2333/2 | | | X | X | X | | 10a/11a | | X |
| 37. | Pickles | P2334 | | 2a | X | X | | | | | |
| **1972** | | | | | | | | | | | |
| 38. | Pig-Wig | P2381 | | | | | | | | | |
| | Grey pig, light blue dress | | | 2a | X | | | | | | |
| | Black pig, dark blue dress | | | | X | X | | | | | |
| **1973** | | | | | | | | | | | |
| 39. | Mr. Alderman Ptolemy | P2424 | | | X | X | X | | | | X |
| 40. | Sir Isaac Newton | P2425 | | | | | | | | | |
| | Dark jacket, striped scarf | | | | X | X | | | | | |
| | Light jacket, spotted scarf | | | | | X | | | | | |
| **1974** | | | | | | | | | | | |
| 41. | Sally Henny Penny | P2452 | | | X | X | X | | | | X |
| 42. | Mr. Jackson | P2453/1 | | | X | | | | | | |
| | | P2453/2 | | | | X | X | | | | |
| **1975** | | | | | | | | | | | |
| 43. | Simpkin | P2508 | | | | X | | | | | |
| 44. | Mr. Benjamin Bunny and Peter Rabbit | P2509 | | | | X | X | | | | |

## Check-off List for Beswick/Royal Albert Beatrix Potter Figures: 1948-2002 (cont.)

| Year | Name of Figure | Doulton Number | Beswick Circle BP-1 | Gold Oval BP-2 | Beswick Brown Straight Line BP-3a | BP-3b | BP-3c | Sig'n BP-4 | Black BP-10/11 | Royal Albert Gold BP-5 | Brown BP-6a |
|------|------|------|------|------|------|------|------|------|------|------|------|
| **1976** | | | | | | | | | | | |
| 45. | Mrs. Rabbit and Bunnies | P2543 | | | X | X | X | | | X | X |
| 46. | Tabitha Twitchit and Miss Moppet | P2544 | | | X | X | X | | | | X |
| 47. | Ginger | P2559 | | | X | | | | | | |
| 48. | Poorly Peter Rabbit | P2560 | | | X | X | X | | | | X |
| **1977** | | | | | | | | | | | |
| 49. | Hunca Munca Sweeping Daisy pattern Dot pattern | P2584 | | | X X | X | X | 10a | | | X |
| 50. | Little Black Rabbit | P2585 | | | X | X | X | | | | X |
| 51. | Fierce Bad Rabbit Feet out | P2586/1 | | | X | | | | | | |
| | Feet in | P2586/2 | | | X | X | X | | | | X |
| **1979** | | | | | | | | | | | |
| 52. | Duchess (Holding a Pie) | P2601 | | | X | | | | | | |
| 53. | Chippy Hackee Light green blanket Yellow blanket | P2627 | | | X | X X | | | | | X |
| 54. | Mr. Drake Puddle-Duck | P2628 | | | X | X | X | 10b | | | X |
| **1981** | | | | | | | | | | | |
| 55. | Rebeccah Puddle-Duck | P2647 | | | X | X | X | 10b | | | X |
| 56. | Thomasina Tittlemouse | P2668 | | | X | X | | | | | X |
| **1982** | | | | | | | | | | | |
| 57. | Diggory Diggory Delvet | P2713 | | | X | X | | | | | X |
| **1983** | | | | | | | | | | | |
| 58. | Susan Dark blue dress Light blue dress | P2716 | | | X X | X | | | | | X |
| 59. | Old Mr. Pricklepin | P2767 | | | X | X | | | | | X |
| 60. | Benjamin Bunny Sat on a Bank eyes down | P2803/1 | | | X | X | | | | | X |
| | eyes up | P2803/2 | | | X | X | | | | | X |
| 61. | The Old Woman Who Lived in a Shoe Knitting | P2804 | | | X | X | | 10a/11a | | | X |
| 62. | Jemima Puddle-Duck Made a Feather Nest | P2823 | | | X | X | X | | | | X |

## Check-off List for Beswick/Royal Albert Beatrix Potter Figures: 1948-2002 (cont.)

| Year | Name of Figure | Doulton Number | Beswick Circle BP-1 | Gold Oval BP-2 | Beswick Brown Straight Line | | | Sig'n BP-4 | Black BP-10/11 | Royal Albert | |
|---|---|---|---|---|---|---|---|---|---|---|---|
| | | | | | BP-3a | BP-3b | BP-3c | | | Gold BP-5 | Brown BP-6a |
| **1985** | | | | | | | | | | | |
| 63. | Mrs. Tiggy Winkle Takes Tea | P2877 | | | | X | X | X | 10a/11a | | X |
| 64. | Cottontail | P2878 | | | | X | X | X | | | X |
| **1986** | | | | | | | | | | | |
| 65. | Old Mr. Bouncer | P2956 | | | | | X | | | | X |
| 66. | Goody and Timmy Tiptoes | P2957 | | | | | X | | | | X |
| 67. | Timmy Willie Sleeping | P2996 | | | | | X | | | | X |
| **1987** | | | | | | | | | | | |
| 68. | Tom Thumb | P2989 | | | | | X | | | | X |
| 69. | Tom Kitten and Butterfly | P3030 | | | | | X | | | | X |
| 70. | Little Pig Robinson Spying | P3031 | | | | | X | | | | X |
| **1988** | | | | | | | | | | | |
| 71. | Mr. Jeremy Fisher Digging | P3090 | | | | | | X | | | X |
| 72. | Mr. Tod | P3091 | | | | | | X | | | X |
| 73. | Johnny Town-Mouse with Bag | P3094 | | | | | | X | X | | X |
| **1989** | | | | | | | | | | | |
| 74. | Mother Ladybird | P2966 | | | | | | | | | X |
| 75. | Babbity Bumble | P2971 | | | | | | | | | X |
| 76. | Peter in the Gooseberry Net | P3157 | | | | | | | | | X |
| **1990** | | | | | | | | | | | |
| 77. | John Joiner | P2965 | | | | | | | | | X |
| 78. | Jemima Puddle-Duck and Foxy Whiskered Gentleman | P3193 | | | | | | | 10a | | X |
| 79. | Mittens and Moppet | P3197 | | | | | | | | | X |
| 80. | Gentleman Mouse made a Bow | P3200 | | | | | | | | | X |
| 81. | Foxy Reading Country News | P3219 | | | | | | | | | X |
| 82. | Lady Mouse Made a Bow | P3220 | | | | | | | | | X |

## Check-off List for Beswick/Royal Albert Beatrix Potter Figures: 1948-2002 (cont.)

| Year | Name of Figure | Doulton Number | Beswick Circle BP-1 | Gold Oval BP-2 | Beswick Brown Straight Line BP-3a | BP-3b | BP-3c | Sig'n BP-4 | Black BP-10/11 | Royal Albert Gold BP-5 | Brown BP-6a |
|------|------|------|------|------|------|------|------|------|------|------|------|
| **1991** | | | | | | | | | | | |
| 83. | Benjamin Wakes Up | P3234 | | | | | | | | | X |
| 84. | Peter and the Red Pocket Handkerchief | P3242 | | | | | | | 10a | | X |
| 85. | Miss Dormouse | P3251 | | | | | | | | | X |
| 86. | Pigling Eats Porridge | P3252 | | | | | | | | | X |
| 87. | Christmas Stocking | P3257 | | | | | | | | | X |
| **1992** | | | | | | | | | | | |
| 88. | Mrs. Rabbit Cooking | P3278 | | | | | | | 10b | | X |
| 89. | Ribby and the Patty Pan | P3280 | | | | | | | | | X |
| 90. | Hunca Munca Spills the Beads | P3288 | | | | | | | | | X |
| 91. | Benjamin Ate a Lettuce Leaf | P3317 | | | | | | | 10a | | X |
| 92. | And This Pig Had None | P3319 | | | | | | | 10a | | X |
| 93. | No More Twist | P3325 | | | | | | | | | X |
| **1995** | | | | | | | | | | | |
| 94. | Peter in Bed | P3473 | | | | | | | 10a/11a | | X |
| 95. | Mr. McGregor Arm up | P3506/1 | | | | | | | 10a/11a | | X |
| | Arm down | P3506/2 | | | | | | | | | X |
| 96. | Peter Ate a Raddish | P3533 | | | | | | | 10b | | X |
| **1996** | | | | | | | | | | | |
| 97. | Peter with Postbag | P3591 | | | | | | | 10b/11a | | X |
| 98. | Peter with Daffodils | P3597 | | | | | | | 10b | | X |
| **1997** | | | | | | | | | | | |
| 99. | Mrs. Rabbit and Peter | P3646 | | | | | | | 10b/11a | | X |
| **1998** | | | | | | | | | | | |
| 100. | Tom Kitten in the Rockery | P4976 | | | | | | | 10a | | |
| 101. | Peter Rabbit Gardening | P4977 | | | | | | | 10a | | |
| 102. | Jemima and her Ducklings | P3786 | | | | | | | 10a/8a* 11a | | |
| 103. | Mrs. Tiggy-Winkle Washing | P3789 | | | | | | | 10a/8a* | | |

\* The above two figures appeared initially with a brown script BP-8a Beswick Ware backstamp (about 1,800 of the Mrs. Tiggy-Winkle's, only a handful of the Jemima's); after the error was detected the intended BP-10 backstamp was used.

# Check-off List for Beswick/Royal Albert Beatrix Potter Figures: 1948-2002 (cont.)

| Year | Name of Figure | Doulton Number | Beswick Circle BP-1 | Gold Oval BP-2 | Beswick Brown Straight Line | | | Sig'n BP-4 | Black BP-10/11 | Royal Albert Gold BP-5 | Brown BP-6a |
|---|---|---|---|---|---|---|---|---|---|---|---|
| | | | | | BP-3a | BP-3b | BP-3c | | | | |
| **1999** | | | | | | | | | | | |
| 104. | Jeremy Fisher Catches a Fish | P3919 | | | | | | | | | |
| | Vee notch open | | | | | | | | 10a | | |
| | Vee notch closed | | | | | | | | 10a | 11a | |
| 105. | Peter in the Watering Can | P3940 | | | | | | | 10a | 11a | |
| **2000** | | | | | | | | | | | |
| 106. | Johnny Town-Mouse Eating Corn | P3931 | | | | | | | 10a | 11a | |
| 107. | Yock-Yock in the Tub | P3946 | | | | | | | 10a | 11a | |
| 108. | Timmy Willie Fetching Milk | P3976 | | | | | | | 10a | 11a | |
| 109. | Farmer Potatoes | P4014 | | | | | | | 10a | 11a | |
| 110. | Mrs. Tittlemouse Style Two | P4015 | | | | | | | 10a | 11a | |
| 111. | Amiable Guinea Pig Style Two | P4031 | | | | | | | 10a | 11a | |
| **2001** | | | | | | | | | | | |
| Note: | A new backstamp design, the BP-11a, was introduced in 2001 for standard range figures, replacing the BP-10 series. The new design is somewhat similar to the BP-10c black circle design except for a "John Beswick" signature rather than the word "BESWICK". The new design does not include the Beswick "P" numbers on standard range figures issued in 2001. | | | | | | | | | | |
| 112. | Hunca Munca with Pan | P4074 | | | | | | | | 11a | |
| 113. | Peter Rabbit Digging | P4075 | | | | | | | | 11a | |
| **2002** | | | | | | | | | | | |
| Note: | Beginning in 2002, the BP-11a backstamp includes the Beswick "P" number on new standard range figures. | | | | | | | | | | |
| 114. | Two Gentleman Rabbits | P4210 | | | | | | | | 11a | |
| 115. | Mrs. Tiggy-Winkle Buys Provisions | P4234 | | | | | | | | 11a | |
| 116. | Head Gardener | P4236 | | | | | | | | 11a | |
| 117. | Little Pig Robinson | P5104 | (Reissue of P1104 with new backstamp and new number) | | | | | | | 11a | |
| 118. | Hunca Munca Sweeping | P5584 | (Reissue of P2584 with new backstamp and new number) | | | | | | | 11a | |
| 119. | Rebeccah Puddle-Duck | P5647 | (Reissue of P2647 with new backstamp and new number) | | | | | | | 11a | |
| 120. | Mr. Benjamin Bunny | P5941 | (Reissue of P1940 with new backstamp and new number) | | | | | | | 11a | |

# BESWICK WARE LIMITED AND SPECIAL EDITION FIGURES

**Notes:**

1. Asterisk (*) items above are re-issues, with gold accents, of figures in the standard Beatrix Potter range.

2. Special edition figures (SpEd) are produced for one year only; limited editions figures (LimEd) are produced in quantities shown.

3. The abbreviation "PR&F" in the 'Sponsor' column identifies Beswick limited and special edition figures commissioned by the firm Peter Rabbit and Friends and sold through their outlets; other limited and special edition figures are Beswick products distributed through Royal Doulton channels.

| Year | Name of Figure | Doulton Number | Limited Ed. Qnty | Beswick Ware BP-8 | BP-9/10d | Sponsor |
|------|----------------|----------------|------------------|-------------------|----------|---------|
| **1997** | | | | | | |
| 1. | Mrs. Rabbit and the Four Bunnies | P3672/LimEd of | 1,997 | 8b | | Beswick |
| 2.* | Peter and the Red Pocket Handkerchief (gold buttons) | PG3242/SpEd | | | 9d | PR&F |
| **1998** | | | | | | |
| 3.* | Jemima Puddle-Duck (gold clip) | PG1092/SpEd | | | 9b | Beswick |
| 4.* | Peter Rabbit (gold buttons) | PG1098/SpEd | | | 9b | Beswick |
| 5.* | Tom Kitten (gold buttons) | PG1100/SpEd | | | 9b | Beswick |
| 6.* | Benjamin Bunny (gold shoes) | PG1105/SpEd | | | 9b | Beswick |
| 7.* | Mrs. Tiggy-Winkle (platinum iron) | PG1107/SpEd | | | 9b | Beswick |
| 8.* | Hunca Munca Sweeping (gold dust pan) | PG2584/SpEd | | | 9b | Beswick |
| 9. | Hiding from the Cat | P3766/LimEd of | 3,500 | 8c | | Beswick |
| 10. | Ginger and Pickles | P3790/LimEd of | 2,750 | | 9d | PR&F |
| **1999** | | | | | | |
| 11. | Mittens, Tom Kitten and Moppet | P3867/SpEd | | 8c | | Beswick |
| 12. | Mrs. Tiggy-Winkle and Lucie | P3867/LimEd of | 2,950 | | 9d | PR&F |
| 13. | Sweet Peter Rabbit | P3886/SpEd of 2,950 | | | 10d | PR&F |

**Note:** The BP-10d backstamp, used on Sweet Peter Rabbit, is a gold lettered version of the BO-10a Beswick black crest backstamp, plus, the words "Peter Rabbit & Friends." While Sweet Peter Rabbit is classified as a special edition figure, production was in fact limited to 2,950; the 'limited edition' number is noted on the base of the figure but not on the accompanying authentication card. Also of interest, at some point after introduction PR&F began including a wood plinth base with the figure.

| Year | Name of Figure | Doulton Number | Limited Ed. Qnty | Beswick Ware BP-8 | BP-9/10d | Sponsor |
|------|----------------|----------------|------------------|-------------------|----------|---------|
| **2000** | | | | | | |
| 14. | Peter and Benjamin Picking Up Onions | P3930/LimEd of | 3,000 | 8c | | Beswick |
| 15. | Duchess and Ribby | P3983/LimEd of | 1,500 | | 9d | PR&F |

## BESWICK WARE LIMITED AND SPECIAL EDITION FIGURES (cont.)

| Year | Name of Figure | Doulton Number | Limited Ed. Qnty | Beswick BP-11a/b | Sponsor |
|---|---|---|---|---|---|
| **2001** | | | | | |
| Note: | The new BP-11b backstamp for limited/special edition figures was introduced in 2001, replacing the BP-8c (Beswick Ware) design. The design is somewhat similar to the BP-10c black circle design except for a "John Beswick" signature rather than the word "BESWICK"; the design also includes the Beswick "P" number. | | | | |
| 17. | Flopsy and Benjamin | P4155/SpEd | | 11b | Beswick |
| 18. | My Dear Son Thomas | P4169/LimEd of | 3,000 | 11b | Beswick |
| **2002** | | | | | |
| 19. | Flopsy, Mopsy and Cottontail | P4161/LimEd of | 1,500 | 11b | Beswick |
| 20. | Peter on His Book | P4217/SpEd | | 11b | Beswick |
| Note: | The backstamp on Peter on His Book figure also has the words "100th anniversary of The Tale of Peter Rabbit." | | | | |
| 21. | Kep & Jemima | P4901/LimEd of | 2,000 | 11b | Beswick |
| 22. | Peter and Benjamin Picking Apples | P4160/LimEd of | 3,000 | 11b | Beswick |
| 23. | Jemima Puddle-Duck Satin | PS1092 | | 11a | Beswick |
| 24. | Peter Rabbit Satin | PS1098 | | 11a | Beswick |
| 25. | Benjamin Bunny Satin | PS1105 | | 11a | Beswick |
| 26. | Mrs. Tiggy-Winkle Satin | PS1107 | | 11a | Beswick |
| 27. | Jeremy Fisher Satin | PS1157 | | 11a | Beswick |
| 28. | Foxy Whiskered Gentleman Satin | PS1277 | | 11a | Beswick |

## LARGE FIGURES

| Year | Name of Figure | Doulton Number | LimEd Qnty | Royal Albert BP-6b | Beswick Ware BP-7 | BP-9a | BP-9c | Sponsor |
|---|---|---|---|---|---|---|---|---|
| **1993** | | | | | | | | |
| 1. | Peter Rabbit | P3356 | | X | X | | | Beswick |
| 2. | Jemima Puddle-Duck | P3373 | | X | | X | | Beswick |
| **1994** | | | | | | | | |
| 3. | Mr. Jeremy Fisher | P3372 | | X | | | | Beswick |
| 4. | Mrs. Rabbit | P3398 | | X | | | | Beswick |
| 5. | Benjamin Bunny | P3403 | | X | | | | Beswick |
| 6. | Tom Kitten | P3405 | | X | | | | Beswick |
| **1995** | | | | | | | | |
| 7. | Tailor of Gloucester | P3449 | | X | | | | Beswick |
| 8. | Foxy Whiskered Gentleman | P3450 | | X | | | | Beswick |
| **1996** | | | | | | | | |
| 9. | Peter and the Red Pocket Handkerchief | P3592 | | X | | | | Beswick |
| **1997** | | | | | | | | |
| 10. | Mrs. Tiggy-Winkle | P3437 | | X | | | | Beswick |
| 11* | Peter Rabbit Gold buttons | PG3356/LimEd of 1,947 | | | | | X | LxP |
| 12* | Benjamin Bunny Gold shoes | PG3403/LimEd of 1,947 | | | | | X | LxP |
| **1998** | | | | | | | | |
| 13.* | Jemima Puddle-Duck Gold clip | PG3373/LimEd of 1,947 | | | | | X | LxP |
| 14* | Mrs. Tiggy-Winkle Platinum iron | PG3437/LimEd of 1,947 | | | | | X | LxP |
| 15* | Mr. Jeremy Fisher Gold accent | PG3372/LimEd of 1,947 | | | | | X | LxP |
| 16* | Tom Kitten Gold buttons | PG3405/LimEd of 1,947 | | | | | X | LxP |
| 17* | Mrs. Rabbit Gold Umbrella | PG3398/LimEd of 1,947 | | | | | X | LxP |
| 18* | Foxy Whiskered Gentleman; Gold accent | PG3450/LimEd of 1,947 | | | | | X | LxP |
| 19.* | Tailor of Gloucester Gold accent | PG3592/LimEd of 1,947 | | | | | X | LxP |
| 20.* | Peter and the Red Pocket Handkerchief Gold buttons | PG3592/LimEd of 1,947 | | | | | X | LxP |

## LARGE FIGURES (cont.)

| Year | Name of Figure | Doulton Number | LimEd Qnty | Royal Albert BP-6b | Beswick Ware BP-7 | BP-9a | BP-9c | Sponsor |
|------|----------------|----------------|------------|--------------------|--------------------|-------|-------|---------|
| **1999** | | | | | | | | |
| 21. | Squirrel Nutkin Gold accent | PG3893/LimEd of 1,947 | | | | | X | LxP |
| 22. | Hunca Munca Sweeping Gold accent | PG3894/LimEd of 1,947 | | | | | X | LxP |
| 23. | Mrs. Rabbit and Peter Gold accent | PG3978/LimEd of 2,500 | | | | | X | LxP |
| **2000** | | | | | | | | |
| 24. | Tabitha Twitchit and Moppet Gold accent | PG4020/LimEd of 2,000 | | | | | X | LxP |

**Note:** When Beswick ended production of the original ten large figures in 1997, Lawley's-by-Post (above abbreviated LxP), a Royal Doulton subsidiary, reissued the same ten figures (*) in limited edition quantities but with gold accents and gold Beswick Ware backstamps. Subsequently, they issued four other gold accented limited edition figures which had not previously been issued in the large size. The first twelve LxP figures were introduced and sold in pairs; the last two were introduced separately and sold singly

# BEATRIX POTTER BACKSTAMPS

## BP-1     BESWICK GOLD CIRCLE AND BESWICK GOLD PARALLEL LINES ISSUED 1948 TO 1954

The Beswick-England gold circle backstamp (BP-1a) was the primary backstamp used from the introduction of the first ten figures in 1948 through 1954. However, three small base figures introduced during that period could not easily accommodate the full gold circle and forced changes in the backstamp design.

The first small base figure, Tailor of Gloucester, introduced in 1949, resulted in the creation of a special backstamp especially for that figure — the BP-1b gold parallel lines backstamp which has the words Beswick and England in very small type. While the BP-1b was used in small quantities on several other figures, such usage was likely simply a matter of production line convenience.

The second figure presenting problems for the full gold circle was Mrs. Rabbit, introduced in 1951. In this instance instead of using the unattractive BP-1b parallel lines design the gold circle was "modified" into a gold oval — which is now called the BP-2. In addition, it appears likely that use of the BP-1b on Tailor of Gloucester was discontinued at this time in favour of the gold oval.

The third small base figure, Johnny Town-Mouse, introduced in 1954, apparently used the new gold oval almost from the start of production and probably led to the decision to simplify the backstamp situation by using the gold oval (BP-2) design for all figures starting in 1955. This much is clear: there are only a tiny handful of gold circle backstamps on the three small base figures introduced prior to 1955 — and all of these are probably pre-production prototypes produced prior to the start of the regular production.

It should be noted that a tiny handful of each of the three figures introduced in 1955 — Tommy Brock, Duchess with Flowers, and Pigling Bland — were produced with the gold circle backstamp. In all likelihood, all of these are pre-production prototypes produced in 1954 for marketing purposes.

BP-1a (gold circle). The first variety has the words "Beswick" and "England" forming a circle; the word "copyright" may or may not appear. While this variety was used on a total of 24 figures plus one variation, it is found only in minuscule quantities on six of these:

Duchess, style one (Holding Flowers)
Johnny Town-Mouse
Mrs. Rabbit, first version
Pigling Bland, first variation
Tailor of Gloucester, first version
Tommy Brock, first version, first variation

BP-1a Beswick Gold Circle

The following is a list of the 18 figures which regularly used the BP-1a backstamp:

Benjamin Bunny, first version
Flopsy, Mopsy and Cottontail, style one
Foxy Whiskered Gentleman, first version, first variation
Hunca Munca, style one
Jemima Puddle-Duck, first version, first variation
Lady Mouse
Little Pig Robinson, first variation
Miss Moppet, first variation
Mr. Jeremy Fisher, first version, first and second variations
Mrs. Tiggy-Winkle, first version, first variation
Mrs. Tittlemouse, style one
Peter Rabbit, first version, first variation
Ribby
Samuel Whiskers
Squirrel Nutkin, first version, first variation
Timmy Tiptoes, first variation
Timmy Willie
Tom Kitten, first version, first variation

BP-1b (gold parallel lines). The second variety has the words "Beswick" and "England" arranged in parallel lines, one atop the other; the word "Copyright" appears in script. This variety was created for use on Tailor of Gloucester but was used in error on several other figures including:

BP-1b Beswick Gold Parallel Lines

Benjamin Bunny, first version
Jemima Puddle-Duck, first version, first variation
Little Pig Robinson, first variation
Peter Rabbit, first version, first variation
Samuel Whiskers
The Tailor of Gloucester, first version
Timmy Tiptoes, first variation
Tom Kitten, first version, first variation

## BP-2 BESWICK GOLD OVAL
### ISSUED 1955 TO 1972

**BP-2a** The gold oval was in use for 18 years, between 1955 and 1972, on 38 figures plus 4 versions/variations. The last gold oval figure, Pig-Wig, was introduced in late 1972. The tiny number of gold oval Pig Wig's produced suggests that they were the usual pre-production prototypes and that, because plans to introduce the brown line backstamp in 1973 were at full throttle, all 1972 regular production Pig-Wig's received the no-copyright-date variety of the new backstamps. The following is a list of figures that can found with a BP-2 backstamp:

BP-2a Beswick Gold Oval

Amiable Guinea-Pig, style one
Anna Maria
Apply Dapply, first version
Aunt Pettitoes
Benjamin Bunny, first and second versions
Cecily Parsley, first version
Cousin Ribby
Duchess, style one (holding flowers)
Flopsy, Mopsy and Cottontail, style one
Foxy Whiskered Gentleman, first version,
    first variation
Goody Tiptoes
Hunca Munca, style one
Jemima Puddle-Duck, first version, first variation
Johnny Town-Mouse
Lady Mouse
Little Pig Robinson, first variation
Miss Moppet, first and second variation
Mr. Benjamin Bunny, first version
Mr. Jeremy Fisher, first version, first variation
Mrs. Flopsy Bunny
Mrs. Rabbit, first version
Mrs. Tiggy-Winkle, first version, first and
    second variations
Mrs. Tittlemouse, style one
Old Mr. Brown
Old Woman Who Lived in a Shoe, The
Peter Rabbit, first version, first variation
Pickles
Pigling Bland, first variation
Pig-Wig
Ribby
Samuel Whiskers
Squirrel Nutkin, first version, first variation
Tabitha Twitchit, first variation
Tailor of Gloucester, first version
Timmy Tiptoes, first and second variations
Timmy Willie From Johnny Town-Mouse
Tom Kitten, first version, first variation
Tommy Brock, first version, first, second and
    third variations

## BP-2b Transitional Gold/Brown
### Issued 1971 - 1972

**BP-2b** Between BP-2 and BP-3 there exist transitional backstamps. These appear on a very limited number of figures. The backstamp is part gold and part brown line; usually "Beatrix Potter" and the figure's name appear in gold with the last three lines in brown.

Part gold, part brown line backstamp

The following is a list of figures known to carry the transitional backstamp:

Flopsy, Mopsy and Cottontail, style one
Mr. Benjamin Bunny, first version
Mr. Benjamin Bunny, second version
Mrs. Tittlemouse, style one
Peter Rabbit, first version, first variation
Squirrel Nutkin, first version, first variation
Timmy Tiptoes, first variation

## BP-3 BESWICK BROWN LINE
### ISSUED 1973 TO 1988

BP-3a Potter's, no date, issued 1973 to 1974
(no copyright date)
Used on 41 figures, plus 9 versions/varieties

The overall BP-3 category groups eight minor backstamp varieties into three major categories, as set forth below. In each category, the words "Beswick" and "England" appear in brown lettering either in a straight line or with "Beswick" atop "England," depending on the size or shape of the base. Over a period of 16 years BP-3 category backstamps were used on a total of 70 figures plus 27 versions/variations.

**Note:** The eight minor varieties are described in Louise Irvine's "Beatrix Potter Figures," 2nd edition, pp74-75. Three of the varieties (B1, B3 and B4) are included in BP-3a; three (B2, B5 and B6) are included in BP-3b; and two (B7 and B8) are included in BP-3c. Similarly, there are two varieties (B9 and B10) included in BP-4."

**BP-3b** Potter's, date, issued 1974 to 1985
(copyright date)
Used on 63 figures, plus 16 versions/varieties

**BP-3c** Potter, date, issued 1985 to 1988
(no "s" on Potter)
Used on 63 figures, plus 16 versions/varieties

**BP-4**         **BESWICK SIGNATURE**
         **ISSUED 1988 TO 1989**

BP-4 Beswick Signature
Used on a total of 29 figures

This era saw the Beswick backstamp converted to the Royal Doulton backstamp. The connection with Beswick was kept by the addition of the John Beswick signature to the backstamp. In use for a year to a year and a half, this is one of the shortest time periods for a backstamp.

**BP-5**         **ROYAL ALBERT GOLD CROWN**
         **ISSUED 1989**

**BP-5** Royal Albert Gold Crown

The gold backstamp was reinstituted for 1989 to mark the change from the Doulton/Beswick backstamps to Royal Albert. It was used on only the following six figures:

Benjamin Bunny, third version, first variation
Flopsy, Mopsy and Cottontail, style one
Hunca Munca, style one
Jemima Puddleduck, first version, first variation
Mrs. Rabbit and Bunnies
Peter Rabbit, first version, second variation

**BP-6**    **ROYAL ALBERT BROWN CROWN**
         **ISSUED 1989 TO 1998**

**BP-6a** Small brown crown    **BP-6b** Large brown crown

This backstamp was issued in two sizes. A small version was used on the standard figures with a larger size for the large size figures. The small size was issued in 1989 and was used on 90 figures. The large size was issued in 1993 and was used on 10 figures. A variation of the small size exists without the crown for small base figures.

**BP-7          BESWICK BROWN OVAL
              ISSUED 1993**

**BP-7** Brown Oval

Issued only on the large size Peter Rabbit to commemorate the 100th anniversary of Peter Rabbit 1893-1993.

**BP-8      BESWICK WARE BROWN SCRIPT
              ISSUED 1994 TO 1998**

"Beswick Ware England" or the mark that followed, "Beswick Ware Made in England" is the earliest printed backstamp of the J. W. Beswick, Baltimore Works, Longton, and it was for the Beswick Centenary that the Beswick Ware logo was reinstated as the primary backstamp of the John Beswick Studio of Royal Doulton.

**BP-8a          General Backstamp Issue 1998**

**BP-8a** Beswick Ware Brown Script

Issued as a general backstamp for a very short period of time in 1998, the brown script may turn out to be the rarest of the Beatrix Potter backstamps. It is found on only two figures.

Jemima and her Ducklings
Mrs. Tiggy-Winkle Washing

**BP-8b      50th Anniversary of Production of
     Beatrix Potter Figures at Beswick, Issued 1997**

**BP-8b** Beswick 50th Anniversary

1997 was the 50th anniversary of production of Beatrix Potter figurines at the John Beswick Studios in Longton. This backstamp was in use only during 1997.

**BP-8c          Limited Edition Backstamp**

**BP-8c** Beswick Ware Brown Script
Limited Edition Backstamp

**BP-8c** is a modification of BP-8a and designed for limited and special edition figurines.

The following is a list of figures that can be found with a BP-8c backstamp:

Hiding From the Cat
Mittens, Tom Kitten and Moppet
Peter and Benjamin Picking Up Onions

## BP-9 BESWICK WARE GOLD SCRIPT
### ISSUED 1997 TO 1999

A gold Beswick Ware script backstamp was coupled with the anniversary, limited edition, gold or platinum highlighted figurines. There are three varieties of this backstamp.

## BP-9a 100th Anniversary of
### John Beswick Studios, Issued 1994

**BP-9a** Beswick Centenary

Issued to commemorate the 100th anniversary of the founding of the Beswick studios. This backstamp was available only on the large Jemima Puddle-Duck.

## BP-9b General Backstamp
### 1997-1998

**BP-9b** Beswick Gold Script

The following small size figures issued with gold accents are coupled with gold Beswick Ware backstamps:

Benjamin Bunny, third version, second variation
Hunca Munca Sweeping, first version, second variation
Jemima Puddle-Duck, first version, second variation
Mrs. Tiggy-Winkle, first version, third variation
Peter Rabbit, first version, third variation
Tom Kitten, first version, third variation

## BP-9c Limited Edition Backstamp

**BP-9c** Beswick Ware Gold Script
Limited Edition

This backstamp, a modification of BP-9b, appears on 12 large size figurines issued by Lawleys By Post between 1997-1999. They were issued in pairs except for Mrs. Rabbit and Peter (1999) and Tabitha Twitchet and Miss Moppet (2000).

**Issued in pairs:**

1. Benjamin Bunny, fourth version, second variation
   Peter Rabbit, second version, second variation

2. Jemima Puddle-Duck, second version, second var.
   Mrs. Tiggy-Winkle, second version, second variation

3. Mr. Jeremy Fisher, second version, second variation
   Tom Kitten, second version, second variation

4. Foxy Whiskered Gentleman, second version, second variation
   Mrs. Rabbit, third version, second variation

5. Peter and the Red Pocket Handkerchief, second version, second variation
   Tailor of Gloucester, second version, second var.

6. Hunca Munca Sweeping, second version
   Squirrel Nutkin, second version

**Issued singly (double figures):**
1. Mrs. Rabbit and Peter, second version
   (Single issue-double figure)
2. Tabitha Twitchit and Moppet, second version

## BP-9d Peter Rabbit and Friends
### Limited Editions

**BP-9d** Peter Rabbit and Friends
Limited Editions

This backstamp is a modification of BP-9b and is found on limited edition figures with gold accents issued by Peter Rabbit and Friends.

Duchess and Ribby
Ginger and Pickles
Mrs. Tiggy-Winkle and Lucie
Peter and the Red Pocket Handkerchief, first version, second variation
This Pig Had a Bit of Meat

## BP-10 BESWICK BLACK CREST
### ISSUED 1998 TO DATE

In 1998 the Beswick backstamp was redesigned and the Beswick crest, first seen in 1968-1969, was re-introduced for the Beswick line of Storybook figurines. There are three varieties of this backstamp.

**BP-10a**  **General Backstamp Issue**

**BP-10a** Beswick Black Crest

This backstamp, now in general use, will be found on the following Beatrix Potter figurines:

Amiable Guinea-Pig, style two
And This Pig Had None
Appley Dapply, second version
Benjamin Ate a Lettuce Leaf
Farmer Potatoes
Foxy Whiskered Gentleman, first version,
  first variation
Hunca Munca Sweeping, first version, first variation
Jemima and her Ducklings
Jemima Puddle-Duck, first version, first variation
Jemima Puddle-Duck with Foxy Whiskered Gentleman
Jeremy Fisher Catches a Fish
Johnny Town-Mouse Eating Corn
Lady Mouse
Mr. Jeremy Fisher, first version, second variation
Mrs. Tiggy Winkle Takes Tea
Mrs. Tiggy-Winkle Washing
Mrs. Tittlemouse, style two
Old Mr. Brown
Peter and the Red Pocket Handkerchief, first version,
  first variation
Peter in Bed
Peter in the Watering Can
Peter Rabbit Gardening
Squirrel Nutkin, first version, second variation
The Old Woman Who Lived in a Shoe Knitting
Timmy Willie Fetching Milk
Tom Kitten in the Rockery
Tommy Brock, second version, third variation
Yock-Yock in the Tub

**BP-10b**  **Beswick Black Arch**

**BP-10b** A modification of backstamp BP-10a

This backstamp is a modification of BP-10a and can be found on the following figurines. The modification was necessary due to base restriction.

Hunca Munca, style one
Miss Moppet, second variation
Mr. Benjamin Bunny, second version
Mr. Drake Puddle-Duck
Mr. McGregor
Mrs. Flopsy Bunny
Mrs. Rabbit and Peter, first version
Mrs. Rabbit Cooking
Peter Ate a Raddish
Peter Rabbit, first version, second variation
Peter with Daffodils
Peter with Postbag
Rebeccah Puddle-Duck

**BP-10c**  **Beswick Black Circle**

**BP-10c** A modification of backstamp BP-10a

This backstamp is a modification of BP-10a. Its modification is also due to base restriction. It can be found on the following figurines:

Benjamin Bunny, third version, first variation
Little Pig Robinson, second variation
Mrs. Rabbit, second version
Mrs. Tiggy-Winkle, first version, second variation
Pigling Bland, second variation
Ribby
Tailor of Gloucester, first version
Tom Kitten, first version, second variation

**BP-10d**  **Peter Rabbit and Friends**
**Limited Editions**

**BP-10d** Beswick Gold Crest

At the time of publication BP-10d was found only on Sweet Peter Rabbit, a limited edition figurine commissioned by Peter Rabbit and Friends. This backstamp is a gold version of BP-10a

**BP-11** **JOHN BESWICK SIGNATURE**
**ISSUED 2001 TO 2002**

Beginning in 2001 all standard range figures and limited/special edition figures carry a "John Beswick" signature in lieu of the word "Beswick". In addition, the Doulton "P" number for each figure is included for all limited/special edition figures beginning in 2001 and for the standard range figures beginning in 2002.

**BP-11a** **General Backstamp Issue**

**BP-11a** John Beswick Signature

**Standard range figures:**

Head Gardener, The
Hunca Munca, style two
Hunca Munca Sweeping, first version, first variation
Little Pig Robinson, second variation
Mr. Benjamin Bunny, second version
Mrs. Tiggy-Winkle Buys Provisions
Peter Rabbit Digging
Rebeccah Puddle-duck
Two Gentlemen Rabbits

**Satin glaze figures:**

Benjamin Bunny, third version, third variation
Foxy Whiskered Gentleman, first version,
  second variation
Jemima Puddle-duck, first version, third variation
Mr. Jeremy Fisher, first version, third variation
Mrs. Tiggy-Winkle, first version, fourth variation
Peter Rabbit, first version, fourth variation

**BP-11b** **Limited/Special Edition Backstamp**

**BP-11b** John Beswick Signature

**Limited/special edition figures:**

Flopsy and Benjamin Bunny
Flopsy, Mopsy and Cottontail, style two
Kep and Jemima
My Dear Son Thomas
Peter and Benjamin Picking Apples
Peter on his Book

## AMIABLE GUINEA-PIG™
### Style One

| | |
|---|---|
| Modeller: | Albert Hallam |
| Height: | 3 ½", 8.9 cm |
| Colour: | Tan jacket, white waistcoat, yellow trousers |
| Issued: | 1967 - 1983 |

| Back Stamp | Beswick Number | Doulton Number | U.K. £ | U.S. $ | Price Can. $ | Aust. $ |
|---|---|---|---|---|---|---|
| BP-2a | 2061 | P2061 | 275. | 500. | 625. | 675. |
| BP-3a | | | 100. | 175. | 225. | 235. |
| BP-3b | | | 100. | 175. | 225. | 235. |

**Note:** The colour of the coat varies from tan to brown.

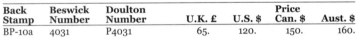

## AMIABLE GUINEA-PIG™
### Style Two

| | |
|---|---|
| Modeller: | Warren Platt |
| Height: | 4 ¼", 10.8 cm |
| Colour: | Brown jacket and waistcoat, beige trousers and hat, blue bowtie and book |
| Issued: | 2000 - 2002 |

| Back Stamp | Beswick Number | Doulton Number | U.K. £ | U.S. $ | Price Can. $ | Aust. $ |
|---|---|---|---|---|---|---|
| BP-10a | 4031 | P4031 | 65. | 120. | 150. | 160. |

## AND THIS PIG HAD NONE™

| | |
|---|---|
| Modeller: | Martyn Alcock |
| Height: | 4", 10.1 cm |
| Colour: | Mauve dress, mottled burgundy and green shawl, brown hat |
| Issued: | 1992 - 1998 |

| Back Stamp | Beswick Number | Doulton Number | U.K. £ | U.S. $ | Price Can. $ | Aust. $ |
|---|---|---|---|---|---|---|
| BP-6a | 3319 | P3319 | 25. | 50. | 65. | 70. |
| BP-10a | | | 35. | 65. | 80. | 90. |

### ANNA MARIA™

| | |
|---|---|
| Modeller: | Albert Hallam |
| Height: | 3", 7.6 cm |
| Colour: | Blue dress and white apron |
| Issued: | 1963 - 1983 |

| Back Stamp | Beswick Number | Doulton Number | U.K. £ | U.S. $ | Price Can. $ | Aust. $ |
|---|---|---|---|---|---|---|
| BP-2a | 1851 | P1851 | 200. | 350. | 425. | 475. |
| BP-3a | | | 100. | 175. | 225. | 235. |
| BP-3b | | | 100. | 175. | 225. | 235. |

**Note:** Dress is bright blue in earlier versions and pale blue in later versions.

### APPLEY DAPPLY™

| | |
|---|---|
| Modeller: | Albert Hallam |
| Height: | 3 ¼", 8.3 cm |
| Colour: | Brown mouse, white apron, blue trim, blue bow, yellow basket, tray of jam tarts |

**FIRST VERSION: BOTTLE OUT**

| Issued: | 1971 - 1975 |
|---|---|

| Back Stamp | Beswick Number | Doulton Number | U.K. £ | U.S. $ | Price Can. $ | Aust. $ |
|---|---|---|---|---|---|---|
| BP-2a | 2333/1 | P2333/1 | 200. | 375. | 475. | 500. |
| BP-3a | | | 75. | 125. | 150. | 175. |
| BP-3b | | | 75. | 125. | 150. | 175. |

First version: Bottle out

BEATRIX POTTER'S
"APPLEY DAPPLY"
F. Warne & Co.Ltd.
© Copyright 1971
BESWICK
ENGLAND

**SECOND VERSION: BOTTLE IN**

| Issued: | 1975 - 2002 |
|---|---|

| Back Stamp | Beswick Number | Doulton Number | U.K. £ | U.S. $ | Price Can. $ | Aust. $ |
|---|---|---|---|---|---|---|
| BP-3b | 2333/2 | P2333/2 | 30. | 55. | 70. | 75. |
| BP-3c | | | 30. | 55. | 70. | 75. |
| BP-6a | | | 40. | 75. | 95. | 100. |
| BP-10a | | | 25. | 45. | 55. | 60. |

Second version: Bottle in

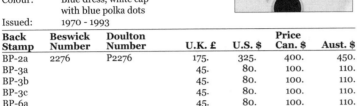

## AUNT PETTITOES™

| | |
|---|---|
| Modeller: | Albert Hallam |
| Height: | 3 ¾", 9.5 cm |
| Colour: | Blue dress, white cap with blue polka dots |
| Issued: | 1970 - 1993 |

| Back Stamp | Beswick Number | Doulton Number | U.K. £ | U.S. $ | Price Can. $ | Aust. $ |
|---|---|---|---|---|---|---|
| BP-2a | 2276 | P2276 | 175. | 325. | 400. | 450. |
| BP-3a | | | 45. | 80. | 100. | 110. |
| BP-3b | | | 45. | 80. | 100. | 110. |
| BP-3c | | | 45. | 80. | 100. | 110. |
| BP-6a | | | 45. | 80. | 100. | 110. |

**Note:** The dress is light blue in earlier versions and bright blue in later versions.

## BABBITTY BUMBLE™

| | |
|---|---|
| Modeller: | Warren Platt |
| Height: | 2 ¾", 7.0 cm |
| Colour: | Black and gold |
| Issued: | 1989 - 1993 |

| Back Stamp | Beswick Number | Doulton Number | U.K. £ | U.S.. $ | Price Can. $ | Aust. $ |
|---|---|---|---|---|---|---|
| BP-6a | 2971 | P2971 | 200. | 350. | 450. | 475. |

## BENJAMIN ATE A LETTUCE LEAF™

| | |
|---|---|
| Modeller: | Martyn Alcock |
| Height: | 4 ¾", 11.9 cm |
| Colour: | Brown, white and yellow |
| Issued: | 1992 - 1998 |

| Back Stamp | Beswick Number | Doulton Number | U.K. £ | U.S. $ | Price Can. $ | Aust. $ |
|---|---|---|---|---|---|---|
| BP-6a | 3317 | P3317 | 30. | 55. | 70. | 75. |
| BP-10a | | | 25. | 45. | 55. | 60. |

First version: Ears out, shoes out

Second version: Ears out, shoes in

Third version: Ears in, shoes in

## BENJAMIN BUNNY™

| | |
|---|---|
| Modeller: | Arthur Gredington |
| Height: | 4", 10.1 cm |
| Size: | Small |

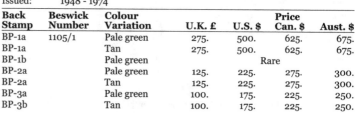

### FIRST VERSION: EARS OUT, SHOES OUT

Colour: Var. No. 1 Pale green jacket
        Var. No. 2 Tan jacket
Issued: 1948 - 1974

| Back Stamp | Beswick Number | Colour Variation | U.K. £ | U.S. $ | Price Can. $ | Aust. $ |
|---|---|---|---|---|---|---|
| BP-1a | 1105/1 | Pale green | 275. | 500. | 625. | 675. |
| BP-1a | | Tan | 275. | 500. | 625. | 675. |
| BP-1b | | Pale green | | | Rare | |
| BP-2a | | Pale green | 125. | 225. | 275. | 300. |
| BP-2a | | Tan | 125. | 225. | 275. | 300. |
| BP-3a | | Pale green | 100. | 175. | 225. | 250. |
| BP-3b | | Tan | 100. | 175. | 225. | 250. |

### SECOND VERSION: EARS OUT, SHOES IN

Colour: Var. No. 1 Pale green jacket; yellow and orange pompon
        Var. No. 2 Tan jacket; yellow and orange pompon
        Var. No. 3 Brown jacket; solid orange pompon
Issued: 1972 - c.1980

| Back Stamp | Beswick Number | Colour Variation | U.K. £ | U.S. $ | Price Can. $ | Aust. $ |
|---|---|---|---|---|---|---|
| BP-2a | 1105/2 | Pale green | | | Very rare | |
| BP-3a | | Pale green | 100. | 175. | 225. | 250. |
| BP-3a | | Tan | 100. | 175. | 225. | 250. |
| BP-3b | | Pale green | 100. | 175. | 225. | 250. |
| BP-3b | | Brown | 100. | 175. | 225. | 250. |

### THIRD VERSION: EARS IN, SHOES IN
### FIRST VARIATION: BROWN OR TAN SHOES

Colour: Var. No. 1 Brown jacket, green beret, solid orange pompon, tan shoes
        Var. No. 2 Light tan jacket and shoes
Issued: c.1980 - 2000

| Back Stamp | Beswick Number | Colour Variation | U.K. £ | U.S. $ | Price Can. $ | Aust. $ |
|---|---|---|---|---|---|---|
| BP-3b | 1105/3 | Brown | 45. | 80. | 100. | 110. |
| BP-3c | | Brown | 45. | 80. | 100. | 110. |
| BP-4 | | Brown | 50. | 90. | 115. | 125. |
| BP-5 | | Brown | 60. | 110. | 140. | 150. |
| BP-6a | | Brown | 25. | 45. | 55. | 60. |
| BP-6a | | Light tan | 25. | 45. | 55. | 60. |
| BP-10c | | Light tan | 25. | 45. | 55. | 60. |

### THIRD VERSION: EARS IN, SHOES IN
### SECOND VARIATION: GOLD SHOES

Colour: Brown jacket, green beret with orange pompon, gold shoes
Issued: 1998 - 1998

| Back Stamp | Beswick Number | Doulton Number | U.K. £ | U.S. $ | Price Can. $ | Aust. $ |
|---|---|---|---|---|---|---|
| BP-9b | 1105/4 | PG1105 | 30. | 55. | 70. | 75. |

### THIRD VERSION: EARS IN, SHOES IN
### THIRD VARIATION: BROWN SHOES, SATIN FINISH

Colour: Pale brown jacket, green beret with solid orange pompon, dark brown shoes
Issued: 2001 - 2002

| Back Stamp | Beswick Number | Doulton Number | U.K. £ | U.S. $ | Price Can. $ | Aust. $ |
|---|---|---|---|---|---|---|
| BP-11a | 1105/5 | PS1105 | 100. | 175. | 225. | 250. |

## BENJAMIN BUNNY™

| | |
|---|---|
| Modeller: | Martyn Alcock |
| Height: | 6 ¼", 15.9 cm |
| Size: | Large |

**FOURTH VERSION: LARGE SIZE, EARS IN, SHOES IN**
**FIRST VARIATION: BROWN SHOES**

| | |
|---|---|
| Colour: | Tan jacket, green beret with orange pompon |
| Issued: | 1994 - 1997 |

| Back Stamp | Beswick Number | Doulton Number | U.K. £ | U.S. $ | Price Can. $ | Aust. $ |
|---|---|---|---|---|---|---|
| BP-6b | 3403/1 | P3403 | 35. | 65. | 80. | 90. |

**FOURTH VERSION: LARGE SIZE, EARS IN, SHOES IN**
**SECOND VARIATION, GOLD SHOES**

| | |
|---|---|
| Colour: | Tan jacket, green beret with orange pompon, gold shoes |
| Issued: | 1997 in a limited edition of 1,947 |
| Series: | Gold edition |

| Back Stamp | Beswick Number | Doulton Number | U.K. £ | U.S. $ | Price Can. $ | Aust. $ |
|---|---|---|---|---|---|---|
| BP-9c | 3403/2 | PG3403 | 50. | 90. | 115. | 125. |

**Note:** Issued, numbered and sold as a pair with Peter Rabbit, second version, second variation.

Benjamin Bunny, large size, gold shoes

## BENJAMIN BUNNY SAT ON A BANK™

| | |
|---|---|
| Modeller: | David Lyttleton |
| Height: | 3 ¾", 9.5 cm |

**FIRST VERSION: HEAD LOOKS DOWN**

| | |
|---|---|
| Colour: | Brown jacket |
| Issued: | 1983 - 1985 |

| Back Stamp | Beswick Number | Doulton Number | U.K. £ | U.S. $ | Price Can. $ | Aust. $ |
|---|---|---|---|---|---|---|
| BP-3b | 2803/1 | P2803/1 | 75. | 135. | 175. | 185. |
| BP-3c | | | 75. | 135. | 175. | 185. |

First version: Head looks down

**SECOND VERSION: HEAD LOOKS UP**

| | |
|---|---|
| Colour: | Golden brown jacket |
| Issued: | 1983 - 1997 |

| Back Stamp | Beswick Number | Doulton Number | U.K. £ | U.S. $ | Price Can. $ | Aust. $ |
|---|---|---|---|---|---|---|
| BP-3b | 2803/2 | P2803/2 | 50. | 90. | 115. | 120. |
| BP-3c | | | 50. | 90. | 115. | 120. |
| BP-6a | | | 30. | 60. | 75. | 80. |

Second version: Head looks up

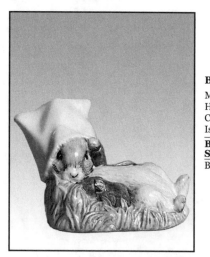

## BENJAMIN WAKES UP™

| Modeller: | Amanda Hughes-Lubeck |
|---|---|
| Height: | 2 ¼", 5.7 cm |
| Colour: | Green, white and orange |
| Issued: | 1991 - 1997 |

| Back Stamp | Beswick Number | Doulton Number | U.K. £ | U.S. $ | Price Can. $ | Aust. $ |
|---|---|---|---|---|---|---|
| BP-6a | 3234 | P3234 | 40. | 75. | 95. | 100. |

First version: Head down

## CECILY PARSLEY™

| Modeller: | Arthur Gredington |
|---|---|
| Height: | 4", 10.1 cm |

### FIRST VERSION: HEAD DOWN, BRIGHT BLUE DRESS

| Colour: | Bright blue dress, white apron, brown pail |
|---|---|
| Issued: | 1965 - 1985 |

| Back Stamp | Beswick Number | Doulton Number | U.K. £ | U.S. $ | Price Can. $ | Aust. $ |
|---|---|---|---|---|---|---|
| BP-2a | 1941/1 | P1941/1 | 100. | 175. | 225. | 250. |
| BP-3a | | | 50. | 90. | 115. | 125. |
| BP-3b | | | 50. | 90. | 115. | 125. |
| BP-3c | | | 50. | 90. | 115. | 125. |

Second version: Head up

### SECOND VERSION: HEAD UP, PALE BLUE DRESS

| Colour: | Pale blue dress, white apron, brown pail |
|---|---|
| Issued: | 1985 - 1993 |

| Back Stamp | Beswick Number | Doulton Number | U.K. £ | U.S. $ | Price Can. $ | Aust. $ |
|---|---|---|---|---|---|---|
| BP-3c | 1941/2 | P1941/2 | 50. | 90. | 115. | 125. |
| BP-6a | | | 50. | 90. | 115. | 125. |

**Note:** Cecily Parsley was issued with both a dark and a light blue dress.

## CHIPPY HACKEE™

| | |
|---|---|
| Modeller: | David Lyttleton |
| Height: | 3 ¾", 9.5 cm |
| Colour: | Pale green blanket, white handkerchief, green foot bath |
| Issued: | 1979 - 1993 |

| Back Stamp | Beswick Number | Doulton Number | U.K. £ | U.S. $ | Price Can. $ | Aust. $ |
|---|---|---|---|---|---|---|
| BP-3b | 2627 | P2627 | 50. | 90. | 115. | 125. |
| BP-3c | | | 50. | 90. | 115. | 125. |
| BP-6a | | | 175. | 325. | 400. | 450. |

**Note:** The colour of the blanket may range from pale green to pale yellow.

## CHRISTMAS STOCKING™

| | |
|---|---|
| Modeller: | Martyn Alcock |
| Height: | 3 ¼", 8.3 cm |
| Colour: | Brown mice, red and white striped stocking |
| Issued: | 1991 - 1994 |

| Back Stamp | Beswick Number | Doulton Number | U.K. £ | U.S. $ | Price Can. $ | Aust. $ |
|---|---|---|---|---|---|---|
| BP-6a | 3257 | P3257 | 200. | 350. | 450. | 475. |

## COTTONTAIL™

| | |
|---|---|
| Modeller: | David Lyttleton |
| Height: | 3 ¾", 9.5 cm |
| Colour: | Blue dress, brown chair |
| Issued: | 1985 - 1996 |

| Back Stamp | Beswick Number | Doulton Number | U.K. £ | U.S. $ | Price Can. $ | Aust. $ |
|---|---|---|---|---|---|---|
| BP-3b | 2878 | P2878 | 40. | 75. | 95. | 100. |
| BP-3c | | | 40. | 75. | 95. | 100. |
| BP-4 | | | 40. | 75. | 95. | 100. |
| BP-6a | | | 30. | 55. | 70. | 75. |

### COUSIN RIBBY™

| | |
|---|---|
| Modeller: | Albert Hallam |
| Height: | 3 ½", 8.9 cm |
| Colour: | Pink skirt and hat, green apron, blue shawl, yellow basket |
| Issued: | 1970 - 1993 |

| Back Stamp | Beswick Number | Doulton Number | U.K. £ | U.S. $ | Price Can. $ | Aust. $ |
|---|---|---|---|---|---|---|
| BP-2a | 2284 | P2284 | 200. | 375. | 475. | 500. |
| BP-3a | | | 45. | 80. | 100. | 110. |
| BP-3b | | | 45. | 80. | 100. | 110. |
| BP-3c | | | 45. | 80. | 100. | 110. |
| BP-6a | | | 60. | 110. | 135. | 150. |

BEATRIX POTTER
"Diggory Diggory Delvet"
© Frederick Warne & Co. 1982
Licensed by Copyrights
BESWICK ENGLAND

### DIGGORY DIGGORY DELVET™

| | |
|---|---|
| Modeller: | David Lyttleton |
| Height: | 2 ¾", 7.0 cm |
| Colour: | Grey mole |
| Issued: | 1982 - 1997 |

| Back Stamp | Beswick Number | Doulton Number | U.K. £ | U.S. $ | Price Can. $ | Aust. $ |
|---|---|---|---|---|---|---|
| BP-3b | 2713 | P2713 | 50. | 90. | 115. | 125. |
| BP-3c | | | 50. | 90. | 115. | 125. |
| BP-6a | | | 35. | 65. | 80. | 90. |

### DUCHESS™
### Style One (Holding Flowers)

| | |
|---|---|
| Modeller: | Graham Orwell |
| Height: | 3 ¾", 9.5 cm |
| Colour: | Black dog, multicoloured flowers |
| Issued: | 1955 - 1967 |

| Back Stamp | Beswick Number | Doulton Number | U.K. £ | U.S. $ | Price Can. $ | Aust. $ |
|---|---|---|---|---|---|---|
| BP-1a | 1355 | P1355 | | Extremely Rare | | |
| BP-2a | | | 2,000. | 3,500. | 4,500. | 4,750. |

## DUCHESS™
### Style Two (Holding a Pie)

| | |
|---|---|
| Modeller: | Graham Tongue |
| Height: | 4", 10.1 cm |
| Colour: | Black dog, blue bow, light brown pie |
| Issued: | 1979 - 1982 |

| Back Stamp | Beswick Number | Doulton Number | U.K. £ | U.S. $ | Price Can. $ | Aust. $ |
|---|---|---|---|---|---|---|
| BP-3b | 2601 | P2601 | 325. | 600. | 750. | 800. |

For **Duchess and Ribby** see the Tableaux Section, page 109.

## FARMER POTATOES™

| | |
|---|---|
| Modeller: | Shane Ridge |
| Height: | 5", 12.7 cm |
| Colour: | Tan jacket, brown trousers, yellow shirt, blue hat and lantern |
| Issued: | 2000 - 2002 |

| Back Stamp | Beswick Number | Doulton Number | U.K. £ | U.S. $ | Price Can. $ | Aust. $ |
|---|---|---|---|---|---|---|
| BP-10a | 4014 | P4014 | 45. | 80. | 100. | 110. |

First version: Feet out

Second version: Feet in

## FIERCE BAD RABBIT™

Modeller: David Lyttleton
Height: 4 ¾", 12.1 cm

### FIRST VERSION: FEET OUT

Colour: Dark brown and white rabbit, red-brown carrot, green seat
Issued: 1977 - 1980

| Back Stamp | Beswick Number | Doulton Number | U.K. £ | U.S. $ | Price Can. $ | Aust. $ |
|---|---|---|---|---|---|---|
| BP-3b | 2586/1 | P2586/1 | 75. | 135. | 175. | 200. |

BEATRIX POTTER'S
"Fierce Bad Rabbit"
F. Warne & Co.Ltd.
© Copyright 1977
BESWICK ENGLAND

### SECOND VERSION: FEET IN

Colour: Light brown and white rabbit, red-brown carrot, green seat
Issued: 1980 - 1997

| Back Stamp | Beswick Number | Doulton Number | U.K. £ | U.S. $ | Price Can. $ | Aust. $ |
|---|---|---|---|---|---|---|
| BP-3b | 2586/2 | P2586/2 | 50. | 90. | 115. | 125. |
| BP-3c | | | 50. | 90. | 115. | 125. |
| BP-4 | | | 70. | 125. | 150. | 175. |
| BP-6a | | | 35. | 65. | 80. | 90. |

BEATRIX POTTER
"Fierce Bad Rabbit"
© Frederick Warne & Co. 1977
Licensed by Copyrights
BESWICK ENGLAND

For **Flopsy and Benjamin Bunny** see the Tableaux Section, page 109.

## FLOPSY, MOPSY AND COTTONTAIL™
### Style One

| | |
|---|---|
| Modeller: | Arthur Gredington |
| Height: | 2 ½", 6.4 cm |
| Colour: | Brown/white rabbits wearing rose-pink cloaks |
| Issued: | 1954 - 1997 |

| Back Stamp | Beswick Number | Doulton Number | U.K. £ | U.S. $ | Price Can. $ | Aust. $ |
|---|---|---|---|---|---|---|
| BP-1a | 1274 | P1274 | 325. | 600. | 750. | 800. |
| BP-2a | | | 100. | 175. | 225. | 250. |
| BP-2b | | | 100. | 175. | 225. | 250. |
| BP-3a | | | 35. | 65. | 80. | 90. |
| BP-3b | | | 35. | 65. | 80. | 90. |
| BP-3c | | | 35. | 65. | 80. | 90. |
| BP-4 | | | 40. | 75. | 95. | 100. |
| BP-5 | | | 100. | 175. | 225. | 250. |
| BP-6a | | | 35. | 65. | 80. | 90. |

**Note:** Colour variations of the cloaks exist. Angle of bunnies heads may vary.

For **Flopsy, Mopsy and Cottontail**, Style Two, see the Tableaux Section, page 109.

## FOXY READING COUNTRY NEWS™

| | |
|---|---|
| Modeller: | Amanda Hughes-Lubeck |
| Height: | 4 ¼", 10.8 cm |
| Colour: | Brown and green |
| Issued: | 1990 - 1997 |

| Back Stamp | Beswick Number | Doulton Number | U.K. £ | U.S. $ | Price Can. $ | Aust. $ |
|---|---|---|---|---|---|---|
| BP-6a | 3219 | P3219 | 40. | 75. | 95. | 100. |

Small size: gloss finish

Small size: satin finish

# FOXY WHISKERED GENTLEMAN™

Modeller:    Arthur Gredington

**FIRST VERSION: SMALL**
**FIRST VARIATION: GLOSS FINISH**

Height:     4 ¾", 12.1 cm
Size:       Small
Colour:     Pale green jacket and trousers,
            pink waistcoat
Issued:     1954 - 2002

| Back Stamp | Beswick Number | Doulton Number | U.K. £ | U.S. $ | Price Can. $ | Aust. $ |
|---|---|---|---|---|---|---|
| BP-1a | 1277/1 | P1277 | 400. | 725. | 900. | 975. |
| BP-2a | | | 75. | 135. | 175. | 190. |
| BP-3a | | | 40. | 75. | 95. | 100. |
| BP-3b | | | 40. | 75. | 95. | 100. |
| BP-3c | | | 40. | 75. | 95. | 100. |
| BP-4 | | | 30. | 55. | 70. | 75. |
| BP-6a | | | 25. | 50. | 65. | 70. |
| BP-10a | | | 25. | 50. | 65. | 70. |

**Note:** 1. Variations occur with the head turned either right or left.
2. Gentleman is spelled as "Gentlemen" on all BP-1a and BP-2 backstamps

**FIRST VERSION: SMALL**
**SECOND VARIATION: SATIN FINISH**

Height:     4 ¾", 12.1 cm
Size:       Small
Colour:     Pale green jacket and trousers,
            pink waistcoat
Issued:     2001 - 2002

| Back Stamp | Beswick Number | Doulton Number | U.K. £ | U.S. $ | Price Can. $ | Aust. $ |
|---|---|---|---|---|---|---|
| BP-11a | 1277/2 | PS1277 | 100. | 175. | 225. | 250. |

**SECOND VERSION: LARGE**
**FIRST VARIATION: GREEN BUTTONS**

Height:     7 ½", 19.1 cm
Size:       Large
Colour:     Pale green jacket and trousers, pink waistcoat
Issued:     1995 - 1997

| Back Stamp | Beswick Number | Doulton Number | U.K. £ | U.S. $ | Price Can. $ | Aust. $ |
|---|---|---|---|---|---|---|
| BP-6b | 3450/1 | P3450 | 60. | 110. | 140. | 150. |

**SECOND VERSION: LARGE**
**SECOND VARIATION: GOLD BUTTONS**

Height:     7 ½", 19.1 cm
Size:       Large
Colour:     Pale green jacket and trousers, pink waistcoat, gold buttons
Issued:     1998 in a limited edition of 1,947
Series:     Gold edition

| Back Stamp | Beswick Number | Doulton Number | U.K. £ | U.S. $ | Price Can. $ | Aust. $ |
|---|---|---|---|---|---|---|
| BP-9c | 3450/2 | PG3450 | 70. | 125. | 160. | 170. |

Large size

**Note:** The gold edition was issued, numbered and sold as a pair with Mrs. Rabbit, third
version, first variation.

## GENTLEMAN MOUSE MADE A BOW™

| | |
|---|---|
| Modeller: | Ted Chawner |
| Height: | 3", 7.6 cm |
| Colour: | Brown, blue and white |
| Issued: | 1990 - 1996 |

| Back Stamp | Beswick Number | Doulton Number | U.K. £ | U.S. $ | Price Can. $ | Aust. $ |
|---|---|---|---|---|---|---|
| BP-6a | 3200 | P3200 | 30. | 55. | 65. | 70. |

## GINGER™

| | |
|---|---|
| Modeller: | David Lyttleton |
| Height: | 3 ¾", 9.5 cm |
| Colour: | Green, white and brown |
| Issued: | 1976 - 1982 |

| Back Stamp | Beswick Number | Doulton Number | U.K. £ | U.S. $ | Price Can. $ | Aust. $ |
|---|---|---|---|---|---|---|
| BP-3b | 2559 | P2559 | 250. | 450. | 550. | 600. |

**Note:** The jacket colour varies from light to dark green.

For **Ginger and Pickles** see the Tableaux Section, page 110.

## GOODY AND TIMMY TIPTOES™

| | |
|---|---|
| Modeller: | David Lyttleton |
| Height: | 4", 10.1 cm |
| Colour: | Timmy - rose coat Goody - pink overdress with green and biege underskirt, green umbrella |
| Issued: | 1986 - 1996 |

| Back Stamp | Beswick Number | Doulton Number | U.K. £ | U.S. $ | Price Can. $ | Aust. $ |
|---|---|---|---|---|---|---|
| BP-3c | 2957 | P2957 | 125. | 225. | 275. | 300. |
| BP-6a | | | 60. | 110. | 135. | 150. |

## GOODY TIPTOES™

| | |
|---|---|
| Modeller: | Arthur Gredington |
| Height: | 3 ½", 8.9 cm |
| Colour: | Grey squirrel wearing pink dress and white apron, brown sack with yellow nuts |
| Issued: | 1961 - 1997 |

| Back Stamp | Beswick Number | Doulton Number | U.K. £ | U.S. $ | Price Can. $ | Aust. $ |
|---|---|---|---|---|---|---|
| BP-2a | 1675 | P1675 | 120. | 220. | 275. | 300. |
| BP-3a | | | 50. | 90. | 115. | 125. |
| BP-3b | | | 50. | 90. | 115. | 125. |
| BP-3c | | | 50. | 90. | 115. | 125. |
| BP-6a | | | 25. | 45. | 55. | 60. |

**Note:** This model has two different bases and the dress comes in various shades of pink.

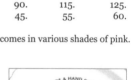

## HEAD GARDENER™

| | |
|---|---|
| Modeller: | Shane Ridge |
| Height: | 3 ½", 8.9 cm |
| Colour: | Brown and green |
| Issued: | 2002 - 2002 |

| Back Stamp | Beswick Number | Doulton Number | U.K. £ | U.S. $ | Price Can. $ | Aust. $ |
|---|---|---|---|---|---|---|
| BP-11a | P4236 | P4236 | 150. | 275. | 350. | 375. |

For **Hiding From the Cat** see the Tableaux Section, page 110.

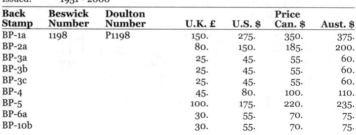

## HUNCA MUNCA™
### Style One

| | |
|---|---|
| Modeller: | Arthur Gredington |
| Height: | 2 ¾", 7.0 cm |
| Colour: | Blue dress, white apron, pink blanket and straw cradle |
| Issued: | 1951 - 2000 |

| Back Stamp | Beswick Number | Doulton Number | U.K. £ | U.S. $ | Price Can. $ | Aust. $ |
|---|---|---|---|---|---|---|
| BP-1a | 1198 | P1198 | 150. | 275. | 350. | 375. |
| BP-2a | | | 80. | 150. | 185. | 200. |
| BP-3a | | | 25. | 45. | 55. | 60. |
| BP-3b | | | 25. | 45. | 55. | 60. |
| BP-3c | | | 25. | 45. | 55. | 60. |
| BP-4 | | | 45. | 80. | 100. | 110. |
| BP-5 | | | 100. | 175. | 220. | 235. |
| BP-6a | | | 30. | 55. | 70. | 75. |
| BP-10b | | | 30. | 55. | 70. | 75. |

## HUNCA MUNCA™
### Style Two

| | |
|---|---|
| Modeller: | Shane Ridge |
| Height: | 4 ¼", 10.8 cm |
| Colour: | Mauve dress, white apron, grey pans |
| Issued: | 2001 - 2002 |

| Back Stamp | Beswick Number | Doulton Number | U.K. £ | U.S. $ | Price Can. $ | Aust. $ |
|---|---|---|---|---|---|---|
| BP-11a | P4074 | P4074 | 70. | 125. | 160. | 170. |

## HUNCA MUNCA SPILLS THE BEADS™

| | |
|---|---|
| Modeller: | Martyn Alcock |
| Height: | 3 ¼", 8.3 cm |
| Colour: | Brown mouse, blue and white rice jar |
| Issued: | 1992 - 1996 |

| Back Stamp | Beswick Number | Doulton Number | U.K. £ | U.S. $ | Price Can. $ | Aust. $ |
|---|---|---|---|---|---|---|
| BP-6a | 3288 | P3288 | 40. | 75. | 95. | 100. |

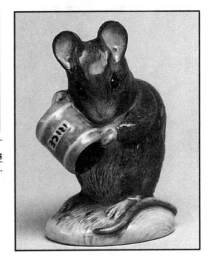

Green broom handle

Gold dustpan

Gold dustpan and broom handle

BEATRIX POTTER'S
"Hunca Munca Sweeping"
F. Warne & Co.Ltd.
© Copyright 1977
BESWICK ENGLAND

## HUNCA MUNCA SWEEPING™

Modeller: David Lyttleton
Height: 3 ½", 8.9 cm
Size: Small

**FIRST VERSION: SMALL SIZE**
**FIRST VARIATION: LIGHT BROWN DUSTPAN**

Colour: Mauve patterned dress, white apron, green broom handle, light brown dustpan
Issued: 1977 - 2002

| Back Stamp | Beswick Number | Doulton Number | U.K. £ | U.S. $ | Price Can. $ | Aust. $ |
|---|---|---|---|---|---|---|
| BP-3b | 2584/1 | P2584 | 40. | 70. | 85. | 95. |
| BP-3c | | | 40. | 70. | 85. | 95. |
| BP-4 | | | 40. | 70. | 85. | 95. |
| BP-6a | | | 30. | 55. | 70. | 75. |
| BP-10a | | | 25. | 45. | 55. | 60. |
| BP-11a | | | 30. | 55. | 70. | 75. |

**FIRST VERSION: SMALL SIZE**
**SECOND VARIATION: GOLD DUSTPAN**

Colour: Mauve patterned dress, white apron, green broom handle, gold dustpan
Issued: 1998 - 1998

| Back Stamp | Beswick Number | Doulton Number | U.K. £ | U.S. $ | Price Can. $ | Aust. $ |
|---|---|---|---|---|---|---|
| BP-9b | 2584/2 | PG2584 | 35. | 65. | 80. | 90. |

**SECOND VERSION: LARGE SIZE, GOLD DUSTPAN AND BROOM HANDLE**

Modeller: Amanda Hughes-Lubeck
Height: 5 ¼", 13.3 cm
Size: Large
Colour: Mauve patterned dress, white apron, gold dustpan and broom handle
Issued: 1999 in a limited edition of 1,947
Series: Gold edition

| Back Stamp | Beswick Number | Doulton Number | U.K. £ | U.S. $ | Price Can. $ | Aust. $ |
|---|---|---|---|---|---|---|
| BP-9c | 3894 | PG3894 | 50. | 90. | 115. | 125. |

**Note:** Issued, numbered and sold as a pair with Squirrel Nutkin, large size.

## JEMIMA AND HER DUCKLINGS™

Modeller: Martyn Alcock
Height: 4 ¼", 10.5 cm
Colour: Mauve shawl, blue bonnet
Issued: 1998 - 2002

| Back Stamp | Beswick Number | Doulton Number | U.K. £ | U.S. $ | Price Can. $ | Aust. $ |
|---|---|---|---|---|---|---|
| BP-8a | 3786 | P3786 | 300. | 550. | 700. | 750. |
| BP-10a | | | 60. | 110. | 135. | 150. |

**Note:** Very few examples of BP-8a are known.

## JEMIMA PUDDLE-DUCK™

Modeller: Arthur Gredington
Height: 4 ¾", 12.1 cm
Size: Small

**FIRST VERSION: SMALL SIZE**
**FIRST VARIATION: GLOSS FINISH, YELLOW SCARF CLIP**

Colour: Mauve or pink shawl, light blue bonnet, yellow scarf clip
Issued: 1948 - 2002

| Back Stamp | Beswick Number | Doulton Number | U.K. £ | U.S. $ | Price Can. $ | Aust. $ |
|---|---|---|---|---|---|---|
| BP-1a | 1092/1 | P1092 | 165. | 300. | 375. | 400. |
| BP-1b | | | Rare | | | |
| BP-2a | | | 70. | 125. | 150. | 170. |
| BP-3a | | | 40. | 75. | 90. | 100. |
| BP-3b | | | 40. | 75. | 90. | 100. |
| BP-3c | | | 40. | 75. | 90. | 100. |
| BP-4 | | | 40. | 75. | 90. | 100. |
| BP-5 | | | 175. | 300. | 375. | 400. |
| BP-6a | | | 30. | 55. | 70. | 75. |
| BP-10a | | | 30. | 55. | 70. | 75. |

Small size, yellow scarf clip

**FIRST VERSION: SMALL SIZE**
**SECOND VARIATION: GLOSS FINISH, GOLD SCARF CLIP**

Colour: Mauve or pink shawl, light blue bonnet, gold scarf clip
Issued: 1997 - 1997

| Back Stamp | Beswick Number | Doulton Number | U.K. £ | U.S. $ | Price Can. $ | Aust. $ |
|---|---|---|---|---|---|---|
| BP-9b | 1092/2 | PG1092 | 35. | 65. | 80. | 90. |

**FIRST VERSION: SMALL SIZE**
**THIRD VARIATION: SATIN FINISH**

Colour: Pink shawl with blue design, light blue bonnet, yellow scarf clip
Issued: 2001 - 2002

| Back Stamp | Beswick Number | Doulton Number | U.K. £ | U.S. $ | Price Can. $ | Aust. $ |
|---|---|---|---|---|---|---|
| BP-11a | 1092/3 | PS1092 | 100. | 175. | 225. | 250. |

Small size, gold scarf clip

Large size, yellow scarf clip

Large size, gold scarf clip

*Beswick Ware*
MADE IN ENGLAND
**BEATRIX POTTER'S
JEMIMA PUDDLE-DUCK**
BESWICK CENTENARY
1894 – 1994
© F. WARNE & CO. 1993
© 1993 ROYAL DOULTON

## JEMIMA PUDDLE-DUCK™

Modeller: Martyn Alcock
Height: 6", 15.0 cm
Size: Large

**SECOND VERSION: LARGE SIZE
FIRST VARIATION: YELLOW SCARF CLIP**

Colour: White duck, mauve shawl, light
blue bonnet, yellow scarf clip
Issued: 1993 - 1997

| Back Stamp | Beswick Number | Doulton Number | U.K. £ | U.S. $ | Price Can. $ | Aust. $ |
|---|---|---|---|---|---|---|
| BP-6b | 3373/1 | P3373 | 40. | 70. | 85. | 95. |
| BP-9a | Beswick Centenary | | 50. | 90. | 115. | 125. |

**SECOND VERSION: LARGE SIZE
SECOND VARIATION: GOLD SCARF CLIP**

Colour: White duck, mauve shawl, light
blue bonnet, gold scarf clip
Issued: 1998 in a limited edition of 1,947
Series: Gold edition

| Back Stamp | Beswick Number | Doulton Number | U.K. £ | U.S. $ | Price Can. $ | Aust. $ |
|---|---|---|---|---|---|---|
| BP-9c | 3373/2 | PG3373 | 50. | 90. | 115. | 125. |

**Note:** The second variation was issued, numbered and sold as a pair with
Mrs. Tiggy-Winkle, second version, second variation.

BEATRIX POTTER'S
Jemima Puddleduck
Made a feather nest
© Frederick Warne PLC. 1983
BESWICK
ENGLAND

## JEMIMA PUDDLE-DUCK MADE A FEATHER NEST™

Modeller: David Lyttleton
Height: 2 ¼", 5.7 cm
Colour: White duck, mauve or
pink shawl, blue hat
Issued: 1983 - 1997

| Back Stamp | Beswick Number | Doulton Number | U.K. £ | U.S. $ | Price Can. $ | Aust. $ |
|---|---|---|---|---|---|---|
| BP-3b | 2823 | P2823 | 45. | 80. | 100. | 110. |
| BP-3c | | | 45. | 80. | 100. | 125. |
| BP-4 | | | 50. | 90. | 115. | 125. |
| BP-6a | | | 30. | 55. | 70. | 75. |

**Note:** This model was issued with either a mauve or pink shawl.

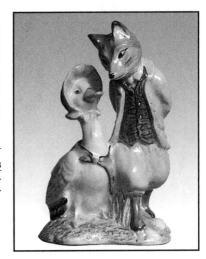

## JEMIMA PUDDLE-DUCK WITH FOXY WHISKERED GENTLEMAN™

| | |
|---|---|
| Modeller: | Ted Chawner |
| Height: | 4 ¾", 12.1 cm |
| Colour: | Brown, green, white and blue |
| Issued: | 1990 - 1999 |

| Back Stamp | Beswick Number | Doulton Number | U.K. £ | U.S. $ | Price Can. $ | Aust. $ |
|---|---|---|---|---|---|---|
| BP-6a | 3193 | P3193 | 30. | 55. | 65. | 75. |
| BP-10a | | | 40. | 70. | 90. | 95. |

## JEREMY FISHER CATCHES A FISH™

| | |
|---|---|
| Modeller: | Martyn Alcock |
| Height: | 3", 7.6 cm |
| Colour: | Green frog with brown spots, lilac coat, green, yellow and red fish |
| Issued: | 1999 - 2002 |

| Back Stamp | Beswick Number | Doulton Number | U.K. £ | U.S. $ | Price Can. $ | Aust. $ |
|---|---|---|---|---|---|---|
| BP-10a | 3919 | P3919 | 55. | 100. | 125. | 135. |
| BP-10a | 3919 | P3919 cut out 'V' | 125. | 225. | 275. | 300. |

**Note:** Two variations of P3919 exist. The base has either a full "V" cut through the lily pad and water, or a shorter "V" cut through the lily pad and water.

## JOHN JOINER™

| | |
|---|---|
| Modeller: | Graham Tongue |
| Height: | 2 ½", 6.4 cm |
| Colour: | Brown dog wearing green jacket |
| Issued: | 1990 - 1997 |

| Back Stamp | Beswick Number | Doulton Number | U.K. £ | U.S. $ | Price Can. $ | Aust. $ |
|---|---|---|---|---|---|---|
| BP-6a | 2965 | P2965 | 40. | 70. | 90. | 95. |

**Note:** John Joiner will vary in shade from black to blue-black.

## JOHNNY TOWN-MOUSE™

| Modeller: | Arthur Gredington |
| --- | --- |
| Height: | 3 ½", 8.9 cm |
| Colour: | Pale blue jacket, white and brown waistcoat |
| Issued: | 1954 - 1993 |

| Back Stamp | Beswick Number | Doulton Number | U.K. £ | U.S. $ | Price Can. $ | Aust. $ |
| --- | --- | --- | --- | --- | --- | --- |
| BP-1a | 1276 | P1276 | | Extremely rare | | |
| BP-2a | | | 90. | 165. | 200. | 225. |
| BP-3a | | | 50. | 90. | 115. | 120. |
| BP-3b | | | 50. | 90. | 115. | 120. |
| BP-3c | | | 50. | 90. | 115. | 120. |
| BP-6a | | | 50. | 90. | 115. | 120. |

**Note:** 1. Jacket colouring varies from pale to deep blue.
2. Because of it's small base very few figures have the BP-1a backstamp.

## JOHNNY TOWN-MOUSE EATING CORN™

| Modeller: | Martyn Alcock |
| --- | --- |
| Height: | 3 ¾", 9.5 cm |
| Colour: | Blue jacket, green and white waistcoat, pink trousers |
| Issued: | 2000 - 2002 |

| Back Stamp | Beswick Number | Doulton Number | U.K. £ | U.S. $ | Price Can. $ | Aust. $ |
| --- | --- | --- | --- | --- | --- | --- |
| BP-10a | 3931 | P3931 | 60. | 110. | 135. | 145. |

BEATRIX POTTER
"Johnny Town–Mouse with Bag"
© Frederick Warne & Co. 1988
Licensed by Copyrights
John Beswick
Studio of Royal Doulton
England

## JOHNNY TOWN-MOUSE WITH BAG™

| Modeller: | Ted Chawner |
| --- | --- |
| Height: | 3 ½", 8.9 cm |
| Colour: | Light brown coat and hat, yellow-cream waistcoat |
| Issued: | 1988 - 1994 |

| Back Stamp | Beswick Number | Doulton Number | U.K. £ | U.S. $ | Price Can. $ | Aust. $ |
| --- | --- | --- | --- | --- | --- | --- |
| BP-4 | 3094 | P3094 | 175. | 300. | 375. | 400. |
| BP-6a | | | 150. | 275. | 350. | 375. |

For **Kep and Jemima** see the Tableaux Section, page 110.

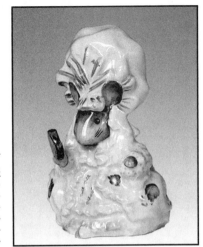

## LADY MOUSE™

| | |
|---|---|
| Modeller: | Arthur Gredington |
| Height: | 4", 10.1 cm |
| Colour: | White dress with yellow trim and blue polka-dot sleeves, white hat with purple and blue highlights |
| Issued: | 1950 - 2000 |

| Back Stamp | Beswick Number | Doulton Number | U.K. £ | U.S. $ | Price Can. $ | Aust. $ |
|---|---|---|---|---|---|---|
| BP-1a | 1183 | P1183 | 150. | 275. | 325. | 375. |
| BP-2a | | | 75. | 125. | 150. | 175. |
| BP-3a | | | 40. | 75. | 90. | 100. |
| BP-3b | | | 40. | 75. | 90. | 100. |
| BP-3c | | | 40. | 75. | 90. | 100. |
| BP-6a | | | 35. | 60. | 75. | 80. |
| BP-10a | | | 45. | 80. | 100. | 110. |

## LADY MOUSE MADE A CURTSY™

| | |
|---|---|
| Modeller: | Amanda Hughes-Lubeck |
| Height: | 3 ¼", 8.3 cm |
| Colour: | Purple-pink and white |
| Issued: | 1990 - 1997 |

| Back Stamp | Beswick Number | Doulton Number | U.K. £ | U.S. $ | Price Can. $ | Aust. $ |
|---|---|---|---|---|---|---|
| BP-6a | 3220 | P3220 | 50. | 90. | 115. | 120. |

## LITTLE BLACK RABBIT™

| | |
|---|---|
| Modeller: | David Lyttleton |
| Height: | 4 ½", 11.4 cm |
| Colour: | Black rabbit wearing green waistcoat |
| Issued: | 1977 - 1997 |

| Back Stamp | Beswick Number | Doulton Number | U.K. £ | U.S. $ | Price Can. $ | Aust. $ |
|---|---|---|---|---|---|---|
| BP-3b | 2585 | P2585 | 55. | 100. | 125. | 135. |
| BP-3c | | | 55. | 100. | 125. | 135. |
| BP-4 | | | | Very rare | | |
| BP-6a | | | 50. | 90. | 115. | 120. |

**Note:** 1. The jacket colouring varies from light to dark green.
2. The BP-4 version is very rare.

First variation: Blue striped dress

## LITTLE PIG ROBINSON™

Modeller:   Arthur Gredington

**FIRST VARIATION: BLUE STRIPED DRESS**

Height:   4", 10.2 cm
Colour:   White and blue striped dress, brown basket with yellow cauliflowers
Issued:   1948 - 1974

| Back Stamp | Beswick Number | Doulton Number | U.K. £ | U.S. $ | Price Can. $ | Aust. $ |
|---|---|---|---|---|---|---|
| BP-1a | 1104/1 | P1104/1 | 225. | 400. | 500. | 550. |
| BP-1b | | | | | Rare | |
| BP-2a | | | 125. | 225. | 275. | 300. |
| BP-3a | | | 100. | 175. | 225. | 250. |
| BP-3b | | | 100. | 175. | 225. | 250. |

Second variation: Blue checked dress

**SECOND VARIATION: BLUE CHECKED DRESS**

Height:   3 ½", 8.9 cm
Colour:   Blue checked dress, brown basket with cream cauliflowers
Issued:   c.1974 - 1999
Re-issued:   2002

| Back Stamp | Beswick Number | Doulton Number | U.K. £ | U.S. $ | Price Can. $ | Aust. $ |
|---|---|---|---|---|---|---|
| BP-3b | 1104/2 | P1104/2 | 40. | 75. | 95. | 100. |
| BP-3c | | | 40. | 75. | 95. | 100. |
| BP-6a | | | 25. | 45. | 55. | 60. |
| BP-10c | | | 25. | 45. | 55. | 60. |
| BP-11a | | | 25. | 45. | 55. | 60. |

## LITTLE PIG ROBINSON SPYING™

Modeller:   Ted Chawner
Height:   3 ½", 8.9 cm
Colour:   Blue and white striped outfit, rose-pink chair
Issued:   1987 - 1993

| Back Stamp | Beswick Number | Doulton Number | U.K. £ | U.S. $ | Price Can. $ | Aust. $ |
|---|---|---|---|---|---|---|
| BP-3c | 3031 | P3031 | 100. | 175. | 225. | 250. |
| BP-6a | | | 100. | 175. | 225. | 250. |

## MISS DORMOUSE™

| | |
|---|---|
| Modeller: | Martyn Alcock |
| Height: | 4", 10.1 cm |
| Colour: | Blue, white and pink |
| Issued: | 1991 - 1995 |

| Back Stamp | Beswick Number | Doulton Number | U.K. £ | U.S. $ | Price Can. $ | Aust. $ |
|---|---|---|---|---|---|---|
| BP-6a | 3251 | P3251 | 75. | 135. | 175. | 185. |

## MISS MOPPET™

| | |
|---|---|
| Modeller: | Arthur Gredington |
| Height: | 3", 7.6 cm |

**FIRST VARIATION: MOTTLED BROWN CAT**

| | |
|---|---|
| Colour: | Mottled brown cat, blue checkered kerchief |
| Issued: | 1954 - c.1978 |

| Back Stamp | Beswick Number | Doulton Number | U.K. £ | U.S. $ | Price Can. $ | Aust. $ |
|---|---|---|---|---|---|---|
| BP-1a | 1275/1 | P1275/1 | 425. | 750. | 925. | 1,000. |
| BP-2a | | | 80. | 135. | 170. | 180. |
| BP-3a | | | 45. | 80. | 100. | 110. |
| BP-3b | | | 45. | 80. | 100. | 110. |

First variation: Mottled brown cat

## SECOND VARIATION: BROWN STRIPED CAT

The BP-1a, BP-2a and some BP-3a striped variations are subtle and appear to be more a matter of decorator discretion than the deliberate bold stripes that began with later BP-3a's.

| | |
|---|---|
| Colour: | Striped brown cat, blue checked kerchief |
| Issued: | 1978 - 2002 |

| Back Stamp | Beswick Number | Doulton Number | U.K. £ | U.S. $ | Price Can. $ | Aust. $ |
|---|---|---|---|---|---|---|
| BP-1a | 1275/2 | P1275/2 | 350. | 625. | 775. | 850. |
| BP-2a | | | 100. | 175. | 225. | 250. |
| BP-3a | | | 35. | 60. | 75. | 80. |
| BP-3b | | | 35. | 60. | 75. | 80. |
| BP-3c | | | 35. | 60. | 75. | 80. |
| BP-6a | | | 35. | 60. | 75. | 80. |
| BP-10b | | | 35. | 60. | 75. | 80. |

Second variation: Brown striped cat

**MITTENS AND MOPPET™**

Modeller: Ted Chawner
Height: 3 ¾", 9.5 cm
Colour: Blue, brown and grey
Issued: 1990 - 1994

| Back Stamp | Beswick Number | Doulton Number | U.K. £ | U.S. $ | Price Can. $. £ Aust. $ | |
|---|---|---|---|---|---|---|
| BP-6a | 3197 | P3197 | 100. | 175. | 225. | 250. |

For **Mittens, Tom Kitten and Moppet** see the Tableaux Section, page 111.

**MOTHER LADYBIRD™**

Modeller: Warren Platt
Height: 2 ½", 6.4 cm
Colour: Red and black
Issued: 1989 - 1996

| Back Stamp | Beswick Number | Doulton Number | U.K. £ | U.S. $ | Price Can. $ | Aust. $ |
|---|---|---|---|---|---|---|
| BP-6a | 2966 | P2966 | 75. | 135. | 165. | 175. |

**MR. ALDERMAN PTOLEMY™**

Modeller: Graham Tongue
Height: 3 ½", 8.9 cm
Colour: Brown, grey and green
Issued: 1973 - 1997

| Back Stamp | Beswick Number | Doulton Number | U.K. £ | U.S. $ | Price Can. $ | Aust. $ |
|---|---|---|---|---|---|---|
| BP-3a | 2424 | P2424 | 65. | 120. | 150. | 160. |
| BP-3b | | | 40. | 75. | 95. | 100. |
| BP-3c | | | 65. | 120. | 150. | 160. |
| BP-6a | | | 40. | 75. | 95. | 100. |

Note: Mr. Alderman Ptolemy and Sir Isaac Newton are the only figures with backstamps using the words "Made in England" vice "England."

## MR. BENJAMIN BUNNY™

Modeller:  Arthur Gredington
Height:    4 ¼", 10.8 cm

### FIRST VERSION: PIPE OUT

Colour:    Var. No. 1 Dark maroon jacket
           Var. No. 2 Lilac jacket
Issued:    1965 - 1974

| Back Stamp | Beswick Number | Colour Variation | U.K. £ | U.S. $ | Price Can. $ | Aust. $ |
|---|---|---|---|---|---|---|
| BP-2a | 1940/1 | Dark maroon | 225. | 400. | 500. | 550. |
| BP-2b | | Dark maroon | 225. | 400. | 500. | 550. |
| BP-3a | | Dark maroon | 200. | 350. | 450. | 475. |
| BP-3a | | Lilac | | Extremely are | | |

First version: Pipe out

### SECOND VERSION: PIPE IN

Colour:    Var. No. 1 Dark maroon jacket
           Var. No. 2 Lilac jacket
Issued:    1. c.1970 - c.1974
           2. 1975 - 2000
Re-issued: 2. 2002

| Back Stamp | Beswick Number | Colour Variation | U.K. £ | U.S. $ | Price Can. $ | Aust. $ |
|---|---|---|---|---|---|---|
| BP-2b | 1940/2 | Lilac | | Rare | | |
| BP-3a | | Dark maroon | 200. | 300. | 375. | 400. |
| BP-3a | | Lilac | 235. | 425. | 525. | 575. |
| BP-3b | | Dark maroon | 200. | 300. | 375. | 400. |
| BP-3b | | Lilac | 35. | 65. | 80. | 90. |
| BP-3c | | Lilac | 35. | 65. | 80. | 90. |
| BP-4 | | Lilac | 40. | 70. | 90. | 95. |
| BP-6a | | Lilac | 35. | 65. | 80. | 90. |
| BP-10b | | Lilac | 35. | 65. | 80. | 90. |
| BP-11a | | Lilac | 35. | 65. | 80. | 90. |

Second version: Pipe in

## MR. BENJAMIN BUNNY AND PETER RABBIT™

Modeller:  Alan Maslankowski
Height:    4", 10.1 cm
Colour:    Benjamin Bunny: lilac jacket, yellow
           waistcoat
           Peter Rabbit: blue jacket
Issued:    1975 - 1995

| Back Stamp | Beswick Number | Doulton Number | U.K. £ | U.S. $ | Price Can. $ | Aust. $ |
|---|---|---|---|---|---|---|
| BP-3b | 2509 | P2509 | 75. | 135. | 165. | 175. |
| BP-3c | | | 75. | 135. | 165. | 175. |
| BP-6a | | | 60. | 110. | 135. | 150. |

### MR. DRAKE PUDDLE-DUCK™

Modeller: David Lyttleton
Height: 4", 10.1 cm
Colour: White duck, blue waistcoat and trousers
Issued: 1979 - 2000

| Back Stamp | Beswick Number | Doulton Number | U.K. £ | U.S. $ | Price Can. $ | Aust. $ |
|---|---|---|---|---|---|---|
| BP-3b | 2628 | P2628 | 40. | 75. | 95. | 100. |
| BP-3c | | | 60. | 110. | 135. | 150. |
| BP-4 | | | 40. | 75. | 95. | 100. |
| BP-6a | | | 30. | 55. | 70. | 75. |
| BP-10b | | | 40. | 75. | 95. | 100. |

BEATRIX POTTER
"Mr. Drake Puddle-Duck"
© Frederick Warne & Co. 1979
Licensed by Copyrights
BESWICK ENGLAND

First variation: Green toad

### MR. JACKSON™

Modeller: Albert Hallam
Height: 2 ¾", 7.0 cm

**FIRST VARIATION: GREEN TOAD**

Colour: Green toad wearing mauve jacket
Issued: 1974 - c.1974

| Back Stamp | Beswick Number | Doulton Number | U.K. £ | U.S. $ | Price Can. $ | Aust. $ |
|---|---|---|---|---|---|---|
| BP-3a | 2453/1 | P2453/1 | 225. | 400. | 500. | 550. |

BEATRIX POTTER'S
"Mr Jackson"
F. Warne & Co. Ltd.
Copyright
BESWICK ENGLAND

Second variation: Brown toad

**SECOND VARIATION: BROWN TOAD**

Colour: Brown toad wearing mauve jacket
Issued: 1975 - 1997

| Back Stamp | Beswick Number | Doulton Number | U.K. £ | U.S. $ | Price Can. $ | Aust. $ |
|---|---|---|---|---|---|---|
| BP-3b | 2453/2 | P2453/2 | 45. | 80. | 100. | 110. |
| BP-3c | | | 45. | 80. | 100. | 110. |
| BP-6a | | | 35. | 60. | 75. | 80. |

BEATRIX POTTER'S
"Mr Jackson"
F. Warne & Co. Ltd.
© Copyright 1974
BESWICK ENGLAND

## MR. JEREMY FISHER™

Modeller: Arthur Gredington
Height: 3", 7.6 cm
Size: Small

### FIRST VERSION: SMALL SIZE
### FIRST VARIATION: SPOTTED LEGS

Colour: Green frog with small brown spots on head and legs, lilac coat
Issued: 1950 - c.1974

| Back Stamp | Beswick Number | Doulton Number | U.K. £ | U.S. $ | Price Can. $ | Aust. $ |
|---|---|---|---|---|---|---|
| BP-1a | 1157/1 | P1157/1 | 250. | 450. | 550. | 600. |
| BP-2a | | | 100. | 175. | 225. | 250. |
| BP-3a | | | 55. | 100. | 125. | 135. |
| BP-3b | | | 55. | 100. | 125. | 135. |

Small size: Spotted legs

### FIRST VERSION: SMALL SIZE
### SECOND VARIATION: STRIPED LEGS

Colour: Green frog with large spots on head and stripes on legs, lilac coat
Issued: c.1950 - 2002

| Back Stamp | Beswick Number | Doulton Number | U.K. £ | U.S. $ | Price Can. $ | Aust. $ |
|---|---|---|---|---|---|---|
| BP-1a | 1157/2 | P1157/2 | 200. | 350. | 425. | 475. |
| BP-3b | | | 40. | 75. | 95. | 100. |
| BP-3c | | | 40. | 75. | 95. | 100. |
| BP-6a | | | 40. | 75. | 95. | 100. |
| BP-10a | | | 30. | 55. | 70. | 75. |

**Note:** BP-3c backstamp name exists with and without "Mr."

### FIRST VERSION: SMALL SIZE; THIRD VARIATION: SATIN FINISH

Colour: Beige frog with large spots on head and stripes on legs, lilac coat
Issued: 2001 - 2002

| Back Stamp | Beswick Number | Doulton Number | U.K. £ | U.S. $ | Price Can. $ | Aust. $ |
|---|---|---|---|---|---|---|
| BP-11a | 1157/3 | PS1157 | 100. | 175. | 225. | 250. |

Small size: Striped legs

### SECOND VERSION: LARGE SIZE
### FIRST VARIATION: LILAC BUTTONS

Modeller: Martyn Alcock
Height: 5", 12.7 cm
Size: Large
Colour: Green frog with stripes on legs, lilac coat
Issued: 1994 - 1997

| Back Stamp | Beswick Number | Doulton Number | U.K. £ | U.S. $ | Price Can. $ | Aust. $ |
|---|---|---|---|---|---|---|
| BP-6b | 3372/1 | P3372 | 40. | 75. | 95. | 100. |

### SECOND VERSION: LARGE SIZE; SECOND VARIATION: GOLD BUTTONS

Colour: Green frog with stripes on legs, lilac coat with gold buttons
Issued: 1998 in a limited edition of 1,947
Series: Gold edition

| Back Stamp | Beswick Number | Doulton Number | U.K. £ | U.S. $ | Price Can. $ | Aust. $ |
|---|---|---|---|---|---|---|
| BP-9c | 3372/2 | PG3372 | 50. | 90. | 115. | 120. |

**Note:** Issued, numbered and sold as a pair with Tom Kitten, second version, second variation.

Large size: Striped legs

## MR. JEREMY FISHER DIGGING™

Modeller: Ted Chawner
Height: 3 ¾", 9.5 cm
Colour: Green frog with brown highlights,
mauve coat, pink waistcoat, white cravat
Issued: 1988 - 1994

| Back Stamp | Beswick Number | Doulton Number | U.K. £ | U.S. $ | Price Can. $ | Aust. $ |
|---|---|---|---|---|---|---|
| BP-4 | 3090 | P3090 | 175. | 300. | 375. | 400. |
| BP-6a | | | 125. | 225. | 275. | 300. |

**Note:** Jeremy Fisher's skin may have dark or light spots.

## MR. MCGREGOR™

Modeller: Martyn Alcock
Height: 5 ¼", 13.5 cm
Colour: Brown hat and trousers, tan vest and
pale blue shirt
Issued: 1995 - 2002

| Back Stamp | Beswick Number | Doulton Number | U.K. £ | U.S. $ | Price Can. $ | Aust. $ |
|---|---|---|---|---|---|---|
| BP-6a | 3506/1 | P3506/1 | 30. | 55. | 70. | 75. |
| BP-10b | | | 35. | 60. | 75. | 80. |

**Note:** A variation of this figure exists with the right arm at chest height.

## MR. TOD™

Modeller: Ted Chawner
Height: 4 ¾", 12.1 cm
Colour: Green suit, red waistcoat, dark brown
walking stick
Issued: 1988 - 1993

| Back Stamp | Beswick Number | Doulton Number | U.K. £ | U.S. $ | Price Can. $ | Aust. $ |
|---|---|---|---|---|---|---|
| BP-4 | 3091/1 | P3091/1 | 250. | 450. | 550. | 600. |
| BP-6a | | | 125. | 225. | 275. | 300. |

**Note:** Variations occur with the head facing right or left, and the base in either green or brown.

## MRS. FLOPSY BUNNY™

| | |
|---|---|
| Modeller: | Arthur Gredington |
| Height: | 4", 10.1 cm |
| Colour: | 1. Dark blue dress, pink bag |
| | 2. Light blue dress, pink bag |
| Issued: | 1965 - 1998 |

| Back Stamp | Beswick Number | Colour Variation | U.K. £ | U.S. $ | Price Can. $ | Aust. $ |
|---|---|---|---|---|---|---|
| BP-2a | 1942 | Dark blue | 100. | 175. | 225. | 235. |
| BP-3a | | Dark blue | 35. | 65. | 80. | 90. |
| BP-3b | | Dark blue | 35. | 65. | 80. | 90. |
| BP-3b | | Light blue | 35. | 65. | 80. | 90. |
| BP-3c | | Light blue | 35. | 65. | 80. | 90. |
| BP-4 | | Light blue | 60. | 110. | 135. | 150. |
| BP-6a | | Light blue | 55. | 100. | 125. | 135. |
| BP-10b | | Light blue | 30. | 55. | 70. | 75. |

## MRS. RABBIT™

| | |
|---|---|
| Modeller: | Arthur Gredington |
| Height: | 4 ¼", 10.8 cm |
| Size: | Small |

### FIRST VERSION: SMALL SIZE UMBRELLA OUT

| | |
|---|---|
| Colour: | 1. Pink and yellow striped dress |
| | 2. Lilac and yellow striped dress |
| Issued: | 1951 - c.1974 |

| Back Stamp | Beswick Number | Colour Variation | U.K. £ | U.S. $ | Price Can. $ | Aust. $ |
|---|---|---|---|---|---|---|
| BP-1a | 1200/1 | Pink | Very Rare | | | |
| BP-2a | | Pink | 125. | 225. | 275. | 300. |
| BP-2a | | Lilac | 125. | 225. | 275. | 300. |
| BP-3a | | Lilac | 90. | 160. | 200. | 220. |
| BP-3b | | Lilac | 90. | 160. | 200. | 220. |

**Note:** 1. Due to its small base a gold oval backstamp was used for the bulk of pre-1955 production; the gold circle backstamp is very rare.
2. The BP-1a umbrella colour was pale green but became darker green with the BP-2 and BP-3a.

First version: Umbrella out

### SECOND VERSION: SMALL SIZE UMBRELLA MOULDED TO DRESS

| | |
|---|---|
| Colour: | Lilac and yellow striped dress, red collar and cap, light straw coloured basket |
| Issued: | c.1975 - 2002 |

| Back Stamp | Beswick Number | Doulton Number | U.K. £ | U.S. $ | Price Can. $ | Aust. $ |
|---|---|---|---|---|---|---|
| BP-3b | 1200/2 | P1200/2 | 40. | 70. | 90. | 95. |
| BP-3c | | | 40. | 70. | 90. | 95. |
| BP-4 | | | 50. | 90. | 110. | 120. |
| BP-6a | | | 35. | 60. | 75. | 80. |
| BP-10c | | | 35. | 60. | 75. | 80. |

Second version: Umbrella moulded to dress

Brown umbrella point and handle

**MRS. RABBIT™**

| | |
|---|---|
| Modeller: | Martyn Alcock |
| Height: | 6 ¼", 15.9 cm |
| Size: | Large |

**THIRD VERSION: LARGE SIZE**
**FIRST VARIATION: BROWN UMBRELLA POINT AND HANDLE**

| | |
|---|---|
| Colour: | White, pink, yellow and green |
| Issued: | 1994 - 1997 |

| Back Stamp | Beswick Number | Doulton Number | U.K. £ | U.S. $ | Price Can. $ | Aust. $ |
|---|---|---|---|---|---|---|
| BP-6b | 3398/1 | P3398 | 50. | 90. | 115. | 125. |

Gold umbrella point and handle

**THIRD VERSION: LARGE SIZE**
**SECOND VARIATION: GOLD UMBRELLA POINT AND HANDLE**

| | |
|---|---|
| Colour: | White, pink, yellow and green, gold umbrella point and handle |
| Issued: | 1998 in a limited edition of 1,947 |
| Series: | Gold edition |

| Back Stamp | Beswick Number | Doulton Number | U.K. £ | U.S. $ | Price Can. $ | Aust. $ |
|---|---|---|---|---|---|---|
| BP-9c | 3398/2 | PG3398 | 60. | 110. | 135. | 150. |

**Note:** Issued, numbered and sold as a pair with Foxy Whiskered Gentleman, second version, second variation.

**MRS. RABBIT AND BUNNIES™**

| | |
|---|---|
| Modeller: | David Lyttleton |
| Height: | 3 ¾", 9.5 cm |
| Colour: | Blue dress, white apron, dark blue chair |
| Issued: | 1976 - 1997 |

| Back Stamp | Beswick Number | Doulton Number | U.K. £ | U.S. $ | Price Can. $ | Aust. $ |
|---|---|---|---|---|---|---|
| BP-3b | 2543 | P2543 | 40. | 75. | 90. | 100. |
| BP-3c | | | 40. | 75. | 90. | 100. |
| BP-4 | | | 50. | 90. | 115. | 120. |
| BP-5 | | | 100. | 175. | 220. | 235. |
| BP-6a | | | 40. | 75. | 90. | 100. |

## MRS. RABBIT AND PETER™

### FIRST VERSION: SMALL SIZE

| Modeller: | Warren Platt |
|---|---|
| Height: | 3 ½", 8.9 cm |
| Size: | Small |
| Colour: | Mrs. Rabbit: Pale blue dress, white apron |
| | Peter: Pale blue coat with yellow buttons |
| Issued: | 1997 - 2002 |

| Back Stamp | Beswick Number | Doulton Number | U.K. £ | U.S. $ | Price Can. $ | Aust. $ |
|---|---|---|---|---|---|---|
| BP-6a | 3646 | P3646 | 40. | 75. | 95. | 100. |
| BP-10b | | | 35. | 65. | 80. | 90. |

First version: Small size

### SECOND VERSION: LARGE SIZE

| Modeller: | Amanda Hughes-Lubeck |
|---|---|
| Height: | 5 ¼", 13.3 cm |
| Size: | Large |
| Colour: | Mrs. Rabbit: Pale blue dress; white apron |
| | Peter: Pale blue coat with gold buttons |
| Issued: | 1999 in a limited edition of 2,500 |

| Back Stamp | Beswick Number | Doulton Number | U.K. £ | U.S. $ | Price Can. $ | Aust. $ |
|---|---|---|---|---|---|---|
| BP-9c | 3978 | PG3978 | 110. | 200. | 250. | 275. |

Second version: Large size, gold buttons

## MRS. RABBIT COOKING™

| Modeller: | Martyn Alcock |
|---|---|
| Height: | 4", 10.1 cm |
| Colour: | Blue dress, white apron |
| Issued: | 1992 - 1999 |

| Back Stamp | Beswick Number | Doulton Number | U.K. £ | U.S. $ | Price Can. $ | Aust. $ |
|---|---|---|---|---|---|---|
| BP-6a | 3278 | P3278 | 30. | 55. | 70. | 75. |
| BP-10b | | | 35. | 65. | 85. | 90. |

For **Mrs. Rabbit and the Four Bunnies** see the Tableaux Section, page 111.

Small size: Diagonal stripes

## MRS. TIGGY-WINKLE™

Modeller:    Arthur Gredington
Height:    3 ¼", 8.3 cm
Size:    Small

**FIRST VERSION: SMALL SIZE**
**FIRST VARIATION: GLOSS FINISH, DIAGONAL STRIPES**

Colour:    Diagonal striped red-brown and white dress, green and blue striped skirt, white apron
Issued:    1948 - 1974

| Back Stamp | Beswick Number | Doulton Number | U.K. £ | U.S. $ | Price Can. $ | Aust. $ |
|---|---|---|---|---|---|---|
| BP-1a | 1107/1 | P1107/1 | 150. | 275. | 350. | 375. |
| BP-2a | | | 100. | 175. | 200. | 235. |
| BP-3a | | | 50. | 90. | 115. | 120. |

**Note:** This figurine is also recognizable by the heavily patterned bustle.

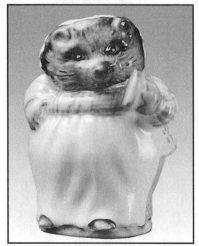

Small size: Plaid

**FIRST VERSION: SMALL SIZE**
**SECOND VARIATION: GLOSS FINISH, PLAID**

Colour:    Red-brown and white plaid dress, green and blue striped skirt, white apron
Issued:    1972 - 2000

| Back Stamp | Beswick Number | Doulton Number | U.K. £ | U.S. $ | Price Can. $ | Aust. $ |
|---|---|---|---|---|---|---|
| BP-2a | 1107/2 | P1107/2 | 75. | 135. | 175. | 185. |
| BP-3a | | | 35. | 65. | 80. | 85. |
| BP-3b | | | 35. | 65. | 80. | 85. |
| BP-3c | | | 35. | 65. | 80. | 85. |
| BP-4 | | | 45. | 60. | 75. | 80. |
| BP-6a | | | 45. | 60. | 75. | 80. |
| BP-10c | | | 45. | 60. | 75. | 80. |

Small size: Platinum iron

**FIRST VERSION: SMALL SIZE**
**THIRD VARIATION: GLOSS FINISH, PLATINUM IRON**

Colour:    Red-brown and white dress, green and blue striped skirt, white apron, platinum iron
Issued:    1998 - 1998

| Back Stamp | Beswick Number | Doulton Number | U.K. £ | U.S. $ | Price Can. $ | Aust. $ |
|---|---|---|---|---|---|---|
| BP-9b | 1107/3 | PG1107 | 50. | 90. | 115. | 120. |

**FIRST VERSION: SMALL SIZE**
**FOURTH VARIATION: SATIN FINISH**

Colour:    Red-brown and white dress, tan and blue striped skirt, white apron; satin glaze
Issued:    2001 - 2002

| Back Stamp | Beswick Number | Doulton Number | U.K. £ | U.S. $ | Price Can. $ | Aust. $ |
|---|---|---|---|---|---|---|
| BP-11a | 1107/4 | PS1107 | 100. | 175. | 225. | 250. |

## MRS. TIGGY-WINKLE™

Modeller:  Amanda Hughes-Lubeck
Height:    4 ½", 11.9 cm
Size:      Large

**SECOND VERSION: LARGE SIZE**
**FIRST VARIATION: CREAMY-BROWN IRON**

Colour:  Brown and white striped dress, white apron, creamy-brown iron
Issued:  1996 - 1997

| Back Stamp | Beswick Number | Doulton Number | U.K. £ | U.S. $ | Price Can. $ | Aust. $ |
|---|---|---|---|---|---|---|
| BP-6b | 3437/1 | P3437 | 40. | 70. | 90. | 95. |

Large size: Creamy-brown iron

**SECOND VERSION: LARGE SIZE**
**SECOND VARIATION: PLATINUM IRON**

Colour:  Brown and white striped dress, white apron, platinum iron
Issued:  1998 in a limited edition of 1,947
Series:  Gold edition

| Back Stamp | Beswick Number | Doulton Number | U.K. £ | U.S. $ | Price Can. $ | Aust. $ |
|---|---|---|---|---|---|---|
| BP-9c | 3437/2 | PG3437 | 55. | 100. | 125. | 135. |

**Note:** Issued, numbered and sold as a pair with Jemima Puddle-Duck, second version, second variation.

Large size: Platinum iron

## MRS. TIGGY-WINKLE BUYS PROVISIONS™

Modeller:  Martin Alcock
Height:    3 ¼", 8.3 cm
Colour:    Pink and white dress, white and brown mobcap
Issued:    2002 - 2002

| Back Stamp | Beswick Number | Doulton Number | U.K. £ | U.S. $ | Price Can. $ | Aust. $ |
|---|---|---|---|---|---|---|
| BP-11a | 4234 | P4234 | 175. | 325. | 400. | 450. |

For **Mrs. Tiggy-Winkle and Lucie** see the Tableaux Section, page 111.

## MRS. TIGGY WINKLE TAKES TEA™

| | | |
|---|---|---|
| Modeller: | David Lyttleton | |
| Height: | 3 ¼", 8.3 cm | |
| Colour: | Pink and white dress, white and brown mobcap | |
| Issued: | 1985 - 2002 | |

| Back Stamp | Beswick Number | Doulton Number | U.K. £ | U.S. $ | Price Can. $ | Aust. $ |
|---|---|---|---|---|---|---|
| BP-3b | 2877 | P2877 | 50. | 90. | 115. | 120. |
| BP-3c | | | 50. | 90. | 115. | 120. |
| BP-4 | | | 50. | 90. | 115. | 120. |
| BP-6a | | | 30. | 55. | 70. | 75. |
| BP-10a | | | 30. | 55. | 70. | 75. |

## MRS. TIGGY-WINKLE WASHING™

| | | |
|---|---|---|
| Modeller: | David Lyttleton | |
| Height: | 2 ½", 6.4 cm | |
| Colour: | Brown and white | |
| Issued: | 1998 - 2000 | |

| Back Stamp | Beswick Number | Doulton Number | U.K. £ | U.S. $ | Price Can. $ | Aust. $ |
|---|---|---|---|---|---|---|
| BP-8a | 3789 | P3789 | 125. | 225. | 275. | 300. |
| BP-10a | | | 55. | 100. | 125. | 135. |

**Note:** Approximately 1,800 pieces were issued with the BP-8a backstamp.

## MRS. TITTLEMOUSE™
### Style One

| | | | | | | |
|---|---|---|---|---|---|---|
| Modeller: | Arthur Gredington | | | | | |
| Height: | 3 ½", 8.9 cm | | | | | |
| Colour: | White and red striped blouse, blue and white striped skirt | | | | | |
| Issued: | 1948 - 1993 | | | | | |

| Back Stamp | Beswick Number | Doulton Number | U.K. £ | U.S. $ | Price Can. $ | Aust. $ |
|---|---|---|---|---|---|---|
| BP-1a | 1103 | P1103 | 100. | 175. | 220. | 235. |
| BP-2a | | | 80. | 150. | 175. | 200. |
| BP-2b | | | 80. | 150. | 175. | 200. |
| BP-3a | | | 45. | 80. | 100. | 110. |
| BP-3b | | | 45. | 80. | 100. | 110. |
| BP-3c | | | 45. | 80. | 100. | 110. |
| BP-6a | | | 65. | 115. | 150. | 160. |

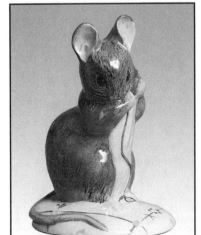

## MRS. TITTLEMOUSE™
### Style Two

| | |
|---|---|
| Modeller: | Shane Ridge |
| Height: | 3 ½", 8.9 cm |
| Colour: | White and red striped blouse, blue and white striped skirt, white apron |
| Issued: | 2000 - 2002 |

| Back Stamp | Beswick Number | Doulton Number | U.K. £ | U.S. $ | Price Can. $ | Aust. $ |
|---|---|---|---|---|---|---|
| BP-10a | 4015 | P4015 | 40. | 75. | 90. | 100. |

For **My Dear Son Thomas** see the Tableaux Section, page 112.

## NO MORE TWIST™

| | |
|---|---|
| Modeller: | Martyn Alcock |
| Height: | 3 ½", 9.2 cm |
| Colour: | Brown and white mouse |
| Issued: | 1992 - 1997 |

| Back Stamp | Beswick Number | Doulton Number | U.K. £ | U.S. $ | Price Can. $ | Aust. $ |
|---|---|---|---|---|---|---|
| BP-6a | 3325 | P3325 | 35. | 60. | 75. | 80. |

BEATRIX POTTER
"Old Mr. Bouncer"
© Frederick Warne & Co. 1986
Licensed by Copyrights
BESWICK ENGLAND

### OLD MR. BOUNCER™

| | |
|---|---|
| Modeller: | David Lyttleton |
| Height: | 3", 7.6 cm |
| Colour: | Brown jacket and trousers, blue scarf |
| Issued: | 1986 - 1995 |

| Back Stamp | Beswick Number | Doulton Number | U.K. £ | U.S. $ | Price Can. $ | Aust. $ |
|---|---|---|---|---|---|---|
| BP-3c | 2956 | P2956 | 50. | 90. | 115. | 120. |
| BP-6a | | | 50. | 90. | 115. | 120. |

BEATRIX POTTER'S
Old Mr. Brown
F. WARNE & Co. Ltd
COPYRIGHT
BESWICK
ENGLAND

### OLD MR. BROWN™

| | |
|---|---|
| Modeller: | Albert Hallam |
| Height: | 3 ¼", 8.3 cm |
| Colour: | 1. Brown owl, red squirrel |
| | 2. Orange owl, red squirrel |
| Issued: | 1963 - 1999 |

| Back Stamp | Beswick Number | Colour Variation | U.K. £ | U.S. $ | Price Can. $ | Aust. $ |
|---|---|---|---|---|---|---|
| BP-2a | 1796 | Brown | 85. | 150. | 200. | 210. |
| BP-3a | | Brown | 40. | 70. | 90. | 95. |
| BP-3b | | Brown | 40. | 70. | 90. | 95. |
| BP-3b | | Orange | 40. | 70. | 90. | 95. |
| BP-3c | | Orange | 40. | 70. | 90. | 95. |
| BP-6a | | Orange | 25. | 45. | 55. | 60. |
| BP-10a | | Orange | 25. | 45. | 55. | 60. |

BEATRIX POTTER'S
"Old Mr Pricklepin"
© Frederick Warne P.L.C. 1983
BESWICK ENGLAND

### OLD MR. PRICKLEPIN™

| | |
|---|---|
| Modeller: | David Lyttleton |
| Height: | 2 ½", 6.4 cm |
| Colour: | Brown |
| Issued: | 1983 - 1989 |

| Back Stamp | Beswick Number | Doulton Number | U.K. £ | U.S. $ | Price Can. $ | Aust. $ |
|---|---|---|---|---|---|---|
| BP-3b | 2767 | P2767 | 100. | 175. | 215. | 235. |
| BP-3c | | | 100. | 175. | 215. | 235. |
| BP-6a | | | 750. | 1,750. | 2,200. | 2,400. |

For **Peter and Benjamin Picking Apples and Peter** and **Benjamin Picking Up Onions** see the Tableaux Section, page 112.

## PETER AND THE RED POCKET HANDKERCHIEF™

Modeller:    Martyn Alcock
Height:      4 ¾", 12.3 cm
Size:        Small

**FIRST VERSION: SMALL SIZE**
**FIRST VARIATION: YELLOW BUTTONS**

Colour:      Light blue jacket with yellow
             buttons, red handkerchief
Issued:      1991 - 1999

| Back Stamp | Beswick Number | Doulton Number | U.K. £ | U.S. $ | Price Can. $ | Aust. $ |
|---|---|---|---|---|---|---|
| BP-6a | 3242 | P3242 | 40. | 75. | 90. | 100. |
| BP-10a | | | 30. | 55. | 70. | 75. |

First version: Small size

**FIRST VERSION: SMALL SIZE**
**SECOND VARIATION: GOLD BUTTONS**

Colour:      Dark blue jacket with gold buttons,
             red handkerchief
Issued:      1997 - 1997
Comm. by:    Peter Rabbit and Friends

| Back Stamp | Beswick Number | Doulton Number | U.K. £ | U.S. $ | Price Can. $ | Aust. $ |
|---|---|---|---|---|---|---|
| BP-9d | 5190 | PG5190 | 60. | 110. | 135. | 150. |

Second version: Small size, gold buttons

Second version: Large size

## PETER AND THE RED POCKET HANDKERCHIEF™

Modeller:    Amanda Hughes-Lubeck
Height:      7 ¼", 18.4 cm
Size:        Large

### SECOND VERSION: LARGE SIZE
### FIRST VARIATION: YELLOW BUTTONS

Colour:      Light blue coat with yellow
             buttons, red handkerchief
Issued:      1996 - 1997

| Back Stamp | Beswick Number | Doulton Number | U.K. £ | U.S. $ | Price Can. $ | Aust. $ |
|---|---|---|---|---|---|---|
| BP-6b | 3592/1 | P3592 | 40. | 70. | 90. | 95. |

**Note:** The backstamp on this version reads Peter "with" the Red Pocket Handkerchief.

Second version: Large size, gold buttons

### SECOND VERSION: LARGE SIZE
### SECOND VARIATION: GOLD BUTTONS

Colour:      Light blue coat with gold buttons,
             red handkerchief
Issued:      1998 in a limited edition of 1,947
Series:      Gold edition

| Back Stamp | Beswick Number | Doulton Number | U.K. £ | U.S. $ | Price Can. $ | Aust. $ |
|---|---|---|---|---|---|---|
| BP-9c | 3592/2 | PG3592 | 55. | 100. | 125. | 135. |

**Note:** Issued, numbered and sold as a pair with The Tailor of Gloucester, second version, second variation.

## PETER ATE A RADISH™

Modeller:    Warren Platt
Height:      4", 10.1 cm
Colour:      Brown and white rabbit,
             blue jacket, red radishes
Issued:      1995 - 1998

| Back Stamp | Beswick Number | Doulton Number | U.K. £ | U.S. $ | Price Can. $ | Aust. $ |
|---|---|---|---|---|---|---|
| BP-6a | 3533 | P3533 | 30. | 55. | 70. | 75. |

**Note:** BP-10b backstamp was reported by Royal Doulton in the backstamp changeover in 1998. We need confirmation that this backstamp was used on an actual issued figure. If it does exist, it is very rare.

## PETER IN BED™

| | | | | | | |
|---|---|---|---|---|---|---|
| Modeller: | Martyn Alcock | | | | | |
| Height: | 2 ¾", 7.0 cm | | | | | |
| Colour: | Blue, white, pink and green | | | | | |
| Issued: | 1995 - 2002 | | | | | |

| Back Stamp | Beswick Number | Doulton Number | U.K. £ | U.S. $ | Price Can. $ | Aust. $ |
|---|---|---|---|---|---|---|
| BP-6a | 3473 | P3473 | 40. | 70. | 90. | 95. |
| BP-10a | | | 40. | 70. | 90. | 95. |

## PETER IN THE GOOSEBERRY NET™

| | | |
|---|---|---|
| Modeller: | David Lyttleton | |
| Height: | 2", 4.6 cm | |
| Colour: | Brown and white rabbit wearing blue jacket, green netting | |
| Issued: | 1989 - 1995 | |

| Back Stamp | Beswick Number | Doulton Number | U.K. £ | U.S. $ | Price Can. $ | Aust. $ |
|---|---|---|---|---|---|---|
| BP-6a | 3157 | P3157 | 75. | 135. | 175. | 185. |

## PETER IN THE WATERING CAN™

| | | |
|---|---|---|
| Modeller: | Warren Platt | |
| Height: | 5", 12.7 cm | |
| Colour: | Brown rabbit in a green watering can | |
| Issued: | 1999 - 2002 | |

| Back Stamp | Beswick Number | Doulton Number | U.K. £ | U.S. $ | Price Can. $ | Aust. $ |
|---|---|---|---|---|---|---|
| BP-10a | 3940 | P3940 | 50. | 90. | 115. | 120. |

## PETER ON HIS BOOK™

| | |
|---|---|
| Modeller: | Martyn Alcock |
| Height: | 5", 12.7 cm |
| Colour: | Pale blue jacket, gold buttons, white book |
| Issued: | 2002 - 2002 |

| Back Stamp | Beswick Number | Doulton Number | U.K. £ | U.S. $ | Price Can. $ | Aust. $ |
|---|---|---|---|---|---|---|
| BP-11b | P4217 | P4217 | 95. | 175. | 225. | 235. |

**Note:** Issued to commemorate the 100th anniversary of the book The Tales of Peter Rabbit.

## PETER RABBIT™

| | |
|---|---|
| Modeller: | Arthur Gredington |
| Height: | 4 ½", 11.4 cm |
| Size: | Small |

### FIRST VERSION: SMALL SIZE
### FIRST VARIATION: DEEP BLUE JACKET

| | |
|---|---|
| Colour: | Dark blue jacket with yellow buttons |
| Issued: | 1948 - c.1980 |

| Back Stamp | Beswick Number | Doulton Number | U.K. £ | U.S. $ | Price Can. $ | Aust. $ |
|---|---|---|---|---|---|---|
| BP-1a | 1098/1 | P1098/1 | 225. | 400. | 500. | 550. |
| BP-1b | | | | Rare | | |
| BP-2a/b | | | 80. | 150. | 185. | 200. |
| BP-3a | | | 50. | 90. | 115. | 125. |
| BP-3b | | | 50. | 90. | 115. | 125. |

Small size: Deep blue jacket

### FIRST VERSION: SMALL SIZE; SECOND VARIATION: LIGHT BLUE JACKET

| | |
|---|---|
| Colour: | Light blue jacket with yellow buttons |
| Issued: | c.1980 - 2002 |

| Back Stamp | Beswick Number | Base Variation | U.K. £ | U.S. $ | Price Can. $ | Aust. $ |
|---|---|---|---|---|---|---|
| BP-3b | 1098/2 | Short base | 35. | 65. | 80. | 90. |
| BP-3b | | Long base | 35. | 65. | 80. | 90. |
| BP-3c | | Long base | 35. | 65. | 80. | 90. |
| BP-4 | | Long base | 45. | 80. | 100. | 110. |
| BP-5 | | Long base | 60. | 110. | 135. | 150. |
| BP-6a | | Long base | 25. | 45. | 55. | 60. |
| BP-10b | | Long base | 25. | 45. | 55. | 60. |

### FIRST VERSION: SMALL SIZE
### THIRD VARIATION: LIGHT BLUE JACKET, GOLD BUTTONS

| | |
|---|---|
| Colour: | Light blue jacket with gold buttons |
| Issued: | 1997 - 1997 |

| Back Stamp | Beswick Number | Doulton Number | U.K. £ | U.S. $ | Price Can. $ | Aust. $ |
|---|---|---|---|---|---|---|
| BP-9b | 1098/3 | PG1098 | 50. | 90. | 115. | 120. |

### FIRST VERSION: SMALL SIZE; FOURTH VARIATION: SATIN FINISH

| | |
|---|---|
| Colour: | Blue jacket with yellow buttons |
| Issued: | 2001 - 2002 |

| Back Stamp | Beswick Number | Doulton Number | U.K. £ | U.S. $ | Price Can. $ | Aust. $ |
|---|---|---|---|---|---|---|
| BP-11a | 1098/4 | PS1098 | 100. | 175. | 225. | 250. |

Small size: Gold buttons

## PETER RABBIT™

| | |
|---|---|
| Modeller: | Martyn Alcock |
| Height: | 6 ¾", 17.1 cm |
| Size: | Large |

**SECOND VERSION: LARGE SIZE**
**FIRST VARIATION: YELLOW BUTTONS**

| | |
|---|---|
| Colour: | Light blue jacket, yellow buttons |
| Issued: | 1993 - 1997 |

| Back Stamp | Beswick Number | Doulton Number | U.K. £ | U.S. $ | Price Can. $ | Aust. $ |
|---|---|---|---|---|---|---|
| BP-6b | 3356/1 | P3356 | 50. | 90. | 115. | 125. |
| BP-7 | 100th Anniversary | | 55. | 100. | 125. | 135. |

**Note:** The BP-7 backstamp was used only in 1993.

Large size: Yellow buttons

**SECOND VERSION: LARGE SIZE**
**SECOND VARIATION: GOLD BUTTONS**

| | |
|---|---|
| Colour: | Blue jacket with gold buttons |
| Issued: | 1997 in a limited edtion of 1,947 |
| Series: | Gold edition |

| Back Stamp | Beswick Number | Doulton Number | U.K. £ | U.S. $ | Price Can. $ | Aust. $ |
|---|---|---|---|---|---|---|
| BP-9c | 3356/2 | PG3356 | 75. | 135. | 175. | 185. |

**Note:** The second variation of this model was issued, numbered and sold as a pair with Benjamin Bunny, fourth version, fourth variation.

Large size: Gold buttons

## PETER RABBIT DIGGING™

| | |
|---|---|
| Modeller: | Martyn Alcock |
| Height: | 5", 12.7 cm |
| Colour: | Pale blue jacket |
| Issued: | 2001 - 2002 |

| Back Stamp | Beswick Number | Doulton Number | U.K. £ | U.S. $ | Price Can. $ | Aust. $ |
|---|---|---|---|---|---|---|
| BP-11a | P4075 | P4075 | 100. | 175. | 225. | 250. |

**PETER RABBIT GARDENING™**

| | |
|---|---|
| Modeller: | Warren Platt |
| Height: | 5", 12.7 cm |
| Colour: | Blue jacket, brown shovel, basket of carrots |
| Issued: | 1998 - 1999 |

| Back Stamp | Beswick Number | Doulton Number | U.K. £ | U.S. $ | Price Can. $ | Aust. $ |
|---|---|---|---|---|---|---|
| BP-10a | 3739 | P3739 | 60. | 110. | 135. | 150. |

**PETER WITH DAFFODILS™**

| | |
|---|---|
| Modeller: | Warren Platt |
| Height: | 4 ¾", 12.1 cm |
| Colour: | Light blue jacket, yellow daffodils |
| Issued: | 1996 - 1999 |

| Back Stamp | Beswick Number | Doulton Number | U.K. £ | U.S. $ | Price Can. $ | Aust. $ |
|---|---|---|---|---|---|---|
| BP-6a | 3597 | P3597 | 35. | 65. | 80. | 90. |
| BP-10b | | | 30. | 55. | 70. | 75. |

**PETER WITH POSTBAG™**

| | |
|---|---|
| Modeller: | Amanda Hughes-Lubeck |
| Height: | 4 ¾", 12.1 cm |
| Colour: | Light brown rabbit and postbag, lilac jacket trimmed in red |
| Issued: | 1996 - 2002 |

| Back Stamp | Beswick Number | Doulton Number | U.K. £ | U.S. $ | Price Can. $ | Aust. $ |
|---|---|---|---|---|---|---|
| BP-6a | 3591 | P3591 | 35. | 65. | 80. | 90. |
| BP-10b | | | 40. | 75. | 90. | 100. |

## PICKLES™

| | |
|---|---|
| Modeller: | Albert Hallam |
| Height: | 4 ½", 11.4 cm |
| Colour: | Black face dog with brown jacket and white apron, pink book |
| Issued: | 1971 - 1982 |

| Back Stamp | Beswick Number | Doulton Number | U.K. £ | U.S. $ | Price Can. $ | Aust. $ |
|---|---|---|---|---|---|---|
| BP-2a | 2334 | P2334 | 300. | 550. | 675. | 750. |
| BP-3a | | | 200. | 350. | 425. | 475. |
| BP-3b | | | 200. | 350. | 425. | 475. |

## PIGLING BLAND™

| | |
|---|---|
| Modeller: | Graham Orwell |
| Height: | 4 ¼", 10.8 cm |

### FIRST VARIATION: DEEP MAROON JACKET

| | |
|---|---|
| Colour: | Purple jacket, blue waistcoat, yellow trousers |
| Issued: | 1955 - 1974 |

| Back Stamp | Beswick Number | Doulton Number | U.K. £ | U.S. $ | Price Can. $ | Aust. $ |
|---|---|---|---|---|---|---|
| BP-1a | 1365/1 | P1365/1 | | Extremely | rare | |
| BP-2a | | | 175. | 300. | 375. | 400. |
| BP-3a | | | 125. | 225. | 275. | 300. |
| BP-3b | | | 125. | 225. | 275. | 300. |

First variation: Purple jacket

### SECOND VARIATION: LILAC JACKET

| | |
|---|---|
| Colour: | Lilac jacket, blue waistcoat, yellow trousers |
| Issued: | c.1975 - 1998 |

| Back Stamp | Beswick Number | Doulton Number | U.K. £ | U.S. $ | Price Can. $ | Aust. $ |
|---|---|---|---|---|---|---|
| BP-3b | 1365/2 | P1365/2 | 35. | 65. | 80. | 90. |
| BP-3c | | | 35. | 65. | 80. | 90. |
| BP-6a | | | 30. | 55. | 65. | 75. |
| BP-10c | | | 30. | 55. | 65. | 75. |

Note: 1. An example is known to exist with a grey jacket, light blue waistcoat, white trousers and tie. (BP-6a).
2. The BP-3b and BP-3c backstamps show an incorrect copyright date (1956), vice the correct date (1955).

Second variation: Lilac jacket

## PIGLING EATS HIS PORRIDGE™

| | |
|---|---|
| Modeller: | Martyn Alcock |
| Height: | 4", 10.1 cm |
| Colour: | Brown coat, blue waistcoat and yellow trousers |
| Issued: | 1991 - 1994 |

| Back Stamp | Beswick Number | Doulton Number | U.K. £ | U.S. $ | Price Can. $ | Aust. $ |
|---|---|---|---|---|---|---|
| BP-6a | 3252 | P3252 | 125. | 225. | 275. | 300. |

## PIG-WIG™

| | |
|---|---|
| Modeller: | Albert Hallam |
| Height: | 4", 10.1 cm |
| Colour: | 1. Grey pig, pale blue dress |
| | 2. Black pig, deep blue dress |
| Issued: | 1972 - 1982 |

| Back Stamp | Beswick Number | Colour Variation | U.K. £ | U.S. $ | Price Can. $ | Aust. $ |
|---|---|---|---|---|---|---|
| BP-2a | 2381 | Grey pig | | Extremely rare | | |
| BP-3a | | Black pig | 225. | 400. | 500. | 550. |
| BP-3b | | Black pig | 225. | 400. | 500. | 550. |

## POORLY PETER RABBIT™

| | |
|---|---|
| Modeller: | David Lyttleton |
| Height: | 3 ¾", 9.5 cm |
| Colour: | Brown-red and white blanket |
| Issued: | 1976 - 1997 |

| Back Stamp | Beswick Number | Doulton Number | U.K. £ | U.S. $ | Price Can. $ | Aust. $ |
|---|---|---|---|---|---|---|
| BP-3b | 2560 | P2560 | 50. | 90. | 115. | 120. |
| BP-3c | | | 50. | 90. | 115. | 120. |
| BP-4 | | | 50. | 90. | 115. | 120. |
| BP-6a | | | 50. | 90. | 115. | 120. |

**Note:** Later models have a lighter brown blanket.

## REBECCAH PUDDLE-DUCK™

Modeller:  David Lyttleton
Height:  3 ¼", 8.3 cm
Colour:  White goose, pale blue coat and hat
Issued:  1981 - 2000
Re-Issued:  2002

| Back Stamp | Beswick Number | Doulton Number | U.K. £ | U.S. $ | Price Can. $ | Aust. $ |
|---|---|---|---|---|---|---|
| BP-3b | 2647 | P2647 | 40. | 70. | 90. | 95. |
| BP-3c | | | 40. | 70. | 90. | 95. |
| BP-4 | | | 65. | 115. | 150. | 160. |
| BP-6a | | | 25. | 45. | 55. | 60. |
| BP-10b | | | 25. | 45. | 55. | 60. |
| BP-11a | | | 25. | 45. | 55. | 60. |

## RIBBY™

Modeller:  Arthur Gredington
Height:  3 ¼", 8.3 cm
Colour:  White dress with blue rings, white apron, pink and white striped shawl
Issued:  1951 - 2000

| Back Stamp | Beswick Number | Doulton Number | U.K. £ | U.S. $ | Price Can. $ | Aust. $ |
|---|---|---|---|---|---|---|
| BP-1a | 1199 | P1199 | 200. | 350. | 450. | 475. |
| BP-2a | | | 80. | 150. | 185. | 200. |
| BP-3a | | | 40. | 75. | 90. | 100. |
| BP-3b | | | 40. | 75. | 90. | 100. |
| BP-3c | | | 40. | 75. | 90. | 100. |
| BP-6a | | | 25. | 45. | 55. | 60. |
| BP-10c | | | 25. | 45. | 55. | 60. |

**Note:** The name shown on BP-6a and BP-10c is Mrs Ribby.

## RIBBY AND THE PATTY PAN™

Modeller:  Martyn Alcock
Height:  3 ½", 8.9 cm
Colour:  Blue dress, white apron
Issued:  1992 - 1998

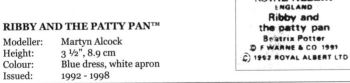

| Back Stamp | Beswick Number | Doulton Number | U.K. £ | U.S. $ | Price Can. $ | Aust. $ |
|---|---|---|---|---|---|---|
| BP-6a | 3280 | P3280 | 25. | 45. | 55. | 60. |

## SALLY HENNY PENNY™

| | |
|---|---|
| Modeller: | Albert Hallam |
| Height: | 4", 10.1 cm |
| Colour: | Brown and gold chicken, black hat and cloak, two yellow chicks |
| Issued: | 1974 - 1993 |

| Back Stamp | Beswick Number | Doulton Number | U.K. £ | U.S. $ | Price Can. $ | Aust. $ |
|---|---|---|---|---|---|---|
| BP-3a | 2452 | P2452 | 75. | 135. | 170. | 180. |
| BP-3b | | | 75. | 135. | 170. | 180. |
| BP-3c | | | 75. | 135. | 170. | 180. |
| BP-6a | | | 85. | 150. | 185. | 200. |

Correct      Error

Backstamp Variations

## SAMUEL WHISKERS™

| | |
|---|---|
| Modeller: | Arthur Gredington |
| Height: | 3 ¼", 8.3 cm |
| Colour: | Light green coat, yellow waistcoat and trousers |
| Issued: | 1948 - 1995 |

| Back Stamp | Beswick Number | Doulton Number | U.K. £ | U.S. $ | Price Can. $ | Aust. $ |
|---|---|---|---|---|---|---|
| BP-1a | 1106 | P1106 | 200. | 350. | 425. | 475. |
| BP-1b | | | | Rare | | |
| BP-2a | | | 100. | 175. | 225. | 250. |
| BP-3a | | | 45. | 80. | 100. | 110. |
| BP-3b | | | 45. | 80. | 100. | 110. |
| BP-3c | | | 45. | 80. | 100. | 110. |
| BP-4 | | | 300. | 550. | 675. | 750. |
| BP-6a | | | 60. | 110. | 135. | 150. |

**Note:** "Samuel" is spelled "Samual" on the BP-4 and BP-6a backstamps.

## SIMPKIN™

| | |
|---|---|
| Modeller: | Alan Maslankowski |
| Height: | 4", 10.1 cm |
| Colour: | Green coat |
| Issued: | 1975 - 1983 |

| Back Stamp | Beswick Number | Doulton Number | U.K. £ | U.S. $ | Price Can. $ | Aust. $ |
|---|---|---|---|---|---|---|
| BP-3b | 2508 | P2508 | 250. | 450. | 550. | 600. |

## SIR ISAAC NEWTON™

Modeller:   Graham Tongue
Height:     3 ¾", 9.5 cm
Colour:     Pale green jacket, yellow
            waistcoat with tan markings
Issued:     1973 - 1984

| Back<br>Stamp | Beswick<br>Number | Doulton<br>Number | U.K. £ | U.S. $ | Price<br>Can. $ | Aust. $ |
|---------------|-------------------|-------------------|--------|--------|-----------------|---------|
| BP-3a | 2425 | P2425 | 225. | 400. | 500. | 550. |
| BP-3b |      |       | 225. | 400. | 500. | 550. |

**Note:** 1. The colour and size of Sir Isaac Newton may vary.
2. Sir Isaac Newton and Mr. Alderman Ptolemy are the only figures with backstamps using the words "Made in England" vice "England."

## SQUIRREL NUTKIN™

Modeller:   Arthur Gredington
Height:     3 ¾", 9.5 cm
Size:       Small

### FIRST VERSION: SMALL SIZE
### FIRST VARIATION: RED-BROWN SQUIRREL

Colour:     Red-brown squirrel, green-brown apple
Issued:     1948 - c.1980

| Back<br>Stamp | Beswick<br>Number | Doulton<br>Number | U.K. £ | U.S. $ | Price<br>Can. $ | Aust. $ |
|---------------|-------------------|-------------------|--------|--------|-----------------|---------|
| BP-1a | 1102/1 | P1102/1 | 175. | 300. | 375. | 400. |
| BP-2a/b |      |         | 100. | 175. | 225. | 250. |
| BP-3a |        |         | 50.  | 90.  | 115. | 125. |
| BP-3b |        |         | 50.  | 90.  | 115. | 125. |

Small size: Red-brown squirrel

### FIRST VERSION: SMALL SIZE
### SECOND VARIATION: GOLDEN BROWN SQUIRREL

Colour:     Golden brown squirrel, green apple
Issued:     c.1980 - 2000

| Back<br>Stamp | Beswick<br>Number | Doulton<br>Number | U.K. £ | U.S. $ | Price<br>Can. $ | Aust. $ |
|---------------|-------------------|-------------------|--------|--------|-----------------|---------|
| BP-3b | 1102/2 | P1102/2 | 40. | 70. | 90. | 95. |
| BP-3c |        |         | 40. | 70. | 90. | 95. |
| BP-6a |        |         | 25. | 45. | 55. | 60. |
| BP-10a |       |         | 25. | 45. | 55. | 60. |

### SECOND VERSION: LARGE SIZE; RED CRAB APPLE, GOLD CORE

Modeller:   Amanda Hughes-Lubeck
Height:     5 ¼", 13.3 cm
Size:       Large
Colour:     Golden brown squirrel, red crab-apple, gold core
Issued:     1999 in a limited edition of 1,947
Series:     Gold edition

| Back<br>Stamp | Beswick<br>Number | Doulton<br>Number | U.K. £ | U.S. $ | Price<br>Can. $ | Aust. $ |
|---------------|-------------------|-------------------|--------|--------|-----------------|---------|
| BP-9c | 3893 | PG3893 | 50. | 90. | 115. | 125. |

**Note:** The second version of Squirrel Nutkin was issued, numbered and sold as a pair with Hunca Munca Sweeping, second version.

Large size: Gold apple core

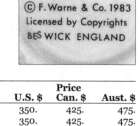

**SUSAN™**

| | |
|---|---|
| Modeller: | David Lyttleton |
| Height: | 4", 10.1 cm |
| Colour: | Blue dress, green, pink and black shawl and hat |
| Issued: | 1983 - 1989 |

| Back Stamp | Beswick Number | Doulton Number | U.K. £ | U.S. $ | Price Can. $ | Aust. $ |
|---|---|---|---|---|---|---|
| BP-3b | 2716 | P2716 | 200. | 350. | 425. | 475. |
| BP-3c | | | 200. | 350. | 425. | 475. |
| BP-6a | | | | Very rare | | |

**Note:** The colour and size of Susan may vary.

**SWEET PETER RABBIT™**

| | |
|---|---|
| Modeller: | Shane Ridge |
| Height: | 4 ¾", 12.1 cm |
| Colour: | Beige and cream rabbit, blue jacket, green and beige base |
| Issued: | 1999 in a special edition of 2,950 |

| Back Stamp | Beswick Number | Doulton Number | U.K. £ | U.S. $ | Price Can. $ | Aust. $ |
|---|---|---|---|---|---|---|
| BP-10d | 3888 | P3888 | 250. | 450. | 550. | 600. |

**Note:** This figure was commissioned by Peter Rabbit and Friends to commemorate the Year of the Rabbit, 1999.

## TABITHA TWITCHIT™

Modeller:   Arthur Gredington
Height:     3 ½", 8.9 cm

### FIRST VARIATION: BLUE STRIPED TOP

Colour:     Blue and white striped dress, white apron
Issued:     1961 - 1974

| Back Stamp | Beswick Number | Doulton Number | U.K. £ | U.S. $ | Price Can. $ | Aust. $ |
|---|---|---|---|---|---|---|
| BP-2a | 1676/1 | P1676/1 | 150. | 275. | 325. | 375. |
| BP-3a | | | 75. | 135. | 175. | 185. |
| BP-3b | | | 75. | 135. | 175. | 185. |

**Note:** Tabitha "Twitchit" is spelled "Twichett" on the BP-3a and BP-3b backstamps.

First variation: Blue striped top

### SECOND VARIATION: WHITE TOP

Colour:     Blue and white striped dress, white apron
Issued:     c.1975 - 1995

| Back Stamp | Beswick Number | Doulton Number | U.K. £ | U.S. $ | Price Can. $ | Aust. $ |
|---|---|---|---|---|---|---|
| BP-3b | 1676/2 | P1676/2 | 50. | 90. | 115. | 120. |
| BP-3c | | | 50. | 90. | 115. | 120. |
| BP-6a | | | 40. | 75. | 90. | 100. |

**Note:** 1. BP-3b has Twitchit spelled "Twitchett."
2. The white face became very dark/mottled shortly after the second variation was introduced.

Second variation: White top

First version: Small size

Second version: Large size

BEATRIX POTTER'S
Tabitha Twitchit and Miss Moppet
F. Warne & Co.Ltd.
© Copyright 1976
BESWICK ENGLAND

## TABITHA TWITCHIT AND MISS MOPPET™

### FIRST VERSION: SMALL SIZE

| | |
|---|---|
| Modeller: | David Lyttleton |
| Height: | 3 ½", 8.9 cm |
| Size: | Small |
| Colour: | Lilac dress, white apron, yellow sponge and hassock |
| Issued: | 1976 - 1993 |

| Back Stamp | Beswick Number | Doulton Number | U.K. £ | U.S. $ | Price Can. $ | Aust. $ |
|---|---|---|---|---|---|---|
| BP-3b | 2544 | P2544 | 75. | 135. | 175. | 185. |
| BP-3c | | | 75. | 135. | 175. | 185. |
| BP-4 | | | 150. | 275. | 350. | 375. |
| BP-6a | | | 125. | 225. | 275. | 300. |

## TABITHA TWITCHIT AND MOPPET™

### SECOND VERSION: LARGE SIZE

| | |
|---|---|
| Modeller: | Martyn Alcock |
| Height: | 5 ½", 14.0 cm |
| Size: | Large |
| Colour: | Tabitha Twitchit: Dark purple dress, white apron |
| | Moppet: Grey striped kitten |
| | Stool: Yellow with gold legs |
| Issued: | 2000 in a limited edition of 2,000 |
| Series: | Gold edition |

| Back Stamp | Beswick Number | Doulton Number | U.K. £ | U.S. $ | Price Can. $ | Aust. $ |
|---|---|---|---|---|---|---|
| BP-9c | 4020 | PG4020 | 100. | 175. | 225. | 250. |

## TAILOR OF GLOUCESTER™

### FIRST VERSION: SMALL SIZE

| | |
|---|---|
| Modeller: | Arthur Gredington |
| Height: | 3 ½", 8.9 cm |
| Size: | Small |
| Colour: | Brown mouse, yellow bobbin of red thread |
| Issued: | 1949 - 2002 |

| Back Stamp | Beswick Number | Doulton Number | U.K. £ | U.S. $ | Price Can. $ | Aust. $ |
|---|---|---|---|---|---|---|
| BP-1a | 1108 | P1108 | | Extremely rare | | |
| BP-1b | | | 400. | 725. | 900. | 975. |
| BP-2a | | | 70. | 125. | 150. | 165. |
| BP-3a | | | 30. | 55. | 70. | 75. |
| BP-3b | | | 30. | 55. | 70. | 75. |
| BP-3c | | | 30. | 55. | 70. | 75. |
| BP-4 | | | 50. | 90. | 115. | 120. |
| BP-6a | | | 30. | 55. | 70. | 75. |
| BP-10c | | | 25. | 45. | 55. | 60. |

**Note:** Only a very small quantity with the BP-1a backstamp are known to exist. The BP-1b backstamp was expressly designed for the small base Tailor of Gloucester and, unlike the other BP-1b's which were brief production line mistakes, was used for more than two years.

First version: Small size

### SECOND VERSION: LARGE SIZE
### FIRST VARIATION: STANDARD COLOURS

| | |
|---|---|
| Modeller: | Arthur Gredington |
| Height: | 6", 15.0 cm |
| Size: | Large |
| Colour: | Brown mouse, yellow bobbin of red thread |
| Issued: | 1995 - 1997 |

| Back Stamp | Beswick Number | Doulton Number | U.K. £ | U.S. $ | Price Can. $ | Aust. $ |
|---|---|---|---|---|---|---|
| BP-6b | 3449/1 | P3449 | 40. | 70. | 90. | 95. |

Second version: Large size

### SECOND VERSION: LARGE SIZE
### SECOND VARIATION: GOLD ACCENTS

| | |
|---|---|
| Colour: | Brown mouse, yellow bobbin of red thread, gold accents |
| Issued: | 1998 in a limited edition of 1,947 |
| Series: | Gold edition |

| Back Stamp | Beswick Number | Doulton Number | U.K. £ | U.S. $ | Price Can. $ | Aust. $ |
|---|---|---|---|---|---|---|
| BP-9c | 3449/2 | PG3449 | 50. | 90. | 115. | 120. |

**Note:** The second version, second variation of this model was issued, numbered and sold as a pair with Peter Rabbit and the Red Pocket Handkerchief, second version, second variation.

Second version: Large size, gold accents

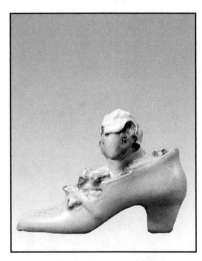

## THE OLD WOMAN WHO LIVED IN A SHOE™

| | |
|---|---|
| Modeller: | Colin Melbourne |
| Size: | 2 ¾" x 3 ¾", 7.0 cm x 9.5 cm |
| Colour: | Blue shoe |
| Issued: | 1959 - 1998 |

| Back Stamp | Beswick Number | Doulton Number | U.K. £ | U.S. $ | Price Can. $ | Aust. $ |
|---|---|---|---|---|---|---|
| BP-2 | 1545 | P1545 | 90. | 160. | 200. | 215. |
| BP-3a | | | 35. | 60. | 75. | 80. |
| BP-3b | | | 35. | 60. | 75. | 80. |
| BP-3c | | | 35. | 60. | 75. | 80. |
| BP-6a | | | 30. | 55. | 70. | 75. |

**Note:** The lettering of the BP-2 backstanp, which is gold, is frequently not very bright.

## THE OLD WOMAN WHO LIVED  IN A SHOE KNITTING™

| | |
|---|---|
| Modeller: | David Lyttleton |
| Height: | 3", 7.5 cm |
| Colour: | Purple dress, white apron, pale blue shawl and mobcap, yellow chair |
| Issued: | 1983 - 2002 |

| Back Stamp | Beswick Number | Doulton Number | U.K. £ | U.S. $ | Price Can. $ | Aust. $ |
|---|---|---|---|---|---|---|
| BP-3b | 2804 | P2804 | 75. | 135. | 175. | 185. |
| BP-3c | | | 75. | 135. | 175. | 185. |
| BP-6a | | | 25. | 45. | 55. | 60. |
| BP-10a | | | 25. | 45. | 55. | 60. |

## THIS PIG HAD A BIT OF MEAT™

| | |
|---|---|
| Modeller: | Martyn Alcock |
| Height: | 4", 10.1 cm |
| Colour: | Lilac dress, grey shawl, white apron and cap, gold-framed spectacles |
| Issued: | 2000 in a special edition of 1,500 |
| Comm. by: | Peter Rabbit and Friends |

| Back Stamp | Beswick Number | Doulton Number | U.K. £ | U.S. $ | Price Can. $ | Aust. $ |
|---|---|---|---|---|---|---|
| BP-9d | 4030 | P4030 | 850. | 1,500. | 1,750. | 2,000. |

## THOMASINA TITTLEMOUSE™

| | |
|---|---|
| Modeller: | David Lyttleton |
| Height: | 3 ¼", 8.3 cm |
| Colour: | Brown and pink highlights |
| Issued: | 1981 - 1989 |

Correct      Incorrect

Backstamp Variations

| Back Stamp | Beswick Number | Doulton Number | U.K. £ | U.S. $ | Price Can. $ | Aust. $ |
|---|---|---|---|---|---|---|
| BP-3b | 2668 | P2668 | 75. | 135. | 170. | 180. |
| BP-3c | | | 75. | 135. | 170. | 180. |
| BP-6a | | | 575. | 1,000. | 1,250. | 1,350. |

**Note:** "Thomasina" is spelled "Tomasina" on the BP-3c backstamp.

## TIMMY TIPTOES™

| | |
|---|---|
| Modeller: | Arthur Gredington |
| Height: | 3 ¾", 9.5 cm |

### FIRST VARIATION: RED JACKET

| | |
|---|---|
| Colour: | 1. Brown-grey squirrel, red jacket |
| | 2. Grey squirrel, red jacket |
| Issued: | 1948 - c.1980 |

| Back Stamp | Beswick Number | Colour Variation | U.K. £ | U.S. $ | Price Can. $ | Aust. $ |
|---|---|---|---|---|---|---|
| BP-1a | 1101/1 | Brown-grey | 125. | 225. | 275. | 300. |
| BP-1a | | Grey | 125. | 225. | 275. | 300. |
| BP-1b | | | | Rare | | |
| BP-2a | | Brown-grey | 85. | 150. | 200. | 220. |
| BP-2a | | Grey | 85. | 150. | 200. | 220. |
| BP-2b | | | 85. | 150. | 200. | 220. |
| BP-3a | | Brown-grey | 50. | 90. | 115. | 120. |
| BP-3a | | Grey | 50. | 90. | 115. | 120. |
| BP-3b | | Brown-grey | 50. | 90. | 115. | 120. |
| BP-3b | | Grey | 50. | 90. | 115. | 120. |

Fist variation: Red jacket

### SECOND VARIATION: LIGHT PINK JACKET

| | |
|---|---|
| Colour: | Grey squirrel, pink jacket |
| Issued: | c.1970 - 1997 |

| Back Stamp | Beswick Number | Doulton Number | U.K. £ | U.S. $ | Price Can. $ | Aust. $ |
|---|---|---|---|---|---|---|
| BP-2a | 1101/2 | P1101/2 | 90. | 160. | 200. | 220. |
| BP-3b | | | 50. | 90. | 115. | 120. |
| BP-3c | | | 50. | 90. | 115. | 120. |
| BP-6a | | | 25. | 45. | 55. | 60. |

**Note:** Second variations will vary in colour in a similar manner as the first.

Second variation: Pink jacket

## TIMMY WILLIE FETCHING MILK™

| | |
|---|---|
| Modeller: | Warren Platt |
| Height: | 3 ¼", 8.3 cm |
| Colour: | Brown and white mouse, blue milk jug |
| Issued: | 2000 - 2002 |

| Back Stamp | Beswick Number | Doulton Number | U.K. £ | U.S. $ | Price Can. $ | Aust. $ |
|---|---|---|---|---|---|---|
| BP-10a | 3976 | P3976 | 60. | 110. | 140. | 150. |

## TIMMY WILLIE FROM JOHNNY TOWN-MOUSE™

| | |
|---|---|
| Modeller: | Arthur Gredington |
| Height: | 2 ½", 6.4 cm |
| Colour: | Brown and white mouse, green or multicoloured base |
| Issued: | 1949 - 1993 |

| Back Stamp | Beswick Number | Doulton Number | U.K. £ | U.S. $ | Price Can. $ | Aust. $ |
|---|---|---|---|---|---|---|
| BP-1a | 1109 | P1109 | 100. | 175. | 200. | 225. |
| BP-2a | | | 85. | 150. | 185. | 200. |
| BP-3a | | | 40. | 70. | 85. | 95. |
| BP-3b | | | 40. | 70. | 85. | 95. |
| BP-3c | | | 40. | 70. | 85. | 95. |
| BP-4 | | | 50. | 90. | 115. | 120. |
| BP-6a | | | 50. | 90. | 115. | 120. |

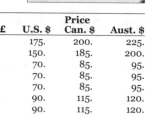

## TIMMY WILLIE SLEEPING™

| | |
|---|---|
| Modeller: | Graham Tongue |
| Size: | 1 ¼" x 3 ¾", 3.2 cm x 9.5 cm |
| Colour: | Green, white and brown |
| Issued: | 1986 - 1996 |

| Back Stamp | Beswick Number | Doulton Number | U.K. £ | U.S. $ | Price Can. $ | Aust. $ |
|---|---|---|---|---|---|---|
| BP-3c | 2996 | P2996 | 100. | 175. | 200. | 225. |
| BP-6a | | | 40. | 70. | 90. | 95. |

## TOM KITTEN™

| | |
|---|---|
| Modeller: | Arthur Gredington |
| Height: | 3 ½", 8.9 cm |
| Size: | Small |

**FIRST VERSION: SMALL SIZE**
**FIRST VARIATION: DEEP BLUE OUTFIT**

| | |
|---|---|
| Colour: | Tabby kitten wearing deep blue jacket and trousers, dark green base |
| Issued: | 1948 - c.1980 |

| Back Stamp | Beswick Number | Doulton Number | U.K. £ | U.S. $ | Price Can. $ | Aust. $ |
|---|---|---|---|---|---|---|
| BP-1a | 1100/1 | P1100/1 | 125. | 225. | 275. | 300. |
| BP-1b | | | | | Rare | |
| BP-2a | | | 75. | 135. | 170. | 180. |
| BP-3a | | | 35. | 60. | 75. | 80. |
| BP-3b | | | 35. | 60. | 75. | 80. |

Small size: Deep blue colourway

**FIRST VERSION: SMALL SIZE**
**SECOND VARIATION: LIGHT BLUE OUTFIT**

| | |
|---|---|
| Colour: | Tabby kitten wearing light blue jacket and trousers, light green base |
| Issued: | c.1980 - 1999 |

| Back Stamp | Beswick Number | Doulton Number | U.K. £ | U.S. $ | Price Can. $ | Aust. $ |
|---|---|---|---|---|---|---|
| BP-3b | 1100/2 | P1100/2 | 35. | 60. | 75. | 80. |
| BP-3c | | | 35. | 60. | 75. | 80. |
| BP-4 | | | 40. | 70. | 90. | 95. |
| BP-6a | | | 25. | 45. | 55. | 60. |
| BP-10c | | | 25. | 45. | 55. | 60. |

Small size: Light blue colourway

**FIRST VERSION: SMALL SIZE**
**THIRD VARIATION: GOLD BUTTONS**

| | |
|---|---|
| Colour: | Tabby kitten wearing light blue jacket and trousers; gold buttons |
| Issued: | 1997 - 1997 |

| Back Stamp | Beswick Number | Doulton Number | U.K. £ | U.S. $ | Price Can. $ | Aust. $ |
|---|---|---|---|---|---|---|
| BP-9b | 1100/3 | PG1100 | 35. | 60. | 75. | 80. |

**Note:** The small version of Tom Kitten was issued with two different style bases.

Small size: Gold buttons

Large size: Yellow buttons

## TOM KITTEN™

**SECOND VERSION: LARGE SIZE**
**FIRST VARIATION: YELLOW BUTTONS**

| Modeller: | Martyn Alcock |
| Height: | 5 ¼", 13.3 cm |
| Size: | Large |
| Colour: | Tabby kitten wearing light blue jacket and trousers; light green base |
| Issued: | 1994 - 1997 |

| Back Stamp | Beswick Number | Doulton Number | U.K. £ | U.S. $ | Price Can. $ | Aust. $ |
|---|---|---|---|---|---|---|
| BP-6b | 3405/1 | P3405 | 40. | 70. | 90. | 95. |

**SECOND VERSION: LARGE SIZE**
**SECOND VARIATION: GOLD BUTTONS**

| Colour: | Light blue jacket and trousers; gold buttons |
| Issued: | 1994 - 1997 |
| Series: | Gold edition |

| Back Stamp | Beswick Number | Doulton Number | U.K. £ | U.S. $ | Price Can. $ | Aust. $ |
|---|---|---|---|---|---|---|
| BP-9c | 3405/2 | PG3405 | 50. | 90. | 115. | 120. |

**Note:** The second variation was issued, numbered and sold as a pair with Mr. Jeremy Fisher, second version, second variation.

## TOM KITTEN AND BUTTERFLY™

| Modeller: | Ted Chawner |
| Height: | 3 ½", 8.9 cm |
| Colour: | Blue outfit, yellow hat |
| Issued: | 1987 - 1994 |

| Back Stamp | Beswick Number | Doulton Number | U.K. £ | U.S. $ | Price Can. $ | Aust. $ |
|---|---|---|---|---|---|---|
| BP-3c | 3030 | P3030 | 150. | 275. | 325. | 375. |
| BP-6a | | | 100. | 175. | 200. | 225. |

## TOM KITTEN IN THE ROCKERY™

| Modeller: | Warren Platt |
| Height: | 3 ½", 8.9 cm |
| Colour: | Pale blue jacket and trousers, yellow hat |
| Issued: | 1998 - 2002 |

| Back Stamp | Beswick Number | Doulton Number | U.K. £ | U.S. $ | Price Can. $ | Aust. $ |
|---|---|---|---|---|---|---|
| BP-10a | 3719 | P3719 | 30. | 55. | 70. | 75. |

## TOM THUMB™

Modeller:   Warren Platt
Height:     3 ¼", 8.3 cm
Colour:     Rose-pink and yellow chimney
Issued:     1987 - 1997

BEATRIX POTTER
"Tom Thumb"
© F. Warne & Co. 1987
Licensed by Copyrights
BESWICK ENGLAND

| Back Stamp | Beswick Number | Doulton Number | U.K. £ | U.S. $ | Price Can. $ | Aust. $ |
|---|---|---|---|---|---|---|
| BP-3c | 2989 | P2989 | 65. | 115. | 150. | 160. |
| BP-6a | | | 35. | 60. | 75. | 80. |

## TOMMY BROCK™

Modeller:   Graham Orwell
Height:     3 ½", 8.9 cm

General note. This figure has appeared in three versions, three variations and with multiple backstamps. Note that the new version 2 and the new variation 1 are new to this edition of Beswick Collectables.

**VERSIONS:**

**Version 1 — Handle out (1955-circa 1973):** white gloved hand around tan shaft of spade handle, tan loop of spade handle fully exposed; BP-1a, BP-2a and BP-3a backstamps;

**Version 2 — Hidden handle (circa 1974):** white gloved hand on top of tan spade handle, no portion of spade handle loop shown. This rare version is newly noted in this edition; BP-3a backstamp;

**Version 3 — Handle in (circa 1974-2002):** white gloved hand around tan shaft of spade handle, tan top of loop shows above white gloved hand. This is the final version; BP-3a, BP-3b et seq. backstamps.

**VARIATIONS:**

**Variation 1 — Original variable size eye patches (1955-circa 1970):** eye patch treatment, which varied considerably, appears to have been a matter of decorator discretion with size varying from somewhat small to somewhat large, and, with the patches having a somewhat feathery appearance, curving inward toward the centre of a grey-ish forehead; BP-1a and BP-2a backstamps;

**Variation 2 — Small eye patches (circa 1970-circa 1974):** ultra small, crisp black eye patches; off-white background; tip of eye patches tend to be in a line with ears; BP-2a, BP-3a and BP-3b backstamps;

**Variation 3 — Large eye patches (circa 1975-2002):** ultra large black eye patches in line with and touching the ears; off-white background; BP-3b et seq backstamps, but note the photo of the rare BP-2a version 1, variation 3.

BEATRIX POTTER'S
TOMMY BROCK
F. WARNE & Co. LTD.
COPYRIGHT
BESWICK
ENGLAND

**FIRST VERSION: SPADE HANDLE OUT**
**FIRST VARIATION: VARIABLE SIZE**
**EYE PATCH**

Colour:   Blue jacket, pink waistcoat, yellow-green trousers
Issued:   1955 - 1973

| Back Stamp | Beswick Number | Doulton Number | U.K. £ | U.S. $ | Price Can. $ | Aust. $ |
|---|---|---|---|---|---|---|
| BP-1a | 1348/1 | P1348/1 | | Extremely rare | | |
| BP-2a | | | 225. | 400. | 500. | 550. |

**Note:** Until circa 1972 the eye patches curved inward towards the centre of the forehead; tended to have a feathery appearance; and varied in size.

Spade handle out, variable eye patch

Spade handle out, small eye patch

## TOMMY BROCK™

Modeller:   Graham Orwell
Height:      3 ½", 8.9 cm

### FIRST VERSION: SPADE HANDLE OUT
### SECOND VARIATION: SMALL EYE PATCH

Colour:     Blue jacket, pink waistcoat,
             yellow trousers
Issued:     c.1972 -1974

| Back Stamp | Beswick Number | Doulton Number | U.K. £ | U.S. $ | Price Can. $ | Aust. $ |
|---|---|---|---|---|---|---|
| BP-2a | 1348/2 | P1348/2 | | | Rare | |
| BP-3a | | | 200. | 350. | 425. | 450. |

**Note:** Beginning in 1972-1974 the eye patches, large and small, tended to run straight up towards the ears; also, they were a solid black.

Spade handle out, large eye patch

### FIRST VERSION: SPADE HANDLE OUT
### THIRD VARIATION: LARGE EYE PATCH

Colour:     Blue jacket, pink waistcoat,
             yellow trousers
Issued:     c.1972 -1974

| Back Stamp | Beswick Number | Doulton Number | U.K. £ | U.S. $ | Price Can. $ | Aust. $ |
|---|---|---|---|---|---|---|
| BP-2a | 1348/3 | P1348/3 | | | Rare | |
| BP-3a | | | | | Rare | |

Spade handle hidden, small eye patch

### SECOND VERSION: SPADE HANDLE HIDDEN
### SECOND VARIATION: SMALL EYE PATCH

Colour:     Blue-grey jacket, pink waistcoat,
             yellow trousers
Issued:     c. 1974

| Back Stamp | Beswick Number | Doulton Number | U.K. £ | U.S. $ | Price Can. $ | Aust. $ |
|---|---|---|---|---|---|---|
| BP-3a | 1348/4 | P1348/4 | | | Rare | |

**Note:** This "hidden handle" version was an initial transition step to the "handle in" version.

**TOMMY BROCK**™

Modeller: Graham Orwell
Height: 3 ½", 8.9 cm

**THIRD VERSION: HANDLE IN
SECOND VARIATION: SMALL EYE PATCH**

Height: 3 ½", 8.9 cm
Colour: Blue-grey jacket, pink waistcoat, yellow trousers
Issued: c.1974 - 1975

| Back Stamp | Beswick Number | Doulton Number | U.K. £ | U.S. $ | Price Can. $ | Aust. $ |
|---|---|---|---|---|---|---|
| BP-3a | 1348/5 | P1348/5 | 70. | 125. | 150. | 165. |
| BP-3b | | | 60. | 110. | 135. | 150. |

Spade handle in, small eye patch

**THIRD VERSION: HANDLE IN
THIRD VARIATION: LARGE EYE PATCH**

Colour: Blue-grey jacket, red waistcoat, yellow trousers
Issued: c.1975 - 2002

| Back Stamp | Beswick Number | Doulton Number | U.K. £ | U.S. $ | Price Can. $ | Aust. $ |
|---|---|---|---|---|---|---|
| BP-3b | 1348/6 | P1348/6 | 40. | 70. | 90. | 95. |
| BP-3c | | | 40. | 70. | 90. | 95. |
| BP-4 | | | 50. | 90. | 115. | 125. |
| BP-6a | | | 25. | 45. | 55. | 60. |
| BP-10a | | | 25. | 45. | 55. | 60. |

**Note:** The jacket colour varies from pale to dark blue in BP-3b.

Spade handle in, large eye patch

## TWO GENTLEMEN RABBITS™

Modeller:   Shane Ridge
Height:     5", 12.5 cm
Colour:     Brown, green and red
Issued:     2002 - 2002

| Back Stamp | Beswick Number | Doulton Number | U.K. £ | U.S. $ | Price Can. $ | Aust. $ |
|---|---|---|---|---|---|---|
| BP-11a | 4210 | P4210 | 225. | 400. | 500. | 550. |

## YOCK-YOCK IN THE TUB™

Modeller:   Warren Platt
Height:     3", 7.6 cm
Colour:     Pink pig, brown tub
Issued:     2000-2002

| Back Stamp | Beswick Number | Doulton Number | U.K. £ | U.S. $ | Price Can. $ | Aust. $ |
|---|---|---|---|---|---|---|
| BP-10a | 3946 | P3946 | 60. | 110. | 135. | 145. |

# BEATRIX POTTER
# TABLEAUX

## DUCHESS AND RIBBY™

| | |
|---|---|
| Modeller: | Martyn Alcock |
| Length: | 7 ¾", 19.7 cm |
| Colour: | Black, lilac, grey and gold |
| Issued: | 2000 in a limited edition of 1,500 |
| Comm. by: | Peter Rabbit and Friends |

| Back Stamp | Beswick Number | Doulton Number | U.K. £ | U.S. $ | Price Can. $ | Aust. $ |
|---|---|---|---|---|---|---|
| BP-9d | 3983 | P3983 | 325. | 600. | 725. | 775. |

## FLOPSY AND BENJAMIN BUNNY™

| | |
|---|---|
| Modeller: | Shane Ridge |
| Height: | 5", 12.7 cm |
| Colour: | Benjamin: Pink jacket Flopsy: Blue dress |
| Issued: | 2001 - 2002 |

| Back Stamp | Beswick Number | Doulton Number | U.K. £ | U.S. $ | Price Can. $ | Aust. $ |
|---|---|---|---|---|---|---|
| BP-11b | 4155 | P4155 | 125. | 225. | 275. | 300. |

## FLOPSY, MOPSY AND COTTONTAIL™
### Style Two

| | |
|---|---|
| Modeller: | Shane Ridge |
| Height: | 3 ¾", 9.5 cm |
| Colour: | Brown, pink and white |
| Issued: | 2002 in a limited edition of 1,500 (C of A) |
| Comm. by: | Doulton-Direct |

| Back Stamp | Beswick Number | Doulton Number | U.K. £ | U.S. $ | Price Can. $ | Aust. $ |
|---|---|---|---|---|---|---|
| BP-11b | 4161 | P4161 | 500. | 900. | 1,100. | 1,200. |

**Note:** Final piece in the series.

### GINGER AND PICKLES™

| Modeller: | David Lyttleton |
|---|---|
| Height: | 3 ¾", 9.5 cm |
| Colour: | Green, white and brown |
| Issued: | 1998 in a limited edition of 2,750 |
| Comm. by: | Peter Rabbit and Friends |

| Back Stamp | Beswick Number | Doulton Number | U.K. £ | U.S. $ | Price Can. $ | Aust. $ |
|---|---|---|---|---|---|---|
| BP-9d | 3790 | P3790 | 175. | 300. | 375. | 400. |

### HIDING FROM THE CAT™

| Modeller: | Graham Tongue |
|---|---|
| Height: | 5", 12.7 cm |
| Colour: | Brown, blue and grey |
| Issued: | 1998 in a limited edition of 3,500 |
| Series: | Tableau of the Year |

| Back Stamp | Beswick Number | Doulton Number | U.K. £ | U.S. $ | Price Can. $ | Aust. $ |
|---|---|---|---|---|---|---|
| BP-8c | 3672 | P3672 | 100. | 175. | 225. | 250. |

### KEP AND JEMIMIA™

| Modeller: | Martyn Alcock |
|---|---|
| Length: | 4 ½", 11.4 cm |
| Colour: | Jemima: Pink and blue shawl |
| | Kep: Brown and white collie |
| Issued: | 2002 in a limited edition of 2,000 (C of A) |

| Back Stamp | Beswick Number | Doulton Number | U.K. £ | U.S. $ | Price Can. $ | Aust. $ |
|---|---|---|---|---|---|---|
| BP-11b | 4901 | P4901 | 250. | 450. | 550. | 600. |

**MITTENS, TOM KITTEN AND MOPPET™**

| | |
|---|---|
| Modeller: | Amanda Hughes-Lubeck |
| Length: | 7", 17.8 cm |
| Colour: | Pale blue and beige |
| Issued: | 1999 - 1999 |
| Series: | Tableau of the Year |

| Back Stamp | Beswick Number | Doulton Number | U.K. £ | U.S. $ | Price Can. $ | Aust. $ |
|---|---|---|---|---|---|---|
| BP-8c | 3792 | P3792 | 75. | 135. | 165. | 180. |

**MRS. RABBIT AND THE FOUR BUNNIES™**

| | |
|---|---|
| Modeller: | Shane Ridge |
| Height: | 4 ½", 11.9 cm |
| Colour: | Mrs Rabbit: Pale blue dress, white apron |
| | Bunnies: Rose cloaks |
| | Peter: Pale blue jacket |
| Issued: | 1997 in a limited edition of 1,997 |
| Series: | Tableau of the Year |

| Back Stamp | Beswick Number | Doulton Number | U.K. £ | U.S. $ | Price Can. $ | Aust. $ |
|---|---|---|---|---|---|---|
| BP-8b | 3672 | P3672 | 250. | 450. | 550. | 600. |

**MRS. TIGGY-WINKLE AND LUCIE™**

| | |
|---|---|
| Modeller: | Martyn Alcock |
| Height: | 4", 10.1 cm |
| Colour: | Mrs. Tiggy-Winkle: Brown, pink and cream dress, yellow and blue striped skirt, white apron, red handkerchief, platinum iron and horseshoe |
| | Lucie: Pink dress, white pinafore |
| Issued: | 1999 in a limited edition of 2,950 |
| Comm. by: | Peter Rabbit and Friends |

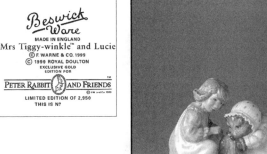

| Back Stamp | Beswick Number | Doulton Number | U.K. £ | U.S. $ | Price Can. $ | Aust. $ |
|---|---|---|---|---|---|---|
| BP-9d | 3867 | P3867 | 125. | 225. | 275. | 300. |

## MY DEAR SON THOMAS™

| | |
|---|---|
| Modeller: | Martyn Alcock |
| Height: | 3 ½", 8.9 cm |
| Colour: | Blue, white, pink, grey and tan |
| Issued: | 2001 in a limited edition of 3,000 |

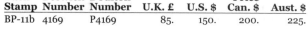

| Back Stamp | Beswick Number | Doulton Number | U.K. £ | U.S. $ | Price Can. $ | Aust. $ |
|---|---|---|---|---|---|---|
| BP-11b | 4169 | P4169 | 85. | 150. | 200. | 225. |

## PETER AND BENJAMIN PICKING APPLES™

| | |
|---|---|
| Modeller: | Martyn Alcock |
| Height: | 4 ¾", 11.4 cm |
| Colour: | Blue, brown, tan, red and green |
| Issued: | 2002 in a limited edition of 3,000 |

| Back Stamp | Beswick Number | Doulton Number | U.K. £ | U.S. $ | Price Can. $ | Aust. $ |
|---|---|---|---|---|---|---|
| BP-11b | 4160 | P4160 | 150. | 275. | 325. | 375. |

## PETER AND BENJAMIN PICKING UP ONIONS™

| | |
|---|---|
| Modeller: | Martyn Alcock |
| Height: | 5", 12.7 cm |
| Colour: | Peter: Pale blue jacket Benjamin: Brown jacket |
| Issued: | 2000 in a limited edition of 3,000 |
| Series: | Tableau of the Year |

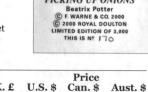

| Back Stamp | Beswick Number | Doulton Number | U.K. £ | U.S. $ | Price Can. $ | Aust. $ |
|---|---|---|---|---|---|---|
| BP-8c | 3930 | P3930 | 100. | 175. | 225. | 250. |

# BEATRIX POTTER

MRS. TIGGY-WINKLE
TAKES TEA

MRS. TIGGY-WINKLE
WASHING

MRS. TITTLEMOUSE
Style One

MRS. TITTLEMOUSE
STYLE TWO

NO MORE TWIST

OLD MR. BOUNCER

OLD MR. BROWN

OLD MR. PRICKLEPIN

PETER AND THE RED POCKET
HANDKERCHIEF
Small Size, Yellow Buttons

PETER AND THE RED POCKET
HANDKERCHIEF
Small Size, Gold Buttons

PETER AND THE RED POCKET
HANDKERCHIEF
Large Size, Yellow Buttons

PETER AND THE RED POCKET
HANDKERCHIEF
Large Size, Gold Buttons

# BEATRIX POTTER

PETER ATE A RADISH

PETER IN BED

PETER IN THE
GOOSEBERRY NET

PETER IN THE
WATERING CAN

PETER ON HIS BOOK

PETER RABBIT
Small Size, Deep Blue Jacket

PETER RABBIT
Small Size, Light Blue Jacket
Yellow Buttons

PETER RABBIT
Small Size, Light Blue Jacket
Gold Buttons

PETER RABBIT
Large Size, Yellow Buttons

PETER RABBIT DIGGING

PETER RABBIT GARDENING

PETER RABBIT
WITH DAFFODILS

# BEATRIX POTTER

PETER WITH POSTBAG

PICKLES

PIGLING BLAND
Deep Maroon Jacket

PIGLING BLAND
Lilac Jacket

PIGLING EATS HIS
PORRIDGE

PIG-WIG

POORLY PETER RABBIT

REBECCAH PUDDLE-DUCK

RIBBY

RIBBY AND
THE PATTY PAN

SALLY HENNY PENNY

SAMUEL WHISKERS

# BEATRIX POTTER

**SIMPKIN**

**SIR ISAAC NEWTON**

**SQUIRREL NUTKIN**
Small Size, Red-brown Squirrel

**SQUIRREL NUTKIN**
Small Size, Golden Brown Squirrel

**SQUIRREL NUTKIN**
Large Size, Gold Apple Core

**SUSAN**

**SWEET PETER RABBIT**

**TABITHA TWITCHIT**
Blue Striped Top

**TABITHA TWITCHIT**
White Top

**TABITHA TWITCHIT AND
MISS MOPPET**
Small Size

**TABITHA TWITCHIT AND
MISS MOPPET**
Large Size, Gold Stool Legs

**TAILOR OF GLOUCESTER**
Small Size

# BEATRIX POTTER

**TAILOR OF GLOUCESTER**
Large Size, Gold Accents

**THE OLD WOMAN WHO
LIVED IN A SHOE**

**THE OLD WOMAN WHO
LIVED IN A SHOE KNITTING**

**THIS PIG HAD A BIT
OF MEAT**

**THOMASINA
TITTLEMOUSE**

**TIMMY TIPTOES**
Red Jacket

**TIMMY TIPTOES**
Light Pink Jacket

**TIMMY WILLIE
FETCHING MILK**

**TIMMY WILLIE FROM
JOHNNY TOWN-MOUSE**

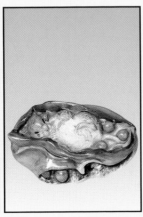

**TIMMY WILLIE SLEEPING**

**TOM KITTEN**
Small Size, Deep Blue Outfit

**TOM KITTEN**
Small Size, Light Blue Outfit
Yellow Buttons

# BEATRIX POTTER

**TOM KITTEN**
Small Size, Light Blue Outfit
Gold Buttons

**TOM KITTEN**
Large Size, Yellow Buttons

**TOM KITTEN
AND BUTTERFLY**

**TOM KITTEN IN
THE ROCKERY**

**TOM THUMB**

**TOMMY BROCK**
Spade Handle Out, Small Eye Patch

**TOMMY BROCK**
Spade Handle Out, Large Eye Patch

**TOMMY BROCK**
Spade Handle In, Small Eye Patch

**TOMMY BROCK**
Spade Handle In, Large Eye Patch

**TWO GENTLEMEN RABBITS**

**YOCK-YOCK IN THE TUB**

# TABLEAUX

DUCHESS AND RIBBY

FLOPSY AND BENJAMIN BUNNY

FLOPSY, MOPSY AND COTTONTAIL
Style Two

GINGER AND PICKLES

HIDING FROM THE CAT

KEP AND JEMIMA

# TABLEAUX

MITTENS, TOM KITTEN AND MOPPET

MRS. RABBIT AND THE FOUR BUNNIES

MRS. TIGGY-WINKLE AND LUCIE

MY DEAR SON THOMAS

PETER AND BENJAMIN PICKING APPLES

PETER AND BENJAMIN PICKING UP ONIONS

# BEATRIX POTTER
# CHARACTER JUGS

## JEMIMA PUDDLE-DUCK
## CHARACTER JUG™

| | |
|---|---|
| Modeller: | Ted Chawner |
| Height: | 4", 10.1 cm |
| Colour: | Blue, pink and white |
| Issued: | 1989 - 1992 |

| Back Stamp | Beswick Number | Doulton Number | U.K. £ | U.S. $ | Price Can. $ | Aust. $ |
|---|---|---|---|---|---|---|
| BP-4 | 3088 | P3088 | 100. | 175. | 225. | 250. |
| BP-6a | | | 65. | 115. | 145. | 155. |

## MR. JEREMY FISHER
## CHARACTER JUG™

| | |
|---|---|
| Modeller: | Graham Tongue |
| Height: | 3", 7.6 cm |
| Colour: | Mauve |
| Issued: | 1987 - 1992 |

| Back Stamp | Beswick Number | Doulton Number | U.K. £ | U.S. $ | Price Can. $ | Aust. $ |
|---|---|---|---|---|---|---|
| BP-4 | 2960 | P2960 | 100. | 175. | 225. | 250. |
| BP-6a | | | 65. | 115. | 145. | 155. |

## MRS. TIGGY-WINKLE
## CHARACTER JUG™

Modeller:    Ted Chawner
Height:      3", 7.6 cm
Colour:      White dress with brown stripes
Issued:      1988 - 1992

| Back Stamp | Beswick Number | Doulton Number | U.K. £ | U.S. $ | Price Can. $ | Aust. $ |
|---|---|---|---|---|---|---|
| BP-4 | 3102 | P3102 | 100. | 175. | 225. | 250. |
| BP-6a | | | 65. | 115. | 145. | 155. |

## OLD MR. BROWN
## CHARACTER JUG™

Modeller:    Graham Tongue
Height:      3", 7.6 cm
Colour:      Brown and cream
Issued:      1987 - 1992

| Back Stamp | Beswick Number | Doulton Number | U.K. £ | U.S. $ | Price Can. $ | Aust. $ |
|---|---|---|---|---|---|---|
| BP-4 | 2959 | P2959 | 90. | 160. | 200. | 215. |
| BP-6a | | | 55. | 100. | 125. | 135. |

## PETER RABBIT
## CHARACTER JUG™

Modeller:    Graham Tongue
Height:      3", 7.6 cm
Colour:      Brown, blue and white
Issued:      1987 - 1992

| Back Stamp | Beswick Number | Doulton Number | U.K. £ | U.S. $ | Price Can. $ | Aust. $ |
|---|---|---|---|---|---|---|
| BP-4 | 3006 | P3006 | 90. | 160. | 200. | 215. |
| BP-6a | | | 55. | 100. | 125. | 135. |

## TOM KITTEN
## CHARACTER JUG™

| | |
|---|---|
| Modeller: | Ted Chawner |
| Height: | 3", 7.6 cm |
| Colour: | Brown, blue and white |
| Issued: | 1989 - 1992 |

BEATRIX POTTER
"Tom Kitten"
© F. Warne & Co. 1988
Licensed by Copyrights
*John Bromist*
Studio of Royal Doulton
England

| Back Stamp | Beswick Number | Doulton Number | U.K. £ | U.S. $ | Price Can. $ | Aust. $ |
|---|---|---|---|---|---|---|
| BP-4 | 3103 | P3103 | 90. | 160. | 200. | 215. |
| BP-6a | | | 55. | 100. | 125. | 135. |

# BEATRIX POTTER PLAQUES

## JEMIMA PUDDLE-DUCK PLAQUE™

| | |
|---|---|
| Modeller: | Albert Hallam |
| Height: | 6", 15.2 cm |
| Colour: | White duck, mauve shawl, pale blue bonnet |
| Issued: | 1967 - 1969 |

| Back Stamp | Beswick Number | Doulton Number | U.K. £ | U.S. $ | Price Can. $ | Aust. $ |
|---|---|---|---|---|---|---|
| BP-2 | 2082 | P2082 | 1,000. | 1,750. | 2,250. | 2,500. |

## JEMIMA PUDDLE-DUCK WITH FOXY WHISKERED GENTLEMAN PLAQUE™

| | |
|---|---|
| Modeller: | Harry Sales and David Lyttleton |
| Size: | 7 ½" x 7 ½", 19.1 cm x 19.1 cm |
| Colour: | Brown, green, white and blue |
| Issued: | 1977 - 1982 |

| Back Stamp | Beswick Number | Doulton Number | U.K. £ | U.S. $ | Price Can. $ | Aust. $ |
|---|---|---|---|---|---|---|
| BP-3 | 2594 | P2594 | 80. | 150. | 185. | 200. |

## MRS. TITTLEMOUSE PLAQUE™

| | | | | | | |
|---|---|---|---|---|---|---|
| Modeller: | Harry Sales | | | | | |
| Height: | 7 ½" x 7 ½", | | | | | |
| | 19.1 cm x 19.1 cm | | | | | |
| Colour: | Blue, pink and green | | | | | |
| Issued: | 1982 - 1984 | | | | | |

| Back Stamp | Beswick Number | Doulton Number | U.K. £ | U.S. $ | Price Can. $ | Aust. $ |
|---|---|---|---|---|---|---|
| BP-3 | 2685 | P2685 | 110. | 200. | 250. | 275. |

## PETER RABBIT PLAQUE™
### First Version

| | |
|---|---|
| Modeller: | Graham Tongue |
| Height: | 6", 15.2 cm |
| Colour: | Brown rabbit wearing a blue coat |
| Issued: | 1967 - 1969 |

| Back Stamp | Beswick Number | Doulton Number | U.K. £ | U.S. $ | Price Can. $ | Aust. $ |
|---|---|---|---|---|---|---|
| BP-2 | 2083 | P2083 | 1,200. | 2,150. | 2,750. | 2,900. |

## PETER RABBIT PLAQUE™
### Second Version

| | |
|---|---|
| Modeller: | Harry Sales and David Lyttleton |
| Size: | 7 ½" x 7 ½", 19.1 cm x 19.1 cm |
| Colour: | Blue, green, brown and orange |
| Issued: | 1979 - 1983 |

| Back Stamp | Beswick Number | Doulton Number | U.K. £ | U.S. $ | Price Can. $ | Aust. $ |
|---|---|---|---|---|---|---|
| BP-3 | 2650 | P2650 | 75. | 135. | 175. | 190. |

**TOM KITTEN PLAQUE**™

Modeller:    Graham Tongue
Height:      6", 15.2 cm
Colour:     Brown, blue and white
Issued:     1967 - 1969

| Back Stamp | Beswick Number | Doulton Number | U.K. £ | U.S. $ | Price Can. $ | Aust. $ |
|---|---|---|---|---|---|---|
| BP-2 | 2085 | P2085 | 1,200. | 2,150. | 2,750. | 2,900. |

# BEATRIX POTTER STANDS

## DISPLAY STAND

| | | | | | | |
|---|---|---|---|---|---|---|
| Modeller: | Andrew Brindley | | | | | |
| Size: | 12 ½" x 12 ½", | | | | | |
| | 31.7 cm x 31.7 cm | | | | | |
| Colour: | Brown, light brown | | | | | |
| Issued: | 1970 - 1997 | | | | | |

| Back Stamp | Beswick Number | Doulton Number | U.K. £ | U.S. $ | Price Can. $ | Aust. $ |
|---|---|---|---|---|---|---|
| Beswick | 2295 | P2295 | 50. | 90. | 115. | 120. |
| Doulton | | | 50. | 90. | 115. | 120. |

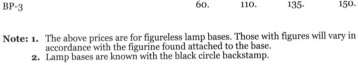

## TREE LAMP BASE™

| | | | | | | |
|---|---|---|---|---|---|---|
| Modeller: | Albert Hallam and | | | | | |
| | James Hayward | | | | | |
| Height: | 7", 17.8 cm | | | | | |
| Colour: | Brown and green | | | | | |
| Issued: | 1958 - 1982 | | | | | |

| Back Stamp | Beswick Number | Doulton Number | U.K. £ | U.S. $ | Price Can. $ | Aust. $ |
|---|---|---|---|---|---|---|
| BP-2 | 1531 | P1531 | 85. | 150. | 185. | 200. |
| BP-3 | | | 60. | 110. | 135. | 150. |

Note: 1. The above prices are for figureless lamp bases. Those with figures will vary in accordance with the figurine found attached to the base.
2. Lamp bases are known with the black circle backstamp.

# BEATRIX POTTER
# RESIN STUDIO SCULPTURES

## FLOPSY BUNNIES™

| | |
|---|---|
| Model No.: | SS 2 |
| Designer: | Harry Sales |
| Modeller: | Graham Tongue |
| Height: | 5", 12.7 cm |
| Colour: | Browns and green |
| Issued: | 1985 - 1985 |

| Back Stamp | Beswick Number | U.K. £ | U.S. $ | Price Can. $ | Aust. $ |
|---|---|---|---|---|---|
| Beswick | SS 2 | 50. | 90. | 115. | 120. |

## MR. JEREMY FISHER™

| | |
|---|---|
| Model No.: | SS 3 |
| Designer: | Harry Sales |
| Modeller: | David Lyttleton |
| Height: | 4", 10.1 cm |
| Colour: | Beige, green and cream |
| Issued: | 1985 - 1985 |

| Back Stamp | Beswick Number | U.K. £ | U.S. $ | Price Can. $ | Aust. $ |
|---|---|---|---|---|---|
| Beswick | SS 3 | 50. | 90. | 115. | 120. |

## MRS. TIGGY-WINKLE™

| | | | | | |
|---|---|---|---|---|---|
| Model No.: | SS 11 | | | | |
| Designer: | Harry Sales | | | | |
| Modeller: | Graham Tongue | | | | |
| Height: | 5", 12.7 cm | | | | |
| Colour: | Browns, green, white and blue | | | | |
| Issued: | 1985 - 1985 | | | | |

| Back Stamp | Beswick Number | U.K. £ | U.S. $ | Price Can. $ | Aust. $ |
|---|---|---|---|---|---|
| Beswick | SS 11 | 50. | 90. | 115. | 120. |

## PETER RABBIT™

| | | | | | |
|---|---|---|---|---|---|
| Model No.: | SS 4 | | | | |
| Designer: | Harry Sales | | | | |
| Modeller: | Graham Tongue | | | | |
| Height: | 7", 17.8 cm | | | | |
| Colour: | Browns, blue and green | | | | |
| Issued: | 1985 - 1985 | | | | |

| Back Stamp | Beswick Number | U.K. £ | U.S. $ | Price Can. $ | Aust. $ |
|---|---|---|---|---|---|
| Beswick | SS 4 | 50. | 90. | 115. | 120. |

## TIMMY WILLIE™

| | | | | | |
|---|---|---|---|---|---|
| Model No.: | SS 1 | | | | |
| Designer: | Harry Sales | | | | |
| Modeller: | Graham Tongue | | | | |
| Height: | 4 ¼", 10.8 cm | | | | |
| Colour: | Green and brown | | | | |
| Issued: | 1985 - 1985 | | | | |

| Back Stamp | Beswick Number | U.K. £ | U.S. $ | Price Can. $ | Aust. $ |
|---|---|---|---|---|---|
| Beswick | SS1 | 40. | 70. | 90. | 95. |

### PETER RABBIT IN WATERING CAN™

| | |
|---|---|
| Model No.: | SS 27 |
| Designer: | Harry Sales |
| Modeller: | David Lyttleton |
| Height: | 3 ¼", 8.3 cm |
| Colour: | Browns and blue |
| Issued: | 1986 - 1986 |

| Back Stamp | Beswick Number | U.K. £ | U.S. $ | Price Can. $ | Aust. $ |
|---|---|---|---|---|---|
| Beswick | SS 27 | 200. | 350. | 450. | 475. |

### YOCK-YOCK™
### (In The Tub)

| | |
|---|---|
| Model No.: | SS 26 |
| Designer: | Harry Sales |
| Modeller: | David Lyttleton |
| Height: | 2", 5.0 cm |
| Colour: | Pink and brown |
| Issued: | 1986 - 1986 |

| Back Stamp | Beswick Number | U.K. £ | U.S. $ | Price Can. $ | Aust. $ |
|---|---|---|---|---|---|
| Beswick | SS 26 | 150. | 275. | 325. | 375. |

# JOAN WALSH ANGLUND

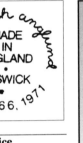

**2272**
**ANGLUND BOY™**

Designer: Albert Hallam
Height: 4 ½", 11.9 cm
Colour: Green dungarees, brown hat
Finish: Gloss
Issued: 1970 - 1971

| Beswick Number | U.K. £ | U.S. $ | Price Can. $ | Aust. $ |
|---|---|---|---|---|
| 2272 | 65. | 115. | 150. | 160. |

**2293**
**ANGLUND GIRL WITH DOLL™**

Designer: Albert Hallam
Height: 4 ½", 11.9 cm
Colour: Green dress and bow, white apron
Finish: Gloss
Issued: 1970 - 1971

| Beswick Number | U.K. £ | U.S. $ | Price Can. $ | Aust. $ |
|---|---|---|---|---|
| 2293 | 65. | 115. | 150. | 160. |

**2317**
**ANGLUND GIRL WITH FLOWERS™**

Designer: Albert Hallam
Height: 4 ¾", 12.1 cm
Colour: White dress, blue leggings, straw hat with blue ribbon
Finish: Gloss
Issued: 1971 - 1971

| Beswick Number | U.K. £ | U.S. $ | Price Can. $ | Aust. $ |
|---|---|---|---|---|
| 2317 | 65. | 115. | 150. | 160. |

# PADDINGTON BEAR

### 3918
### PADDINGTON™ AT THE STATION

| | |
|---|---|
| Modeller: | Warren Platt |
| Height: | 3 ¼", 8.5 cm |
| Colour: | Brown bear, blue coat, red hat, grey sack, gold suitcase corners |
| Finish: | Gloss |
| Issued: | 1999 in a limited edition of 2,000 |
| Comm. by: | Paddington and Friends |

| Beswick Number | | U.K. £ | U.S. $ | Price Can. $ | Aust. $ |
|---|---|---|---|---|---|
| 3918 | | 45. | 80. | 100. | 110. |

# PETER PAN

## 1301
## NANA™

| | |
|---|---|
| Designer: | Jan Granoska |
| Height: | 3 ¼", 8.3 cm |
| Colour: | Brown dog, white frilled cap with blue ribbon |
| Finish: | Gloss |
| Issued: | 1953 - 1965 |

| Beswick Number | U.K. £ | U.S. $ | Price Can. $ | Aust. $ |
|---|---|---|---|---|
| 1301 | 375. | 675. | 850. | 900. |

## 1302
## SMEE™

| | |
|---|---|
| Designer: | Jan Granoska |
| Height: | 4 ¼", 10.8 cm |
| Colour: | Blue and white shirt, blue pants, red cap, green bottle |
| Finish: | Gloss |
| Issued: | 1953 - 1965 |

| Beswick Number | U.K. £ | U.S. $ | Price Can. $ | Aust. $ |
|---|---|---|---|---|
| 1302 | 550. | 975. | 1,200. | 1,300. |

### 1307
### PETER PAN™

| | |
|---|---|
| Designer: | Jan Granoska |
| Height: | 5", 12.7 cm |
| Colour: | Light green, dark green, brown and red |
| Finish: | Gloss |
| Issued: | 1953 - 1965 |

| Beswick Number | | U.K. $ | U.S. $ | Price Can. $ | Aust. $ |
|---|---|---|---|---|---|
| 1307 | | 550. | 975. | 1,200. | 1,300. |

### 1312
### TINKER BELL™

| | |
|---|---|
| Designer: | Jan Granoska |
| Height: | 5", 12.7 cm |
| Colour: | Light green dress, dark green wings and shoes |
| Finish: | Gloss |
| Issued: | 1953 - 1965 |

| Beswick Number | | U.K. £ | U.S. $ | Price Can. $ | Aust. $ |
|---|---|---|---|---|---|
| 1312 | | 675. | 1,200. | 1,500. | 1,600. |

# WIND IN THE WILLOWS

**AW1 (2942)**
**TOAD™**
**Style One**

| | |
|---|---|
| Designer: | Harry Sales |
| Modeller: | David Lyttleton |
| Height: | 3 ½", 8.9 cm |
| Colour: | Green, yellow, white and red |
| Finish: | Gloss |
| Issued: | 1987 – 1989 |

| Beswick Number | U.K. £ | U.S. $ | Price Can. $ | Aust. $ |
|---|---|---|---|---|
| AW 1 (2942) | 60. | 110. | 135. | 150. |

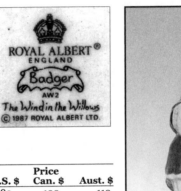

**AW2 (2940)**
**BADGER™**
**Style One**

| | |
|---|---|
| Designer: | Harry Sales |
| Modeller: | David Lyttleton |
| Height: | 3", 7.6 cm |
| Colour: | Black, white and salmon |
| Finish: | Gloss |
| Issued: | 1987 – 1989 |

| Beswick Number | U.K. £ | U.S. $ | Price Can. $ | Aust. $ |
|---|---|---|---|---|
| AW2 (2940) | 45. | 80. | 100. | 110. |

**AW 3 (2941)**
**RATTY™**
**Style One**

| | |
|---|---|
| Designer: | Harry Sales |
| Modeller: | David Lyttleton |
| Height: | 3 ½", 8.9 cm |
| Colour: | Blue and white |
| Finish: | Gloss |
| Issued: | 1987 – 1989 |

| Beswick Number | U.K. £ | U.S. $ | Price Can. $ | Aust. $ |
|---|---|---|---|---|
| AW 3 (2941) | 45. | 80. | 100. | 110. |

**AW 4 (2939)**
**MOLE™**
**Style One**

| | |
|---|---|
| Designer: | Harry Sales |
| Modeller: | David Lyttleton |
| Height: | 3", 7.6 cm |
| Colour: | Dark grey and brown |
| Finish: | Gloss |
| Issued: | 1987 - 1989 |

| Beswick Number | U.K. £ | U.S. $ | Price Can. $ | Aust. $ |
|---|---|---|---|---|
| AW 4 (2939) | 70. | 125. | 150. | 165. |

**AW 5 (3065)**
**PORTLY™**
**(Otter)**

| | |
|---|---|
| Modeller: | Alan Maslankowski |
| Height: | 2 ¾", 7.0 cm |
| Colour: | Brown, blue, green and yellow |
| Finish: | Gloss |
| Issued: | 1988 - 1989 |

| Beswick Number | U.K. £ | U.S. $ | Price Can. $ | Aust. $ |
|---|---|---|---|---|
| AW 5 (3065) | 375. | 675. | 850. | 900. |

**AW 6 (3076)**
**WEASEL GAMEKEEPER™**

| | |
|---|---|
| Modeller: | Alan Maslankowski |
| Height: | 4", 10.1 cm |
| Colour: | Brown, green and yellow |
| Finish: | Gloss |
| Issued: | 1988 – 1989 |

| Beswick Number | U.K. £ | U.S. $ | Price Can. $ | Aust. $ |
|---|---|---|---|---|
| AW 6 (3076) | 200. | 350. | 450. | 475. |

**WIW 1 (3956)**
**ON THE RIVER™**
**(Mole and Ratty)**

| | |
|---|---|
| Designer: | Warren Platt |
| Size: | 3 ½" x 6 ½", 8.9 x 16.5 cm |
| Colour: | Yellow, black, blue and red |
| Finish: | Gloss |
| Issued: | 2000 in a limited edition of 1,908 |
| Series: | Tableau |

| Beswick Number | U.K. £ | U.S. $ | Price Can. $ | Aust. $ |
|---|---|---|---|---|
| WIW 1 (3956) | 125. | 225. | 275. | 300. |

**WIW 2 (4011)**
**TOAD™**
**Style Two**

| | |
|---|---|
| Designer: | Warren Platt |
| Height: | 4 ¾", 12.1 cm |
| Colour: | Orange-brown, browns and grey |
| Finish: | Gloss |
| Issued: | 2000 in a limited edition of 2,000 (C of A) |
| Comm. by: | Doulton-Direct |

| Beswick Number | U.K. £ | U.S. $ | Price Can. $ | Aust. $ |
|---|---|---|---|---|
| WIW 2 (4011) | 45. | 80. | 100. | 110. |

### WIW 3 (4010)
### BADGER™
### Style Two

| | |
|---|---|
| Designer: | Warren Platt |
| Height: | 5 ½", 14.0 cm |
| Colour: | Red, blue and white |
| Issued: | 2000 in a limited edition of 2,000 (C of A) |
| Comm. by: | Doulton-Direct |

| Beswick Number | U.K. £ | U.S. $ | Price Can. $ | Aust. $ |
|---|---|---|---|---|
| WIW 3 (4010) | 45. | 80. | 100. | 110. |

### WIW 4 (4038)
### RATTY™
### Style Two

| | |
|---|---|
| Designer: | Warren Platt |
| Height: | 5", 12.7 cm |
| Colour: | Mustard, yellow, white and red |
| Issued: | 2001 in a limited edition of 2,000 (C of A) |
| Comm. by: | Doulton-Direct |

| Beswick Number | U.K. £ | U.S. $ | Price Can. $ | Aust. $ |
|---|---|---|---|---|
| WIW 4 (4038) | 40. | 70. | 90. | 95. |

### WIW 5 (4039)
### MOLE™
### Style Two

| | |
|---|---|
| Designer: | Warren Platt |
| Height: | 4 ½", 11.9 cm |
| Colour: | Blue, yellow, white and black |
| Issued: | 2001 in a limited edition of 2,000 (C of A) |
| Comm. by: | Doulton-Direct |

| Beswick Number | U.K. £ | U.S. $ | Price Can. $ | Aust. $ |
|---|---|---|---|---|
| WIW 5 (4039) | 40. | 70. | 90. | 95. |

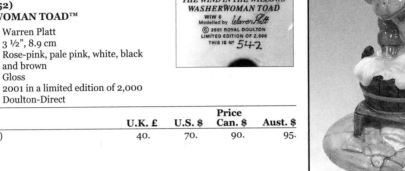

## WIW 6 (4152)
## WASHERWOMAN TOAD™

Designer:    Warren Platt
Height:    3 ½", 8.9 cm
Colour:    Rose-pink, pale pink, white, black and brown
Finish:    Gloss
Issued:    2001 in a limited edition of 2,000
Comm. by:    Doulton-Direct

| Beswick Number | U.K. £ | U.S. $ | Price Can. $ | Aust. $ |
|---|---|---|---|---|
| WIW 6 (4152) | 40. | 70. | 90. | 95. |

**Note:** For a continuation of "Wind in the Willows" figures see *Royal Doulton Collectables*, 4th edition

# WINNIE THE POOH

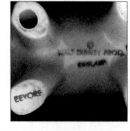

### 2193
### WINNIE THE POOH™
| | |
|---|---|
| Designer: | Albert Hallam |
| Height: | 2 ½", 6.4 cm |
| Colour: | Golden brown and red |
| Finish: | Gloss |
| Issued: | 1968 - 1990 |

| Back Stamp | Beswick Number | U.K. £ | U.S. $ | Price Can. $ | Aust. $ |
|---|---|---|---|---|---|
| Gold | 2193 | 80. | 145. | 175. | 195. |
| Brown | | 60. | 110. | 135. | 150. |

### 2196
### EEYORE™
| | |
|---|---|
| Designer: | Albert Hallam |
| Height: | 2", 5.0 cm |
| Colour: | Grey with black markings |
| Finish: | Gloss |
| Issued: | 1968 - 1990 |

| Back Stamp | Beswick Number | U.K. £ | U.S. $ | Price Can. $ | Aust. $ |
|---|---|---|---|---|---|
| Gold | 2196 | 65. | 110. | 135. | 150. |
| Brown | | 55. | 100. | 125. | 135. |

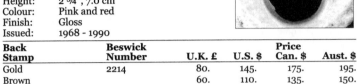

**2214**
**PIGLET™**

| | |
|---|---|
| Designer: | Albert Hallam |
| Height: | 2 ¾", 7.0 cm |
| Colour: | Pink and red |
| Finish: | Gloss |
| Issued: | 1968 - 1990 |

| Back Stamp | Beswick Number | U.K. £ | U.S. $ | Price Can. $ | Aust. $ |
|---|---|---|---|---|---|
| Gold | 2214 | 80. | 145. | 175. | 195. |
| Brown | | 60. | 110. | 135. | 150. |

**2215**
**RABBIT™**

| | |
|---|---|
| Designer: | Albert Hallam |
| Height: | 3 ¼", 8.3 cm |
| Colour: | Brown and beige |
| Finish: | Gloss |
| Issued: | 1968 - 1990 |

| Back Stamp | Beswick Number | U.K. £ | U.S. $ | Price Can. $ | Aust. $ |
|---|---|---|---|---|---|
| Gold | 2215 | 95. | 175. | 215. | 230. |
| Brown | | 80. | 145. | 175. | 195. |

**2216**
**OWL™**

| | |
|---|---|
| Designer: | Albert Hallam |
| Height: | 3", 7.6 cm |
| Colour: | Brown, white and black |
| Finish: | Gloss |
| Issued: | 1968 - 1990 |

| Back Stamp | Beswick Number | U.K. £ | U.S. $ | Price Can. $ | Aust. $ |
|---|---|---|---|---|---|
| Gold | 2216 | 65. | 110. | 135. | 150. |
| Brown | | 55. | 100. | 125. | 135. |

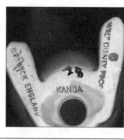

**2217**
**KANGA™**

| | |
|---|---|
| Designer: | Albert Hallam |
| Height: | 3 ¼", 8.3 cm |
| Colour: | Dark and light brown |
| Finish: | Gloss |
| Issued: | 1968 - 1990 |

| Back Stamp | Beswick Number | U.K. £ | U.S. $ | Price Can. $ | Aust. $ |
|---|---|---|---|---|---|
| Gold | 2217 | 80. | 145. | 175. | 195. |
| Brown | | 60. | 110. | 135. | 150. |

**2394**
**TIGGER™**

| | |
|---|---|
| Designer: | Graham Tongue |
| Height: | 3", 7.6 cm |
| Colour: | Yellow with black stripes |
| Finish: | Gloss |
| Issued: | 1971 - 1990 |

| Back Stamp | Beswick Number | U.K. £ | U.S. $ | Price Can. $ | Aust. $ |
|---|---|---|---|---|---|
| Gold | 2394 | 150. | 275. | 335. | 375. |
| Brown | | 110. | 200. | 250. | 275. |

**2395**
**CHRISTOPHER ROBIN™**

| | |
|---|---|
| Designer: | Graham Tongue |
| Height: | 4 ¾", 12.1 cm |
| Colour: | Yellow, blue and white |
| Finish: | Gloss |
| Issued: | 1971 - 1990 |

| Back Stamp | Beswick Number | U.K. $ | U.S. $ | Price Can. $ | Aust. $ |
|---|---|---|---|---|---|
| Gold | 2395 | 150. | 275. | 335. | 375. |
| Brown | | 125. | 225. | 275. | 300. |

# SECTION TWO

## CARTOON AND FILM CHARACTERS

Snow White and the Seven Dwarfs (1954-1967)

# DISNEY CHARACTERS

The first model to be designed in 1952, was as you might guess, perhaps the most famous of them all, *Mickey Mouse.*

The popularity of these figures must in part be due to the fact that we have all seen them on the big screen, and for many of us they bring back nostalgic memories of childhood.

The meticulous attention to detail, by Jan Granoska, makes them some of the best models ever produced. Despite being in production for a period of about twelve years, they are hard to find. In 1954 there followed figures of the classic cartoon characters *Snow White and the Seven Dwarfs*, superbly modelled by Arthur Gredington, and equally scarce.

Characters from Disneyland were also used, in 1954, as a decoration on some Beswick Nursery Ware (see the *Charlton Standard Catalogue of Beswick Pottery*).

### 1278
### MICKEY MOUSE™

| | |
|---|---|
| Designer: | Jan Granoska |
| Height: | 4", 10.1 cm |
| Colour: | Black, white and red |
| Finish: | Gloss |
| Issued: | 1952 - 1965 |

| Back Stamp | Beswick Number | U.K. £ | U.S. $ | Price Can. $ | Aust. $ |
|---|---|---|---|---|---|
| Beswick Gold | 1278 | 550. | 1,000. | 1,250. | 1,350. |

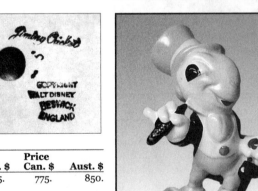

### 1279
### JIMINY CRICKET™

| | |
|---|---|
| Designer: | Jan Granoska |
| Height: | 4", 10.1 cm |
| Colour: | Black, white, beige and blue |
| Finish: | Gloss |
| Issued: | 1952 - 1965 |

| Back Stamp | Beswick Number | U.K. £ | U.S. $ | Price Can. $ | Aust. $ |
|---|---|---|---|---|---|
| Beswick Gold | 1279 | 350. | 625. | 775. | 850. |

**1280**
**PLUTO™**

| | |
|---|---|
| Designer: | Jan Granoska |
| Height: | 3 ½", 8.9 cm |
| Colour: | Brown dog with red collar |
| Finish: | Gloss |
| Issued: | 1953 - 1965 |

| Back Stamp | Beswick Number | U.K. £ | U.S. $ | Price Can. $ | Aust. $ |
|---|---|---|---|---|---|
| Beswick Gold | 1280 | 350. | 625. | 775. | 850. |

**1281**
**GOOFY™**

| | |
|---|---|
| Designer: | Jan Granoska |
| Height: | 4 ¼", 10.8 cm |
| Colour: | Red jersey, blue trousers, black suspenders, white gloves, brown and black hat, brown boots |
| Finish: | Gloss |
| Issued: | 1953 - 1965 |

| Back Stamp | Beswick Number | U.K. £ | U.S. $ | Price Can. $ | Aust. $ |
|---|---|---|---|---|---|
| Beswick Gold | 1281 | 350. | 625. | 775. | 850. |

**1282**
**PINOCCHIO™**

| | |
|---|---|
| Designer: | Jan Granoska |
| Height: | 4", 10.1 cm |
| Colour: | White and yellow jacket, red trousers, blue bowtie and shoes, brown cap |
| Finish: | Gloss |
| Issued: | 1953 - 1965 |

| Back Stamp | Beswick Number | U.K. £ | U.S. $ | Price Can. $ | Aust. $ |
|---|---|---|---|---|---|
| Beswick Gold | 1282 | 475. | 850. | 1,100. | 1,200. |

**1283**
**DONALD DUCK™**

| | |
|---|---|
| Designer: | Jan Granoska |
| Height: | 4", 10.1 cm |
| Colour: | White duck, blue sailor's jacket, red bow, blue and black hat |
| Finish: | Gloss |
| Issued: | 1953 - 1965 |

| Back Stamp | Beswick Number | U.K. £ | U.S. $ | Price Can. $ | Aust. $ |
|---|---|---|---|---|---|
| Beswick Gold | 1283 | 450. | 800. | 1,000. | 1,200. |

**1289**
**MINNIE MOUSE™**

| | |
|---|---|
| Designer: | Jan Granoska |
| Height: | 4", 10.1 cm |
| Colour: | Black and white mouse; yellow top, red skirt with white spots, white gloves and hair bow, brown shoes |
| Finish: | Gloss |
| Issued: | 1953 - 1965 |

| Back Stamp | Beswick Number | U.K. £ | U.S. $ | Price Can. $ | Aust. $ |
|---|---|---|---|---|---|
| Beswick Gold | 1289 | 450. | 800. | 1,000. | 1,200. |

**1291**
**THUMPER™**

| | |
|---|---|
| Designer: | Jan Granoska |
| Height: | 3 ¾", 9.5 cm |
| Colour: | Grey and white rabbit; yellow, red and pink flowers on brown base |
| Finish: | Gloss |
| Issued: | 1953 - 1965 |

| Back Stamp | Beswick Number | U.K. £ | U.S. $ | Price Can. $ | Aus.t $ |
|---|---|---|---|---|---|
| Beswick Gold | 1291 | 250. | 450. | 550. | 600. |

# SNOW WHITE AND THE SEVEN DWARFS

**1325**
**DOPEY™**

| | |
|---|---|
| Designer: | Arthur Gredington |
| Height: | 3 ½", 8.9 cm |
| Colour: | Green coat, maroon cap, grey shoes |
| Finish: | Gloss |
| Issued: | 1954 - 1967 |

| Back Stamp | Beswick Number | U.K. £ | U.S. $ | Price Can. $ | Aust. $ |
|---|---|---|---|---|---|
| Beswick Gold | 1325 | 125. | 225. | 275. | 300. |

**1326**
**HAPPY™**

| | |
|---|---|
| Designer: | Arthur Gredington |
| Height: | 3 ½", 8.9 cm |
| Colour: | Purple tunic, light blue trousers, light brown cap, brown shoes |
| Finish: | Gloss |
| Issued: | 1954 - 1967 |

| Back Stamp | Beswick Number | U.K. £ | U.S. $ | Price Can. $ | Aust. $ |
|---|---|---|---|---|---|
| Beswick Gold | 1326 | 125. | 225. | 275. | 300. |

**1327**
**BASHFUL™**

| Designer: | Arthur Gredington |
| Height: | 3 ½", 8.9 cm |
| Colour: | Brown tunic, purple trousers, grey cap, brown shoes |
| Finish: | Gloss |
| Issued: | 1954 - 1967 |

| Back Stamp | Beswick Number | U.K. £ | U.S. $ | Price Can. $ | Aust. $ |
|---|---|---|---|---|---|
| Beswick Gold | 1327 | 125. | 225. | 275. | 300. |

**1328**
**SNEEZY™**

| Designer: | Arthur Gredington |
| Height: | 3 ½", 8.9 cm |
| Colour: | Green tunic, purple trousers brown cap and shoes |
| Finish: | Gloss |
| Issued: | 1954 - 1967 |

| Back Stamp | Beswick Number | U.K. £ | U.S. $ | Price Can. $ | Aust. $ |
|---|---|---|---|---|---|
| Beswick Gold | 1328 | 125. | 225. | 275. | 300. |

**1329**
**DOC™**

| Designer: | Arthur Gredington |
| Height: | 3 ½", 8.9 cm |
| Colour: | Brown tunic, blue trousers, yellow cap, brown shoes |
| Finish: | Gloss |
| Issued: | 1954 - 1967 |

| Back Stamp | Beswick Number | U.K. £ | U.S. $ | Price Can. $ | Aus.t. $ |
|---|---|---|---|---|---|
| Beswick Gold | 1329 | 125. | 225. | 275. | 300. |

**1330**
**GRUMPY™**

| Designer: | Arthur Gredington |
|---|---|
| Height: | 3 ¾", 9.5 cm |
| Colour: | Purple tunic, red trousers blue cap, brown shoes |
| Finish: | Gloss |
| Issued: | 1954 - 1967 |

| Back Stamp | Beswick Number | U.K. £ | U.S. $ | Price Can. $ | Aust. $ |
|---|---|---|---|---|---|
| Beswick Gold | 1330 | 125. | 225. | 275. | 300. |

**1331**
**SLEEPY™**

| Designer: | Arthur Gredington |
|---|---|
| Height: | 3 ½", 8.9 cm |
| Colour: | Tan tunic, red trousers, green hat, grey shoes |
| Finish: | Gloss |
| Issued: | 1954 - 1967 |

| Back Stamp | Beswick Number | U.K. £ | U.S. $ | Price Can. $ | Aust. $ |
|---|---|---|---|---|---|
| Beswick Gold | 1331 | 125. | 225. | 275. | 300. |

**1332A**
**SNOW WHITE™**
**First Version (Hair in Flounces)**

| Designer: | Arthur Gredington |
|---|---|
| Height: | 5 ½", 14.0 cm |
| Colour: | Yellow and purple dress, red cape, white collar |
| Finish: | Gloss |
| Issued: | 1954 - 1955 |

| Back Stamp | Beswick Number | U.K. £ | U.S. $ | Price Can. $ | Aust. $ |
|---|---|---|---|---|---|
| Beswick Gold | 1332A | | Extremely rare | | |

**Note:** Re-modelled in 1955 see 1332B.

**1332B**
**SNOW WHITE**™
**Second Version (Hair Flat to Head)**

| | |
|---|---|
| Designer: | Arthur Gredington |
| Height: | 5 ½", 14.0 cm |
| Colour: | Yellow and purple dress, red cape, white collar |
| Finish: | Gloss |
| Issued: | 1955 - 1967 |

| Back Stamp | Beswick Number | U.K. £ | U.S. $ | Price Can. $ | Aust. $ |
|---|---|---|---|---|---|
| Beswick Gold | 1332B | 275. | 500. | 625. | 675. |

# DAVID HAND'S ANIMALAND

David Hand, who died in California at the age of eighty-six, was an American film cartoon animator who worked for Disney for fifteen years and was the supervising director for such films as *Snow White* and *Bambi*.

The real Animaland was in a pretty little village in Berkshire, England, situated on the banks of the River Thames. There in a country house two hundred clever writers, artists, animators and technicians worked hard in order to create the characters we know so well today.

The eight figures which were produced by Beswick were beautifully modeled by Arthur Gredington in 1949.

**1148**
**DINKUM PLATYPUS™**

| | |
|---|---|
| Designer: | Arthur Gredington |
| Height: | 4 ¼", 10.8 cm |
| Colour: | Brown and beige platypus, green base |
| Finish: | Gloss |
| Issued: | 1949 - 1955 |

| Beswick Number | U.K. £ | U.S. $ | Price Can. $ | Aust. $ |
|---|---|---|---|---|
| 1148 | 175. | 300. | 375. | 400. |

**1150**
**ZIMMY LION™**

| | |
|---|---|
| Designer: | Arthur Gredington |
| Height: | 3 ¾", 9.5 cm |
| Colour: | Brown lion with white face |
| Finish: | Gloss |
| Issued: | 1949 - 1955 |

| Beswick Number | U.K. £ | U.S. $ | Price Can. $ | Aust. $ |
|---|---|---|---|---|
| 1150 | 300. | 550. | 675. | 750. |

**1151**
**FELIA™**

| Designer: | Arthur Gredington |
| Height: | 4", 10.1 cm |
| Colour: | Green cat |
| Finish: | Gloss |
| Issued: | 1949 - 1955 |

| Beswick Number | | | Price | |
| | U.K. £ | U.S. $ | Can. $ | Aust. $ |
|---|---|---|---|---|
| 1151 | 400. | 725. | 900. | 1,000. |

**1152**
**GINGER NUTT™**

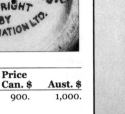

| Designer: | Arthur Gredington |
| Height: | 4", 10.1 cm |
| Colour: | Brown and beige squirrel, green base |
| Finish: | Gloss |
| Issued: | 1949 - 1955 |

| Beswick Number | | | Price | |
| | U.K. £ | U.S. $ | Can. $ | Aust. $ |
|---|---|---|---|---|
| 1152 | 400. | 725. | 900. | 1,000. |

**1153**
**HAZEL NUTT™**

| Designer: | Arthur Gredington |
| Height: | 3 ¾", 9.5 cm |
| Colour: | Brown and beige squirrel, green base |
| Finish: | Gloss |
| Issued: | 1949 - 1955 |

| Beswick Number | | | Price | |
| | U.K. £ | U.S. $ | Can. $ | Aust. $ |
|---|---|---|---|---|
| 1153 | 400. | 725. | 900. | 1,000. |

**1154**
**OSCAR OSTRICH™**

| Designer: | Arthur Gredington |
|---|---|
| Height: | 3 ¾", 9.5 cm |
| Colour: | Beige and mauve ostrich, brown base |
| Finish: | Gloss |
| Issued: | 1949 - 1955 |

| Beswick Number | | | Price | |
|---|---|---|---|---|
| | U.K. £ | U.S. $ | Can. $ | Aust. $ |
| 1154 | 500. | 900. | 1,100. | 1,200. |

**1155**
**DUSTY MOLE™**

| Designer: | Arthur Gredington |
|---|---|
| Height: | 3 ½", 8.9 cm |
| Colour: | Blue mole, white face |
| Finish: | Gloss |
| Issued: | 1949 - 1955 |

| Beswick Number | | | Price | |
|---|---|---|---|---|
| | U.K. $ | U.S. $ | Can. $ | Aust. $ |
| 1155 | 250. | 450. | 550. | 600. |

**1156**
**LOOPY HARE™**

| Designer: | Arthur Gredington |
|---|---|
| Height: | 4 ¼", 10.8 cm |
| Colour: | Brown and beige hare |
| Finish: | Gloss |
| Issued: | 1949 - 1955 |

| Beswick Number | | | Price | |
|---|---|---|---|---|
| | U.K. £ | U.S. $ | Can. $ | Aust. $ |
| 1156 | 450. | 800. | 1,000. | 1,100. |

# FELIX THE CAT

Joe Oriolo's *Felix the Cat* was originally created by Otto Messmer in Pat Sullivan's New York Animation Studios. His film debut was in 1922 when he featured in the film *Felix Saves The Day*. His career was put on hold when Pat Sullivan died in 1933, but Felix re-appeared in 1959 in cartoons for television. Although his career had it's ups and downs he managed to survive over many decades whilst still retaining his nine lives.

This model, a one off, was a special commission for U.K. International Ceramics in a limited edition of 1,000. Each one came with a numbered Certificate of Authenticity.

**3854**
**FELIX**

| | |
|---|---|
| Designer: | Unknown |
| Height: | 5 ½", 14.0 cm |
| Colour: | Black cat, white around eyes and mouth; red tongue |
| Finish: | Gloss |
| Issued: | 1998 in a limited edition of 1,000 |
| Comm. by: | U.K. International Ceramics |

| Beswick Number | Price | | | |
|---|---|---|---|---|
| | U.K. £ | U.S. $ | Can. $ | Aust. $ |
| 3854 | 65. | 115. | 150. | 160. |

# THE FLINTSTONES

In 1960 Hanna-Barbera created a clan of Cro-Magnon cave dwellers, the Flintstones and the Rubbles, who lived in the modern Stone Age town of Bedrock. The stories follow the adventures of these two "average" families.

Their first appearance was on television and the appeal of these characters was so great that their popularity spread throughout the U.S.A. to seventy-three countries worldwide.

This set of seven main characters was commissioned by U.K. International Ceramics. Each one came with a numbered Certificate of Authenticity.

**3577**
**PEBBLES FLINTSTONE™**

| | |
|---|---|
| Designer: | Simon Ward |
| Height: | 3 ½", 8.9 cm |
| Colour: | Green dress, blue pants, red hair, light brown base |
| Finish: | Gloss |
| Issued: | 1997 in a limited edition of 2,000 |
| Comm. by: | U.K. International Ceramics |

| Beswick Number | U.K. £ | U.S. $ | Price Can. $ | Aust. $ |
|---|---|---|---|---|
| 3577 | 35. | 65. | 80. | 90. |

**3579**
**BAMM-BAMM RUBBLE™**

| | |
|---|---|
| Designer: | Simon Ward |
| Height: | 3", 7.6 cm |
| Colour: | Light and dark brown pants, white hair, yellow club |
| Finish: | Gloss |
| Issued: | 1997 in a limited edition of 2,000 |
| Comm. by: | U.K. International Ceramics |

| Beswick Number | U.K. £ | U.S. $ | Price Can. $ | Aust. $ |
|---|---|---|---|---|
| 3579 | 35. | 65. | 80. | 90. |

**3583**
**WILMA FLINTSTONE™**

| Designer: | Simon Ward |
|---|---|
| Height: | 4 ¾", 12.1 cm |
| Colour: | White dress, red hair, light brown base |
| Finish: | Gloss |
| Issued: | 1996 in a limited edition of 2,000 |
| Comm. by: | U.K. International Ceramics |

| Beswick Number | U.K. £ | U.S. $ | Price Can. $ | Aust. $ |
|---|---|---|---|---|
| 3583 | 45. | 80. | 100. | 110. |

**3584**
**BETTY RUBBLE™**

| Designer: | Simon Ward |
|---|---|
| Height: | 4", 10.1 cm |
| Colour: | Blue dress, black hair, light brown base |
| Finish: | Gloss |
| Issued: | 1996 in a limited edition of 2,000 |
| Comm. by: | U.K. International Ceramics |

| Beswick Number | U.K. £ | U.S. $ | Price Can. $ | Aust. $ |
|---|---|---|---|---|
| 3584 | 50. | 90. | 115. | 125. |

**3587**
**BARNEY RUBBLE™**

| Designer: | Simon Ward |
|---|---|
| Height: | 3 ½", 8.9 cm |
| Colour: | Reddish brown shirt, yellow hair, light brown base |
| Finish: | Gloss |
| Issued: | 1996 in a limited edition of 2,000 |
| Comm. by: | U.K. International Ceramics |

| Beswick Number | U.K. £ | U.S. $ | Price Can. $ | Aust. $ |
|---|---|---|---|---|
| 3587 | 50. | 90. | 115. | 125. |

**3588**
**FRED FLINTSTONE™**

| | |
|---|---|
| Designer: | Simon Ward |
| Height: | 4 ¾", 12.1 cm |
| Colour: | Light brown shirt with dark patches, black hair, blue tie |
| Finish: | Gloss |
| Issued: | 1996 in a limited edition of 2,000 |
| Comm. by: | U.K. International Ceramics |

| Beswick Number | U.K. £ | U.S. $ | Price Can. $ | Aust. $ |
|---|---|---|---|---|
| 3588 | 45. | 80. | 100. | 110. |

**3590**
**DINO™**

| | |
|---|---|
| Designer: | Simon Ward |
| Height: | 4 ¾", 12.1 cm |
| Colour: | Purple, white and black |
| Finish: | Gloss |
| Issued: | 1997 in a limited edition of 2,000 |
| Comm. by: | U.K. International Ceramics |

| Beswick Number | U.K. £ | U.S. $ | Price Can. $ | Aust. $ |
|---|---|---|---|---|
| 3590 | 50. | 90. | 115. | 125. |

# RUPERT AND HIS FRIENDS

Rupert Bear was originally created by Mary Tourtel in 1920. The popularity and fame of Rupert Bear rapidly spread following his first annual, which was published in 1936 by the Express Newspapers.

The stories and drawings in this annual were the products of Alfred Bestall.

Cartoons in the Express and illustrated stories were continued until 1973.

**2694**
**RUPERT THE BEAR™**

| | |
|---|---|
| Designer: | Harry Sales |
| Height: | 4 ¼", 10.8 cm |
| Colour: | Red sweater, yellow check trousers and scarf |
| Finish: | Gloss |
| Issued: | 1980 - 1986 |

| Beswick Number | U.K. £ | U.S. $ | Price Can. $ | Aust. |
|---|---|---|---|---|
| 2694 | 225. | 400. | 500. | 550. |

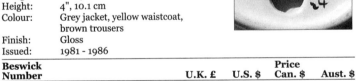

**2710**
**ALGY PUG™**

| | |
|---|---|
| Designer: | Harry Sales |
| Height: | 4", 10.1 cm |
| Colour: | Grey jacket, yellow waistcoat, brown trousers |
| Finish: | Gloss |
| Issued: | 1981 - 1986 |

| Beswick Number | U.K. £ | U.S. $ | Price Can. $ | Aust. $ |
|---|---|---|---|---|
| 2710 | 200. | 350. | 450. | 475. |

**2711**
**PONG PING™**

| | |
|---|---|
| Designer: | Harry Sales |
| Height: | 4 ¼", 10.8 cm |
| Colour: | Dark green jacket, gold trousers |
| Finish: | Gloss |
| Issued: | 1981 - 1986 |

| Beswick Number | U.K. £ | U.S. $ | Price Can. $ | Aust. $ |
|---|---|---|---|---|
| 2711 | 200. | 350. | 450. | 475. |

**2720**
**BILL BADGER™**
**Style One**

| | |
|---|---|
| Designer: | Harry Sales |
| Height: | 2 ¾", 7.0 cm |
| Colour: | Dark grey jacket, light grey trousers and red bowtie |
| Finish: | Gloss |
| Issued: | 1981 - 1986 |

| Beswick Number | U.K. £ | U.S. $ | Price Can. $ | Aust. $ |
|---|---|---|---|---|
| 2720 | 250. | 450. | 550. | 600. |

**2779**
**RUPERT "SNOWBALLING"™**

| | |
|---|---|
| Designer: | Harry Sales |
| Height: | 4 ¼", 10.8 cm |
| Colour: | Red coat, yellow check trousers and scarf |
| Finish: | Gloss |
| Issued: | 1982 - 1986 |

| Beswick Number | U.K. £ | U.S. $ | Price Can. $ | Aust. $ |
|---|---|---|---|---|
| 2779 | 300. | 550. | 675. | 750. |

**3951**
**EDWARD TRUNK**™

| | |
|---|---|
| Modeller: | Martyn Alcock |
| Height: | 5 ¼", 13.3 cm |
| Colour: | Blue coat, red scarf, yellow check trousers |
| Finish: | Gloss |
| Issued: | 2000 in a limited edition of 1,920 |
| Comm. by: | Doulton-Direct |

| Beswick Number | U.K. £ | U.S. $ | Price Can. $ | Aust. $ |
|---|---|---|---|---|
| 3951 | 65. | 115. | 150. | 160. |

**3955**
**BILL BADGER**™
**Style Two**

| | |
|---|---|
| Modeller: | Martyn Alcock |
| Height: | 5", 12.7 cm |
| Colour: | Turquoise, yellow and purple |
| Finish: | Gloss |
| Issued: | 2000 in a limited edition of 1,920 |
| Comm. by: | Doulton-Direct |

| Beswick Number | U.K. £ | U.S. $ | Price Can. $ | Aust. $ |
|---|---|---|---|---|
| 3955 | 65. | 115. | 150. | 160. |

**3975**
**RUPERT BEAR AND ALGY PUG GO-CARTING**™

| | |
|---|---|
| Modeller: | Martyn Alcock |
| Size: | 4 ½", x 5", 11.9 x 12.7 cm |
| Colour: | Red, yellow, blue, burgundy and brown |
| Finish: | Gloss |
| Issued: | 2000 in a limited edition of 2,500 |
| Comm. by: | Doulton-Direct |

| Beswick Number | U.K. £ | U.S. $ | Price Can. $ | Aust. $ |
|---|---|---|---|---|
| 3975 | 125. | 225. | 275. | 300. |

**4002**
**RUPERT WITH SATCHEL™**

| | |
|---|---|
| Modeller: | Martyn Alcock |
| Height: | 5", 12.7 cm |
| Colour: | Red, yellow, white and brown |
| Finish: | Gloss |
| Issued: | 2000 in a limited edition of 2,000 |
| Comm. by: | Doulton-Direct |

| Beswick Number | U.K. £ | U.S. $ | Price Can. $ | Aust. $ |
|---|---|---|---|---|
| 4002 | 175. | 300. | 375. | 400. |

**PODGY PIG**

| | |
|---|---|
| Modeller: | Martyn Alcock |
| Height: | 5 ¾", 14.6 cm |
| Colour: | Brown suit, red scarf, black socks, white shoes |
| Issued: | 1998 in a limited edition of 1,920 |
| Comm. by: | Lawleys by Post |

| Beswick Number | U.K. £ | U.S. $ | Price Can. $ | Aust. $ |
|---|---|---|---|---|
| — | 65. | 115. | 150. | 160. |

**RUPERT BEAR**

| | |
|---|---|
| Modeller: | Martyn Alcock |
| Height: | 5 ¾", 14.6 cm |
| Colour: | Red sweater, yellow check trousers and scarf |
| Issued: | 1998 in a limited edition of 1,920 |
| Comm. by: | Lawleys by Post |

| Beswick Number | U.K. £ | U.S. $ | Price Can. $ | Aust. $ |
|---|---|---|---|---|
| — | 65. | 115. | 150. | 160. |

# THELWELL

The Shetland pony *Kipper* and his rider *Penelope* have been immortalized in the cartoons by Norman Thelwell.

His first cartoon of the pair appeared in Punch magazine in the 1950s, and showed clearly that battle of wills being raged between the little fat pony and his equally diminutive and tubby mistress, whose bottom rarely made contact with the saddle.

Over the years the appeal of this subject has increased. Thelwell's first book *Angles on Horseback* was published in 1957 and since then his cartoons have appeared on all kinds of merchandise including Birthday and Christmas cards, calendars and jigsaws.

Sadly Norman Thelwell passed away in early 2004.

He was also a master of landscape and watercolour and a retrospective exhibition of his work was based on some 3,500 drawings that he had kept over a period of seventy years.

Ten models make up the Beswick stable, six are made in earthenware and four are in resin.

**2704A**
**AN ANGEL ON HORSEBACK™**
**First Variation**

| | |
|---|---|
| Designer: | Harry Sales |
| Modeller: | David Lyttleton |
| Height: | 4 ½", 11.4 cm |
| Colour: | Grey horse, rider wears brown jacket, yellow jodhpurs |
| Finish: | Gloss |
| Issued: | 1982 - 1989 |
| Varieties: | 2704B |

| Beswick Number | U.K. £ | U.S. $ | Price Can. $ | Aust. $ |
|---|---|---|---|---|
| 2704A | 175. | 300. | 375. | 400. |

**2704B**
**AN ANGEL ON HORSEBACK™**
**Second Variation**

| | |
|---|---|
| Designer: | Harry Sales |
| Modeller: | David Lyttleton |
| Height: | 4 ½", 11.4 cm |
| Colour: | Bay horse, rider wears red jacket, yellow jodhpurs |
| Finish: | Gloss |
| Issued: | 1982 - 1989 |
| Varieties: | 2704A |

| Beswick Number | U.K. £ | U.S. $ | Price Can. $ | Aust. $ |
|---|---|---|---|---|
| 2704B | 175. | 300. | 375. | 400. |

**2769A**
**KICK-START™**
**First Variation**

| | |
|---|---|
| Designer: | Harry Sales |
| Modeller: | David Lyttleton |
| Height: | 3 ½", 8.9 cm |
| Colour: | Grey horse, rider wears red jacket and yellow jodhpurs |
| Finish: | Gloss |
| Issued: | 1983 - 1989 |
| Varieties: | 2769B |

| Beswick Number | U.K. £ | U.S. $ | Price Can. $ | Aust. $ |
|---|---|---|---|---|
| 2769A | 175. | 300. | 375. | 400. |

**2769B**
**KICK-START™**
**Second Variation**

| | |
|---|---|
| Designer: | Harry Sales |
| Modeller: | David Lyttleton |
| Height: | 3 ½", 8.9 cm |
| Colour: | Bay horse, rider wears red jacket and yellow jodhpurs |
| Finish: | Gloss |
| Issued: | 1983 - 1989 |
| Varieties: | 2769A |

| Beswick Number | U.K. £ | U.S. $ | Price Can. $ | Aust. $ |
|---|---|---|---|---|
| 2769B | 175. | 300. | 375. | 400. |

**2789A**
**PONY EXPRESS™**
**First Variation**

| | |
|---|---|
| Designer: | Harry Sales |
| Modeller: | David Lyttleton |
| Height: | 4 ½", 11.4 cm |
| Colour: | Grey horse, rider wears green jacket and yellow jodhpurs |
| Finish: | Gloss |
| Issued: | 1983 - 1989 |
| Varieties: | 2789B |

| Beswick Number | U.K. £ | U.S. $ | Price Can. $ | Aust. $ |
|---|---|---|---|---|
| 2789A | 375. | 675. | 850. | 900. |

**2789B**
**PONY EXPRESS™**
**Second Variation**

| | |
|---|---|
| Designer: | Harry Sales |
| Modeller: | David Lyttleton |
| Height: | 4 ½", 11.4 cm |
| Colour: | Bay horse, rider wears red jacket and yellow jodhpurs |
| Finish: | Gloss |
| Issued: | 1983 - 1989 |
| Varieties: | 2789A |

| Beswick Number | U.K. £ | U.S. $ | Price Can. $ | Aust. $ |
|---|---|---|---|---|
| 2789B | 250. | 450. | 550. | 600. |

**SS7A**
**I FORGIVE YOU™**
**First Variation**

| | |
|---|---|
| Designer: | Harry Sales |
| Modeller: | David Lyttleton |
| Height: | 4", 10.1 cm |
| Colour: | Grey horse, rider wears red jacket and yellow jodhpurs |
| Finish: | Resin |
| Issued: | 1985 - 1985 |
| Series: | Studio Sculptures |
| Varieties: | SS7B |

| Beswick Number | U.K. £ | U.S. $ | Price Can. $ | Aust. $ |
|---|---|---|---|---|
| SS7A | 100. | 175. | 225. | 250. |

**SS7B**
**I FORGIVE YOU™**
**Second Variation**

| | |
|---|---|
| Designer: | Harry Sales |
| Modeller: | David Lyttleton |
| Height: | 4", 10.1 cm |
| Colour: | Bay horse, rider wears red jacket and yellow jodhpurs |
| Finish: | Resin |
| Issued: | 1985 - 1985 |
| Series: | Studio Sculptures |
| Varieties: | SS7A |

| Beswick Number | U.K. £ | U.S. $ | Price Can. $ | Aust. $ |
|---|---|---|---|---|
| SS7B | 100. | 175. | 225. | 250. |

### SS12A
### EARLY BATH™
### First Variation

| | |
|---|---|
| Designer: | Harry Sales |
| Modeller: | David Lyttleton |
| Height: | 4 ¾", 12.1 cm |
| Colour: | Grey horse, rider wears redjacket and yellow jodhpurs |
| Finish: | Resin |
| Issued: | 1985 - 1985 |
| Series: | Studio Sculptures |
| Varieties: | SS12B |

| Beswick Number | U.K. £ | U.S. $ | Price Can. $ | Aust. $ |
|---|---|---|---|---|
| SS12A | 125. | 225. | 275. | 300. |

### SS12B
### EARLY BATH™
### Second Variation

| | |
|---|---|
| Designer: | Harry Sales |
| Modeller: | David Lyttleton |
| Height: | 4 ¾", 12.1 cm |
| Colour: | Bay horse, rider wears red jacket and yellow jodhpurs |
| Finish: | Resin |
| Issued: | 1985 - 1985 |
| Series: | Studio Sculptures |
| Varieties: | SS12A |

| Beswick Number | U.K. £ | U.S. $ | Price Can. $ | Aust. $ |
|---|---|---|---|---|
| SS12B | 125. | 225. | 275. | 300. |

# THUNDERBIRDS

Towards the end of October 1963, television producer Gerry Anderson was faced with a dilemma. He and his colleagues at the AP Films Studios in Slough, England, were coming to the end of filming the television series *Stingray* and were faced with a deadline to come up with an idea for a new series.

At that time there was a terrible mine disaster in Germany, three men were rescued but others were trapped underground. A huge drill was needed to try to rescue the remaining men, one existed, but it was in Bremen and would therefore take eight hours to get to the site.

Anderson thought that there should be dumps around the world with rescue equipment standing by to be rushed to disaster zones. This was the start of his idea to create a science fiction International Rescue organisation. From a luxurious island base somewhere in the Pacific Ocean the members of this new International Rescue Force would be on the alert. Their efforts, of course, would always be attacked by villains.

During the Second World War there was an air field in Arizona known as Thunderbird Field and Anderson realized that Thunderbird was the perfect name for the International Rescue vehicles.

A new television series was born.

(Adapted from the *Complete Book of Thunderbirds* by Chris Bentley.)

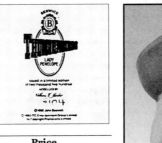

**3337**
**LADY PENELOPE™**

| Designer: | William K. Harper |
| Height: | 4", 10.1 cm |
| Colour: | Pink hat and coat, blonde hair |
| Finish: | Gloss |
| Issued: | 1992 in a limited edition of 2,500 |

| Beswick Number | | | Price | |
|---|---|---|---|---|
| | U.K. £ | U.S. $ | Can. $ | Aust. $ |
| 3337 | 100. | 180. | 225. | 250. |

**3339**
**BRAINS™**

| Designer: | William K. Harper |
| Height: | 4", 10.1 cm |
| Colour: | Black and blue uniform, blue glasses, black hair |
| Finish: | Gloss |
| Issued: | 1992 in a limited edition of 2,500 |

| Beswick Number | | | Price | |
|---|---|---|---|---|
| | U.K. £ | U.S. $ | Can. $ | Aust. $ |
| 3339 | 100. | 180. | 225. | 250. |

### 3344
### SCOTT TRACY™

| | |
|---|---|
| Designer: | William K. Harper |
| Height: | 4", 10.1 cm |
| Colour: | Blue uniform, light blue band |
| Finish: | Gloss |
| Issued: | 1992 in a limited edition of 2,500 |

| Beswick Number | U.K. £ | U.S. $ | Price Can. $ | Aust. $ |
|---|---|---|---|---|
| 3344 | 100. | 180. | 225. | 250. |

### 3345
### VIRGIL TRACY™

| | |
|---|---|
| Designer: | William K. Harper |
| Height: | 4", 10.1 cm |
| Colour: | Blue uniform, yellow band |
| Finish: | Gloss |
| Issued: | 1992 in a limited edition of 2,500 |

| Beswick Number | U.K. £ | U.S. $ | Price Can. $ | Aust. $ |
|---|---|---|---|---|
| 3345 | 100. | 180. | 225. | 250. |

## 3346
## PARKER™

| | |
|---|---|
| Designer: | William K. Harper |
| Height: | 4", 10.1 cm |
| Colour: | Blue-grey uniform |
| Finish: | Gloss |
| Issued: | 1992 in a limited edition of 2,500 |

| Beswick Number | U.K. £ | U.S. $ | Price Can. $ | Aust. $ |
|---|---|---|---|---|
| 3346 | 100. | 180. | 225. | 250. |

## 3348
## THE HOOD™

| | |
|---|---|
| Designer: | William K. Harper |
| Height: | 4", 10.1 cm |
| Colour: | Browns |
| Finish: | Gloss |
| Issued: | 1992 in a limited edition of 2,500 |

| Beswick Number | U.K. £ | U.S. $ | Price Can. $ | Aust. $ |
|---|---|---|---|---|
| 3348 | 100. | 180. | 225. | 250. |

# TOM, JERRY AND DROOPY

The carton character of Tom must be known to most of us. Although he was born over fifty years ago he still continues to turn up unexpectedly on our television screens.

His partner Jerry has been stealing scenes, and our hearts, since their first appearance together in 1939 in the MGM cartoon film *Puss Gets the Boot*.

Together Tom and Jerry have appeared in over two hundred classic cartoons and have received eight Academy Awards.

To celebrate fifty-five years of their antics U.K. International Ceramics commissioned these models.

**3547**
**DROOPY™**

| | |
|---|---|
| Designer: | Simon Ward |
| Height: | 4 ½", 11.4 cm |
| Colour: | White dog with black ears, red cap |
| Finish: | Gloss |
| Issued: | 1995 in a special edition of 2,000 |
| Comm. by: | U.K. International Ceramics |

| Beswick Number | U.K. £ | U.S. $ | Price Can. $ | Aust. $ |
|---|---|---|---|---|
| 3547 | 40. | 70. | 90. | 95. |

**3549**
**JERRY™**

| | |
|---|---|
| Designer: | Simon Ward |
| Height: | 3", 7.6 cm |
| Colour | Red-brown and cream mouse, white base |
| Finish: | Gloss |
| Issued: | 1995 in special edition of 2,000 |
| Series: | Tom and Jerry |
| Comm. by: | U.K. International Ceramics |

| Beswick Number | U.K. £ | U.S. $ | Price Can. $ | Aust. $ |
|---|---|---|---|---|
| 3549 | 35. | 60. | 75. | 80. |

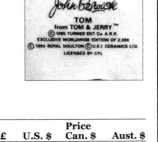

**3552**
**TOM™**

| | |
|---|---|
| Designer: | Simon Ward |
| Height: | 4 ½", 11.4 cm |
| Colour: | Grey-blue and pink cat, white base |
| Finish: | Gloss |
| Issued: | 1995 in a special edition of 2,000 |
| Series: | Tom and Jerry |
| Comm. by: | U.K. International Ceramics |

| Beswick Number | U.K. £ | U.S. $ | Price Can. $ | Aust. $ |
|---|---|---|---|---|
| 3552 | 60. | 110. | 135. | 150. |

# TOP CAT AND FRIENDS

In 1962 Top Cat and his gang made their television debut.

Top Cat (or TC as he is known) is a Con-Man type of character and as such he tries to outwit the policeman, Officer Dribble, unfortunately his gang of friends hamper his attempts to win the day.

These seven characters were created by Hanna-Barbera, and the Beswick models were commissioned by Sinclairs, Sheffield, England.

**3581**
**TOP CAT™**

| Designer: | Andy Moss |
| Height: | 4 ½", 11.9 cm |
| Colour: | Yellow cat wearing a mauve waistcoat and hat |
| Finish: | Gloss |
| Issued: | 1996 in a limited edition of 2,000 |
| Comm. by: | Sinclairs |

*John Beswick*
**TOP CAT** ™
© 1996 H-B PROD., INC
LICENSED BY CPL
© 1996 ROYAL DOULTON
EXCLUSIVE EDITION OF 2,000
FOR THE DOULTON &
BESWICK FAIRS IN ENGLAND

| Beswick Number | U.K. £ | U.S. $ | Price Can. $ | Aust. $ |
|---|---|---|---|---|
| 3581 | 75. | 135. | 160. | 175. |

**3586**
**CHOO-CHOO™**

| Designer: | Andy Moss |
| Height: | 4 ½", 11.9 cm |
| Colour: | Pink cat wearing a white shirt |
| Finish: | Gloss |
| Issued: | 1996 in a limited edition of 2,000 |
| Comm. by: | Sinclairs |

*John Beswick*
**CHOO-CHOO** ™
© 1996 H-B PROD., INC.
LICENSED BY CPL
© 1996 ROYAL DOULTON
EXCLUSIVE EDITION OF 2,000
FOR THE DOULTON &
BESWICK FAIRS IN ENGLAND

| Beswick Number | U.K. £ | U.S. $ | Price Can. $ | Aust. $ |
|---|---|---|---|---|
| 3586 | 75. | 135. | 160. | 175. |

## 3624
### FANCY FANCY™

| | |
|---|---|
| Designer: | Andy Moss |
| Height: | 4 ½", 11.9 cm |
| Colour: | Pink cat, black tip on tail, white scarf |
| Finish: | Gloss |
| Issued: | 1997 in a limited edition of 2,000 |
| Comm. by: | Sinclairs |

| Beswick Number | U.K. £ | U.S. $ | Price Can. $ | Aust. $ |
|---|---|---|---|---|
| 3624 | 40. | 75. | 95. | 100. |

## 3627
### BENNY™

| | |
|---|---|
| Designer: | Andy Moss |
| Height: | 3 ¾", 8.5 cm |
| Colour: | Lilac cat wearing a white jacket |
| Finish: | Gloss |
| Issued: | 1997 in a limited edition of 2,000 |
| Comm. by: | Sinclairs |

| Beswick Number | U.K. £ | U.S. $ | Price Can. $ | Aust. $ |
|---|---|---|---|---|
| 3627 | 40. | 75. | 95. | 100. |

## 3671
### OFFICER DIBBLE™

| | |
|---|---|
| Designer: | Andy Moss |
| Height: | 6 ¾", 17.5 cm |
| Colour: | Dark blue police officer's uniform |
| Finish: | Gloss |
| Issued: | 1998 in a limited edition of 2,000 |
| Comm. by: | Sinclairs |

| Beswick Number | U.K. £ | U.S. $ | Price Can. $ | Aust. $ |
|---|---|---|---|---|
| 3671 | 120. | 200. | 250. | 275. |

**3673**
**SPOOK™**

| | |
|---|---|
| Designer: | Andy Moss |
| Height: | 4 ½", 11.9 cm |
| Colour: | Beige cat wearing black tie |
| Finish: | Gloss |
| Issued: | 1998 in a limited edition of 2,000 |
| Comm. by: | Sinclairs |

| Beswick Number | U.K. £ | U.S. $ | Price Can. $ | Aust. $ |
|---|---|---|---|---|
| 3673 | 40. | 75. | 95. | 100. |

**3674**
**BRAIN™**

| | |
|---|---|
| Designer: | Andy Moss |
| Height: | 4", 10.1 cm |
| Colour: | Yellow cat wearing a purple shirt |
| Finish: | Gloss |
| Issued: | 1998 in a limited edition of 2,000 |
| Comm. by: | Sinclairs |

| Beswick Number | U.K. £ | U.S. $ | Price Can. $ | Aust. $ |
|---|---|---|---|---|
| 3674 | 40. | 75. | 95. | 100. |

# TRUMPTONSHIRE

It was planned originally to make this series a set of thirteen figures, but possibly due to the fact that Beswick's days were numbered, only ten of these figures were put into production. No. 4207 Sergeant Major Grout, No. 4220 Peter Hazel and No. 4221 Chippy Minton were never produced.

Not many models exist and these figures will be hard to find and become rare in the future.

## 4054
## PC MCGARRY™

| Designer: | Robert Simpson |
|---|---|
| Height: | 5 ¾", 14.6 cm |
| Colour: | Black police uniform; white shirt |
| Finish: | Gloss |
| Issued: | 2001 in a limited edition of 2,500 |
| Comm. by: | Doulton-Direct |

| Beswick Number | U.S. $ | Can. $ | Price U.K. £ | Aust. $ |
|---|---|---|---|---|
| 4054 | 75. | 135. | 170. | 180. |

## 4055
## WINDY MILLER™

| Designer: | Robert Simpson |
|---|---|
| Height: | 5 ½", 14.0 cm |
| Colour: | Blue shirt, red trousers and scarf black hat and shoes |
| Finish: | Gloss |
| Issued: | 2001 in a limited edition of 2,500 |
| Comm. by: | Doulton-Direct |

| Beswick Number | U.S. $ | Can. $ | Price U.K. £ | Aust. $ |
|---|---|---|---|---|
| 4055 | 50. | 90. | 110. | 120. |

### 4063
### CAPTAIN FLACK™

| | |
|---|---|
| Designer: | Gordon Murray |
| Modeller: | Robert Simpson |
| Height: | 6", 15.0 cm |
| Colour: | Navy, gold, yellow and black |
| Finish: | Gloss |
| Issued: | 2001 in a limited edition of 2,500 |
| Comm. by: | Doulton-Direct |

| Beswick Number | U.K. £ | U.S. $ | Price Can. $ | Aust. $ |
|---|---|---|---|---|
| 4063 | 50. | 90. | 110. | 120. |

### 4065
### DR. MOPP™

| | |
|---|---|
| Designer: | Gordon Murray |
| Modeller: | Robert Simpson |
| Height: | 5 ¾", 14.6 cm |
| Colour: | Purple, blue, white, yellow and black |
| Finish: | Gloss |
| Issued: | 2001 in a limited edition of 2,500 |
| Comm. by: | Doulton-Direct |

| Beswick Number | U.K. £ | U.S. $ | Price Can. $ | Aust. $ |
|---|---|---|---|---|
| 4065 | 45. | 80. | 100. | 110. |

### 4066
### THE MAYOR™

| | |
|---|---|
| Designer: | Gordon Murray |
| Modeller: | Robert Simpson |
| Height: | 5 ½", 14.0 cm |
| Colour: | Black, red, blue and gold |
| Finish: | Gloss |
| Issued: | 2001 in a limited edition of 2,500 |
| Comm. by: | Doulton-Direct |

| Beswick Number | U.K. £ | U.S. $ | Price Can. $ | Aust. $ |
|---|---|---|---|---|
| 4066 | 45. | 80. | 100. | 110. |

**4067**
**MRS. HONEYMAN**™

| Designer: | Gordon Murray |
| Modeller: | Robert Simpson |
| Height: | 5 ½", 14.0 cm |
| Colour: | Pink, black, white, yellow and purple |
| Finish: | Gloss |
| Issued: | 2001 in a limited edition of 2,500 |
| Comm. by: | Doulton-Direct |

| Beswick Number | U.K. £ | U.S. $ | Price Can. $ | Aust. $ |
|---|---|---|---|---|
| 4067 | 45. | 80. | 100. | 110. |

**4184**
**MRS. DINGLE**™

| Designer: | Gordon Murray |
| Modeller: | Robert Simpson |
| Height: | 5 ¼", 13.3 cm |
| Colour: | Blue, red and white |
| Finish: | Gloss |
| Issued: | 2001 in a limited edition of 2,500 |
| Comm. by: | Doulton-Direct |

| Beswick Number | U.K. £ | U.S. $ | Price Can. $ | Aust. $ |
|---|---|---|---|---|
| 4184 | 75. | 135. | 170. | 180. |

**4185**
**JONATHAN BELL**™

| Designer: | Gordon Murray |
| Modeller: | Robert Simpson |
| Height: | 5 ¼", 13.3 cm |
| Colour: | Brown, yellow, green and black |
| Finish: | Gloss |
| Issued: | 2001 in a limited edition of 2,500 |
| Comm. by: | Doulton-Direct |

| Beswick Number | U.K. £ | U.S.. $ | Price Can. $ | Aust. $ |
|---|---|---|---|---|
| 4185 | 75. | 135. | 170. | 180. |

**4186**
**MICKEY MURPHY**™

| | |
|---|---|
| Designer: | Gordon Murray |
| Modeller: | Robert Simpson |
| Height: | 5 ½", 14.0 cm |
| Colour: | White, blue and yellow |
| Finish: | Gloss |
| Issued: | 2001 in a limited edition of 2,500 |
| Comm. by: | Doulton-Direct |

| Beswick Number | U.K. £ | U.S. $ | Price Can. $ | Aust. $ |
|---|---|---|---|---|
| 4186 | 75. | 135. | 170. | 180. |

**4187**
**MRS. COBBIT**™

| | |
|---|---|
| Designer: | Gordon Murray |
| Modeller: | Robert Simpson |
| Height: | 5 ¼", 13.3 cm |
| Colour: | Yellow, navy and light blue |
| Finish: | Gloss |
| Issued: | 2001 in a limited edition of 2,500 |
| Comm. by: | Doulton-Direct |

| Beswick Number | U.K. £ | U.S. $ | Price Can. $ | Aust. $ |
|---|---|---|---|---|
| 4187 | 75. | 135. | 170. | 180. |

# SECTION THREE

## MISCELLANEOUS CHARACTERS

Fairy Drinking,   Fairy Baking,   Fairy Crying,   Fairy Sewing

# BEDTIME CHORUS

### 1801
### PIANIST™

| | |
|---|---|
| Designer: | Albert Hallam |
| Height: | 3", 7.6 cm |
| Colour: | Pale blue and yellow |
| Finish: | Gloss |
| Issued: | 1962 - 1969 |

| Beswick Number | U.K. £ | U.S. $ | Price Can. $ | Aust. $ |
|---|---|---|---|---|
| 1801 | 90. | 160. | 200. | 215. |

### 1802
### PIANO™

| | |
|---|---|
| Designer: | Albert Hallam |
| Height: | 3", 7.6 cm |
| Colour: | Brown and white |
| Finish: | Gloss |
| Issued: | 1962 - 1969 |

| Beswick Number | U.K. £ | U.S. $ | Price Can. $ | Aus.t $ |
|---|---|---|---|---|
| 1802 | 50. | 90. | 115. | 120. |

### 1803
### CAT - SINGING™

| | |
|---|---|
| Designer: | Albert Hallam |
| Height: | 1 ¼", 3.2 cm |
| Colour: | Ginger stripe |
| Finish: | Gloss |
| Issued: | 1962 - 1971 |

| Beswick Number | U.K. £ | U.S. $ | Price Can. $ | Aust. $ |
|---|---|---|---|---|
| 1803 | 35. | 65. | 80. | 90. |

### 1804
### BOY WITHOUT SPECTACLES™

| | |
|---|---|
| Designer: | Albert Hallam |
| Height: | 3 ½", 8.9 cm |
| Colour: | Yellow, white and blue |
| Finish: | Gloss |
| Issued: | 1962 - 1969 |

| Beswick Number | U.K. £ | U.S. $ | Price Can. $ | Aust. $ |
|---|---|---|---|---|
| 1804 | 100. | 175. | 225. | 250. |

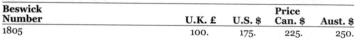

### 1805
### BOY WITH SPECTACLES™

| | |
|---|---|
| Designer: | Albert Hallam |
| Height: | 3", 7.6 cm |
| Colour: | Green, white and blue |
| Finish: | Gloss |
| Issued: | 1962 - 1969 |

| Beswick Number | U.K. £ | U.S. $ | Price Can. $ | Aust. $ |
|---|---|---|---|---|
| 1805 | 100. | 175. | 225. | 250. |

**1824**
**DOG - SINGING**™

| | |
|---|---|
| Designer: | Albert Hallam |
| Height: | 1 ½", 3.8 cm |
| Colour: | Tan |
| Finish: | Gloss |
| Issued: | 1962 - 1971 |

| Beswick Number | U.K. £ | U.S. $ | Price Can. $ | Aust. $ |
|---|---|---|---|---|
| 1824 | 40. | 70. | 90. | 95. |

**1825**
**BOY WITH GUITAR**™

| | |
|---|---|
| Designer: | Albert Hallam |
| Height: | 3", 7.6 cm |
| Colour: | Blue-grey, brown and blue |
| Finish: | Gloss |
| Issued: | 1962 - 1969 |

| Beswick Number | U.K. £ | U.S. $ | Price Can. $ | Aust. $ |
|---|---|---|---|---|
| 1825 | 100. | 175. | 225. | 250. |

**1826**
**GIRL WITH HARP**™

| | |
|---|---|
| Designer: | Albert Hallam |
| Height: | 3 ½", 8.9 cm |
| Colour: | Purple, red and brown |
| Finish: | Gloss |
| Issued: | 1962 - 1969 |

| Beswick Number | U.K. £ | U.S. $ | Price Can. $ | Aust. $ |
|---|---|---|---|---|
| 1826 | 100. | 175. | 225. | 250. |

# BESWICK BEARS

### BB001
### WILLIAM™

| Height: | 2 ¼", 5.7 cm |
| Colour: | Brown bear, blue apron, white and rose book |
| Finish: | Resin |
| Issued: | 1993 - 1993 |

| Beswick Number | | U.K. £ | U.S. $ | Price Can. $ | Aust. $ |
|---|---|---|---|---|---|
| BB001 | | 40. | 70. | 90. | 95. |

BILLY
kicked his ball up high
and it landed "SPLAT"
in the apple pie.
*Beswick Bears*
BB002

### BB002
### BILLY™

| Height: | 4", 10.1 cm |
| Colour: | Brown bear, green waistcoat, blue hat, yellow, red and blue ball |
| Finish: | Resin |
| Issued: | 1993 - 1993 |

| Beswick Number | | U.K. £ | U.S. $ | Price Can. $ | Aust. $ |
|---|---|---|---|---|---|
| BB002 | | 35. | 60. | 75. | 80. |

**BB003**
**HARRY™**

| | |
|---|---|
| Height: | 3 ¼", 8.3 cm |
| Colour: | Brown bear, blue waistcoat, brown hat, white plates |
| Finish: | Resin |
| Issued: | 1993 - 1993 |

| Beswick Number | U.K. £ | U.S. $ | Price Can. $ | Aust. $ |
|---|---|---|---|---|
| BB003 | 35. | 60. | 75. | 80. |

**BB004**
**BOBBY™**

| | |
|---|---|
| Height: | 4", 10.1 cm |
| Colour: | Brown bear, blue waistcoat, brown hat, yellow ball, black and red bat |
| Finish: | Resin |
| Issued: | 1993 - 1993 |

| Beswick Number | U.K. £ | U.S. $ | Price Can. $ | Aust. $ |
|---|---|---|---|---|
| BB004 | 35. | 60. | 75. | 80. |

**BB005**
**JAMES™**

| | |
|---|---|
| Height: | 3 ¾", 9.5 cm |
| Colour: | Brown bear, yellow waistcoat, blue hat, blue gift box with pink ribbon |
| Finish: | Resin |
| Issued: | 1993 - 1993 |

| Beswick Number | U.K. £ | U.S. $ | Price Can. $ | Aust. $ |
|---|---|---|---|---|
| BB005 | 35. | 60. | 75. | 80. |

**BB006**
**SUSIE™**

| Height: | 3 ½", 8.9 cm |
| Colour: | Brown bear, blue dress, brown recorder |
| Finish: | Resin |
| Issued: | 1993 - 1993 |

| Beswick Number | U.K. £ | U.S. $ | Price Can. $ | Aus.t $ |
|---|---|---|---|---|
| BB006 | 35. | 60. | 75. | 80. |

**BB007**
**ANGELA™**

| Height: | 3 ¼", 8.3 cm |
| Colour: | Brown bear, yellow dress, white flowers |
| Finish: | Resin |
| Issued: | 1993 - 1993 |

| Beswick Number | U.K. £ | U.S. $ | Price Can. $ | Aust. $ |
|---|---|---|---|---|
| BB007 | 35. | 60. | 75. | 80. |

**BB008**
**CHARLOTTE™**

| Height: | 4", 10.1 cm |
| Colour: | Brown bear, pink dress, blue and yellow parasol |
| Finish: | Resin |
| Issued: | 1993 - 1993 |

| Beswick Number | U.K. £ | U.S. $ | Price Can. $ | Aust. $ |
|---|---|---|---|---|
| BB008 | 35. | 60. | 75. | 80. |

**BB009**
**SAM™**

Height:     3 ½", 8.9 cm
Colour:     Brown bear, rose waistcoat, yellow banjo
Finish:     Resin
Issued:     1993 - 1993

| Beswick Number | U.K. £ | U.S. $ | Price Can. $ | Aust. $ |
|---|---|---|---|---|
| BB009 | 35. | 60. | 75. | 80. |

**BB010**
**LIZZY™**

Height:     2 ¼", 5.7 cm
Colour:     Brown bear, pink dress, paint box
Finish:     Resin
Issued:     1993 - 1993

| Beswick Number | U.K. £ | U.S. $ | Price Can. $ | Aust. $ |
|---|---|---|---|---|
| BB010 | 35. | 60. | 75. | 80. |

**BB011**
**EMILY™**

Height:     3 ½", 8.9 cm
Colour:     Brown bear, pale blue dress, brown
              picnic hamper
Finish:     Resin
Issued:     1993 - 1993

| Beswick Number | U.K. £ | U.S. $ | Price Can. $ | Aust. $ |
|---|---|---|---|---|
| BB011 | 35. | 60. | 75. | 80. |

SARAH
is sipping her afternoon tea
Perched on the stump
of an old oak tree.

*Beswick Bears*

BB012

**BB012**
**SARAH™**

| | |
|---|---|
| Height: | 3 ¼", 8.3 cm |
| Colour: | Brown bear, green dress, white cup and saucer |
| Finish: | Resin |
| Issued: | 1993 - 1993 |

| Beswick Number | U.K. £ | U.S. $ | Price Can. $ | Aust. $ |
|---|---|---|---|---|
| BB012 | 35. | 60. | 75. | 80. |

# FAIRIES

## 1010
### FAIRY, CRYING

| | |
|---|---|
| Designer: | Arthur Gredington |
| Height: | 6", 15.0 cm |
| Colour: | Pale mauve dress, yellow hair, green base |
| Finish: | Gloss |
| Issued: | 1944 |
| Set: | 1011, 1012, 1013 |

| Beswick Number | U.K. £ | U.S. $ | Price Can. $ | Aust. $ |
|---|---|---|---|---|
| 1010 | | | Very rare | |

## 1011
### FAIRY, DRINKING

| | |
|---|---|
| Designer: | Arthur Gredington |
| Height: | 4", 10.1 cm |
| Colour: | Pale mauve dress, yellow hair, green base |
| Finish: | Gloss |
| Issued: | 1944 |
| Set: | 1010, 1012, 1013 |

| Beswick Number | U.K. £ | U.S. $ | Price Can. $ | Aust. $ |
|---|---|---|---|---|
| 1011 | | | Very rare | |

**1012**
**FAIRY, SEWING**

| | |
|---|---|
| Designer: | Arthur Gredington |
| Height: | 4 ¼", 10.8 cm |
| Colour: | Pale mauve dress, yellow hair, green base |
| Finish: | Gloss |
| Issued: | 1944 - 1954 |
| Set: | 1010, 1011, 1013 |

| Beswick Number | U.K. £ | U.S. $ | Price Can. $ | Aust. $ |
|---|---|---|---|---|
| 1012 | | | Very rare | |

**1013**
**FAIRY, BAKING**

| | |
|---|---|
| Designer: | Arthur Gredington |
| Height: | 6 ¼", 15.9 cm |
| Colour: | Pale mauve dress, yellow hair, green base |
| Finish: | Gloss |
| Issued: | 1944 - 1954 |
| Set: | 1010, 1011, 1012 |

| Beswick Number | U.K. £ | U.S. $ | Price Can. $ | Aust. $ |
|---|---|---|---|---|
| 1013 | | | Very rare | |

# LITTLE LOVABLES

Please note that LL35 was allocated to the Beswick Collectors Circle, but never produced.

**LL1 (3328)**
**HAPPY BIRTHDAY**™

| | |
|---|---|
| Designer: | Amanda Hughes-Lubeck |
| Height: | 4 ½", 11.9 cm |
| Colour: | White, pink and orange |
| Finish: | Gloss |
| Issued: | 1992 - 1994 |
| Varieties: | LL8; LL15; also unnamed LL22 |

| Beswick Number | U.K. £ | U.S. $ | Price Can. $ | Aust. $ |
|---|---|---|---|---|
| LL1 (3328) | 30. | 50. | 60. | 70. |

**LL2 (3320)**
**I LOVE YOU**™

| | |
|---|---|
| Designer: | Amanda Hughes-Lubeck |
| Height: | 4 ½", 11.9 cm |
| Colour: | White, green and pink |
| Finish: | Gloss |
| Issued: | 1992 - 1994 |
| Varieties: | LL9, LL16; also unnamed LL23 |

| Beswick Number | U.K. £ | U.S. $ | Price Can. $ | Aust. $ |
|---|---|---|---|---|
| LL2 (3320) | 25. | 45. | 55. | 60. |

## LL3 (3336)
### GOD LOVES ME™

| | |
|---|---|
| Designer: | Amanda Hughes-Lubeck |
| Height: | 3 ¾", 9.5 cm |
| Colour: | White, green and turquoise |
| Finish: | Gloss |
| Issued: | 1992 - 1993 |
| Varieties: | LL10, LL17; also called Please, LL33, LL34; also unnamed LL24 |

| Beswick Number | U.K. £ | U.S. $ | Price Can. $ | Aust. $ |
|---|---|---|---|---|
| LL3 (3336) | 75. | 125. | 150. | 160. |

## LL4 (3361)
### JUST FOR YOU™

| | |
|---|---|
| Designer: | Warren Platt |
| Height: | 4 ½", 11.9 cm |
| Colour: | White, pink and blue |
| Finish: | Gloss |
| Issued: | 1992 - 1994 |
| Varieties: | LL11, LL18; also unnamed LL25 |

| Beswick Number | U.K. £ | U.S. $ | Price Can. $ | Aust. $ |
|---|---|---|---|---|
| LL4 (3361) | 25. | 45. | 55. | 60. |

## LL5 (3331)
### TO MOTHER™

| | |
|---|---|
| Designer: | Amanda Hughes-Lubeck |
| Height: | 4 ½", 11.9 cm |
| Colour: | White, blue and purple |
| Finish: | Gloss |
| Issued: | 1992 - 1994 |
| Varieties: | LL12, LL19; also called To Daddy LL29, also unnamed LL26 |

| Beswick Number | U.K. £ | U.S. $ | Price Can. $ | Aust. $ |
|---|---|---|---|---|
| LL5 (3331) | 25. | 45. | 55. | 60. |

## LL6 (3340)
### CONGRATULATIONS™

| | |
|---|---|
| Designer: | Warren Platt |
| Height: | 4 ½", 11.9 cm |
| Colour: | White, green and pink |
| Finish: | Gloss |
| Issued: | 1992 - 1994 |
| Varieties: | LL13, LL20; also unnamed LL27 |

| Beswick Number | U.K. £ | U.S. $ | Price Can. $ | Aust. $ |
|---|---|---|---|---|
| LL6 (3340 ) | 25. | 45. | 55. | 60. |

## LL7 (3334)
### PASSED™

| | |
|---|---|
| Designer: | Amanda Hughes-Lubeck |
| Height: | 3", 7.6 cm |
| Colour: | White, lilac and pink |
| Finish: | Gloss |
| Issued: | 1992 - 1994 |
| Varieties: | LL14, LL21; also unnamed LL28 |

| Beswick Number | U.K. £ | U.S. $ | Price Can. $ | Aust. $ |
|---|---|---|---|---|
| LL7 (3334) | 40. | 70. | 85. | 95. |

## LL8 (3328)
### HAPPY BIRTHDAY™

| | |
|---|---|
| Designer: | Amanda Hughes-Lubeck |
| Height: | 4 ½", 11.9 cm |
| Colour: | White, yellow and green |
| Finish: | Gloss |
| Issued: | 1992 - 1994 |
| Varieties: | LL1, LL15; also unnamed LL22 |

| Beswick Number | U.K. £ | U.S. $ | Price Can. $ | Aust. $ |
|---|---|---|---|---|
| LL8 (3328) | 25. | 45. | 55. | 60. |

**LL9 (3320)**
**I LOVE YOU™**

| | |
|---|---|
| Designer: | Amanda Hughes-Lubeck |
| Height: | 4 ½", 11.9 cm |
| Colour: | White, blue and orange |
| Finish: | Gloss |
| Issued: | 1992 - 1994 |
| Varieties: | LL2, LL16; also unnamed LL23 |

| Beswick Number | U.K. £ | U.S. $ | Price Can. $ | Aust. $ |
|---|---|---|---|---|
| LL9 (3320) | 25. | 45. | 55. | 60. |

**LL10 (3336)**
**GOD LOVES ME™**

| | |
|---|---|
| Designer: | Amanda Hughes-Lubeck |
| Height: | 3 ¾", 9.5 cm |
| Colour: | White, gold and blue |
| Finish: | Gloss |
| Issued: | 1992 - 1993 |
| Varieties: | LL3, LL17; also called Please, LL33, LL34; also unnamed LL24 |

| Beswick Number | U.K. £ | U.S. $ | Price Can. $ | Aust. $ |
|---|---|---|---|---|
| LL10 (3336) | 50. | 90. | 110. | 120. |

**LL11 (3361)**
**JUST FOR YOU™**

| | |
|---|---|
| Designer: | Warren Platt |
| Height: | 4 ½", 11.9 cm |
| Colour: | White, yellow and pale green |
| Finish: | Gloss |
| Issued: | 1992 - 1994 |
| Varieties: | LL4, LL18; also unnamed LL25 |

| Beswick Number | U.K. £ | U.S. $ | Price Can. $ | Aust. $ |
|---|---|---|---|---|
| LL11 (3361) | 25. | 45. | 55. | 60. |

**LL12 (3331)**
**TO MOTHER™**

Designer: Amanda Hughes-Lubeck
Height: 4 ½", 11.9 cm
Colour: White, yellow and pink
Finish: Gloss
Issued: 1992 - 1994
Varieties: LL5, LL19; also called To Daddy, LL29;
also unnamed LL26

| Beswick Number | U.K. £ | U.S. $ | Price Can. $ | Aust. $ |
|---|---|---|---|---|
| LL12 (3331) | 25. | 45. | 55. | 60. |

**LL13 (3340)**
**CONGRATULATIONS™**

Designer: Warren Platt
Height: 4 ½", 11.9 cm
Colour: White, pale blue and yellow
Finish: Gloss
Issued: 1992 - 1994
Varieties: LL6, LL20; also unnamed LL27

| Beswick Number | U.K. £ | U.S. $ | Price Can. $ | Aust. $ |
|---|---|---|---|---|
| LL13 (3340 ) | 25. | 45. | 55. | 60. |

**LL14 (3334)**
**PASSED™**

Designer: Amanda Hughes-Lubeck
Height: 3", 7.6 cm
Colour: White, light blue and orange
Finish: Gloss
Issued: 1992 - 1994
Varieties: LL7, LL21; also unnamed LL28

| Beswick Number | U.K. £ | U.S. $ | Price Can. $ | Aust. $ |
|---|---|---|---|---|
| LL14 (3334) | 40. | 70. | 85. | 95. |

### LL15 (3407)
### HAPPY BIRTHDAY™

| | |
|---|---|
| Designer: | Amanda Hughes-Lubeck |
| Height: | 4 ½", 11.9 cm |
| Colour: | White, salmon and green |
| Finish: | Matt |
| Issued: | 1992 - 1993 |
| Varieties: | LL8, LL15; also unnamed LL22 |

| Beswick Number | | Price | | |
|---|---|---|---|---|
| | U.K. £ | U.S. $ | Can. $ | Aust. $ |
| LL15 (3407) | 65. | 115. | 140. | 150. |

### LL16 (3406)
### I LOVE YOU™

| | |
|---|---|
| Designer: | Amanda Hughes-Lubeck |
| Height: | 4 ½", 11.9 cm |
| Colour: | White, green and yellow |
| Finish: | Matt |
| Issued: | 1992 - 1993 |
| Varieties: | LL2, LL9; also unnamed LL23 |

| Beswick Number | | Price | | |
|---|---|---|---|---|
| | U.K. £ | U.S. $ | Can. $ | Aust. $ |
| LL16 (3406) | 65. | 115. | 140. | 150. |

### LL17 (3410)
### GOD LOVES ME™

| | |
|---|---|
| Designer: | Amanda Hughes-Lubeck |
| Height: | 3 ¾", 9.5 cm |
| Colour: | White, purple and yellow |
| Finish: | Matt |
| Issued: | 1992 - 1993 |
| Varieties: | LL3, LL10; also called Please, LL33, LL34; also unnamed LL24 |

| Beswick Number | | Price | | |
|---|---|---|---|---|
| | U.K. £ | U.S. $ | Can. $ | Aust. $ |
| LL17 (3410) | 75. | 125. | 150. | 165. |

## LL18 (3412)
## JUST FOR YOU™

| | |
|---|---|
| Designer: | Warren Platt |
| Height: | 4 ½", 11.9 cm |
| Colour: | White, yellow and dark blue |
| Finish: | Matt |
| Issued: | 1992 - 1993 |
| Varieties: | LL4, LL11; also unnamed LL25 |

| Beswick Number | U.K. £ | U.S. $ | Price Can. $ | Aus.t $ |
|---|---|---|---|---|
| LL18 (3412) | 65. | 115. | 140. | 150. |

## LL19 (3408)
## TO MOTHER™

| | |
|---|---|
| Designer: | Amanda Hughes-Lubeck |
| Height: | 4 ½", 11.9 cm |
| Colour: | White, green and orange |
| Finish: | Matt |
| Issued: | 1992 - 1993 |
| Varieties: | LL5, LL12; also called To Daddy, LL29; also unnamed LL26 |

| Beswick Number | U.K. £ | U.S. $ | Price Can. $ | Aust. $ |
|---|---|---|---|---|
| LL19 (3408 ) | 65. | 115. | 140. | 150. |

## LL20 (3411)
## CONGRATULATIONS™

| | |
|---|---|
| Designer: | Warren Platt |
| Height: | 4 ½", 11.9 cm |
| Colour: | White, blue and red |
| Finish: | Matt |
| Issued: | 1992 - 1993 |
| Varieties: | LL6, LL13; also unnamed LL27 |

| Beswick Number | U.K. £ | U.S. $ | Price Can. $ | Aust. $ |
|---|---|---|---|---|
| LL20 (3411) | 65. | 115. | 140. | 150. |

## LL21 (3409)
### PASSED™

| | |
|---|---|
| Designer: | Amanda Hughes-Lubeck |
| Height: | 3", 7.6 cm |
| Colour: | White, blue and orange |
| Finish: | Matt |
| Issued: | 1992 - 1993 |
| Varieties: | LL7, LL14; also unnamed LL28 |

| Beswick Number | U.K. £ | U.S. $ | Price Can. $ | Aust. $ |
|---|---|---|---|---|
| LL21 (3409) | 75. | 125. | 150. | 165. |

## LL22 (3329)
### (No Name)

| | |
|---|---|
| Designer: | Amanda Hughes-Lubeck |
| Height: | 4 ½", 11.9 cm |
| Colour: | White, pink and orange |
| Finish: | Gloss |
| Issued: | 1993 - 1993 |
| Varieties: | Also called Happy Birthday, LL1, LL8, LL15 |

| Beswick Number | U.K. £ | U.S. $ | Price Can. $ | Aust. $ |
|---|---|---|---|---|
| LL22 (3329) | 40. | 70. | 85. | 95. |

## LL23 (3320)
### (No Name)

| | |
|---|---|
| Designer: | Amanda Hughes-Lubeck |
| Height: | 4 ½", 11.9 cm |
| Colour: | White, green and pink |
| Finsh: | Gloss |
| Issued: | 1993 - 1993 |
| Varieties: | Also called I Love You, LL2, LL9, LL16 |

| Beswick Number | U.K. £ | U.S. $ | Price Can. $ | Aust. $ |
|---|---|---|---|---|
| LL23 (3320) | 40. | 70. | 85. | 95. |

## LL24 (3336)
### (No Name)

| | |
|---|---|
| Designer: | Amanda Hughes-Lubeck |
| Height: | 3 ¾", 9.5 cm |
| Colour: | White, green and turquoise |
| Finish: | Gloss |
| Issued: | 1993 - 1993 |
| Varieties: | Also called God Loves Me, LL3, LL10, LL17; Please, LL33, LL34 |

| Beswick Number | U.K. £ | U.S. $ | Price Can. $ | Aust. $ |
|---|---|---|---|---|
| LL24 (3336) | 50. | 90. | 110. | 120. |

## LL25 (3361)
### (No Name)

| | |
|---|---|
| Designer: | Warren Platt |
| Height: | 4 ½", 11.9 cm |
| Colour: | White, pink and blue |
| Finish: | Gloss |
| Issued: | 1993 - 1993 |
| Varieties: | Also called Just For You, LL4, LL11, LL18 |

| Beswick Number | U.K. £ | U.S. $ | Price Can. $ | Aus.t $ |
|---|---|---|---|---|
| LL25 (3361) | 50. | 90. | 110. | 120. |

## LL26 (3331)
### (No Name)

| | |
|---|---|
| Designer: | Amanda Hughes-Lubeck |
| Height: | 4 ¼", 10.8 cm |
| Colour: | White, blue and purple |
| Finish: | Gloss |
| Issued: | 1993 - 1993 |
| Varieties: | Also called To Mother, LL5, LL12, LL19; To Daddy, LL29 |

| Beswick Number | U.K. £ | U.S. $ | Price Can. $ | Aust. $ |
|---|---|---|---|---|
| LL26 (3331) | 50. | 90. | 110. | 120. |

**LL27 (3340)**
**(No Name)**

| | |
|---|---|
| Designer: | Warren Platt |
| Height: | 4 ½", 11.9 cm |
| Colour: | White, green and pink |
| Finish: | Gloss |
| Issued: | 1993 - 1993 |
| Varieties: | Also called Congratulations, LL6, LL13, LL20 |

| Beswick Number | U.K. £ | U.S. $ | Price Can. $ | Aust. $ |
|---|---|---|---|---|
| LL27 (3340) | 40. | 70. | 85. | 95. |

**LL28 (3334)**
**(No Name)**

| | |
|---|---|
| Designer: | Amanda Hughes-Lubeck |
| Height: | 3", 7.6 cm |
| Colour: | White, lilac and pink |
| Finish: | Gloss |
| Issued: | 1993 - 1993 |
| Varieties: | Also called Passed, LL7, LL14, LL21 |

| Beswick Number | U.K. £ | U.S. $ | Price Can. $ | Aust. $ |
|---|---|---|---|---|
| LL28 (3334) | 40. | 70. | 85. | 95. |

**LL29 (3331)**
**TO DADDY™**

| | |
|---|---|
| Designer: | Amanda Hughes-Lubeck |
| Height: | 4 ½", 11.9 cm |
| Colour: | White, light blue and green |
| Finish: | Gloss |
| Issued: | 1994 - 1994 |
| Varieties: | Also called To Mother, LL5, LL12, LL19; also unnamed LL26 |

| Beswick Number | U.K. £ | U.S. $ | Price Can. $ | Aust. $ |
|---|---|---|---|---|
| LL29 (3331) | 30. | 50. | 60. | 70. |

# STORYBOOK CHARACTERS
## Winnie the Pooh

Christopher Robin

Tigger

Kanga

Rabbit

Winnie the Pooh

Piglet

Owl

Eeyore

# ANIMAL FUN
## Monkey Band

Monkey with Banjo

Monkey with Drum

Monkey with Tuba

Monkey with Fiddle

Monkey with Saxophone

Monkey with Guitar

# ANIMAL FUN
## Bush Babies, Tortoise and Penguin Families

Bush Baby - with Mirror

Bush Baby - with Candlestick

Bush Baby - with Book

Tortoise Mother with Hat

Tortoise Boy with Cap

Tortoise Girl with Bonnet

Penguin - with
Walking Stick

Penguin - Chick

Penguin - Chick

Penguin - with
Umbrella

# CARTOON AND FILM CHARACTERS
## Thelwell

An Angel on Horseback

Kick-Start

Pony Express

# CARTOON AND FILM CHARACTERS
## Rupert and His Friends

Rupert The Bear

Rupert "Snowballing"

Bill Badger

Algy Pug

Pong Ping

# CARTOON AND FILM CHARACTERS
## David Hand's Animaland

Felia

Loopy Hare

Oscar Ostrich

Dinkum Platypus

Zimmy Lion

Dusty Mole

Hazel Nutt

Ginger Nutt

# CARTOON AND FILM CHARACTERS
## Disney Characters

Goofy

Pinocchio

Donald Duck

Mickey Mouse

Minnie Mouse

Jiminy Cricket

Thumper

Pluto

# MISCELLANEOUS CHARACTERS
## Beswick Bears

Emily

Susie

Billy

Sam

Charlotte

**LL30 (3389)**
**MERRY CHRISTMAS™**

| | |
|---|---|
| Designer: | Amanda Hughes-Lubeck |
| Height: | 4", 10.1 cm |
| Colour: | White, red and green |
| Finish: | Gloss |
| Issued: | 1993 - 1994 |

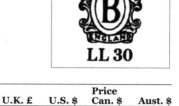

| Beswick Number | U.K. £ | U.S. $ | Price Can. $ | Aust. $ |
|---|---|---|---|---|
| LL30 (3389) | 40. | 70. | 85. | 95. |

**LL31 (3388)**
**GOOD LUCK™**

| | |
|---|---|
| Designer: | Amanda Hughes-Lubeck |
| Height: | 4 ¼", 10.8 cm |
| Colour: | White, pink and green |
| Finish: | Gloss |
| Issued: | 1993 - 1994 |

| Beswick Number | U.K. £ | U.S. $ | Price Can. $ | Aust. $ |
|---|---|---|---|---|
| LL31 (3388) | 30. | 50. | 60. | 70. |

**LL32 (3390)**
**GET WELL SOON™**

| | |
|---|---|
| Designer: | Amanda Hughes-Lubeck |
| Height: | 4 ¼", 10.8 cm |
| Colour: | White, green and purple |
| Finish: | Gloss |
| Issued: | 1994 - 1994 |

| Beswick Number | U.K. £ | U.S. $ | Price Can. $ | Aust. $ |
|---|---|---|---|---|
| LL32 (3390) | 40. | 70. | 85. | 95. |

**LL33 (3336)**
**PLEASE™**

| | |
|---|---|
| Designer: | Amanda Hughes-Lubeck |
| Height: | 3 ¾", 9.5 cm |
| Colour: | White, green and blue |
| Finish: | Gloss |
| Issued: | 1993 - 1994 |
| Varieties: | LL34; also called God Loves Me, LL3, LL10, LL17; also unnamed LL24 |

| Beswick Number | U..K. £ | U.S. $ | Price Can. $ | Aust. $ |
|---|---|---|---|---|
| LL33 (3336) | 50. | 90. | 110. | 120. |

**LL34 (3336)**
**PLEASE™**

| | |
|---|---|
| Designer: | Amanda Hughes-Lubeck |
| Height: | 3 ¾", 9.5 cm |
| Colour: | White, gold and light blue |
| Finish: | Gloss |
| Issued: | 1993 - 1994 |
| Varieties: | LL33; also called God Loves Me, LL3, LL10, LL17; also unnamed LL24 |

| Beswick Number | U.K. £ | U.S. $ | Price Can. $ | Aust. $ |
|---|---|---|---|---|
| LL34 (3336) | 50. | 90. | 110. | 120. |

**LL35** a matt version of 'Please" was not put into production..

**LL36 (3320)**
**I LOVE BESWICK™**

| | |
|---|---|
| Designer: | Amanda Hughes-Lubeck |
| Height: | 4 ½", 11.9 cm |
| Colour: | White, green and pink |
| Finish: | Gloss |
| Issued: | 1995 in a limited edition of 442 |

| Beswick Number | U.K. £ | U.S. $ | Price Can. $ | Aust. $ |
|---|---|---|---|---|
| LL36 (3320) | 75. | 130. | 160. | 175. |

**Note:** This piece was specially commissioned for the 10th Anniversary of the Beswick Collectors Circle.

# PUNCH AND JUDY

These models conjure up memories of childhood for most of us, sitting on the sand on a sunny day, by the seaside and shouting "He's behind you".

Punch and Judy are timeless and have delighted children for many generations.

These models will keep alive these memories if you are fortunate enough to be able to come across them. Not many were produced and this pair will become rare in the years to come. They were sold as a pair.

**4188**
**PUNCH**

| | |
|---|---|
| Modeller: | Shane Ridge |
| Height: | 5 ½", 14.0 cm |
| Colour: | Red, yellow, cream and green |
| Finish: | Gloss |
| Issued: | 2001 in a limited edition of 2,500 |
| Comm. by: | Doulton-Direct |

| Beswick Number | U.K. £ | U.S. $ | Price Can. $ | Aust. $ |
|---|---|---|---|---|
| 4188 | 50. | 90. | 110. | 120. |

**4189**
**JUDY**

| | |
|---|---|
| Modeller: | Shane Ridge |
| Height: | 5 ¼", 13.3 cm |
| Colour: | Blue, white, brown and orange |
| Finish: | Gloss |
| Issued: | 2001 in a limited edition of 2,500 |
| Comm. by: | Doulton-Direct |

| Beswick Number | U.K. £ | U.S. $ | Price Can. $ | Aust. $ |
|---|---|---|---|---|
| 4189 | 50. | 90. | 110. | 120. |

# TEDDY BEARS

### 3626
### BENJAMIN™

| | |
|---|---|
| Height: | 4 ½", 11.9 cm |
| Colour: | Brown bear wearing a bright yellow scarf |
| Finish: | Gloss |
| Issued: | 1996 |
| Comm. by: | Compton & Woodhouse Ltd. |

| Beswick Number | U.K. £ | U.S. $ | Price Can. $ | Aust. $ |
|---|---|---|---|---|
| 3626 | 50. | 90. | 115. | 125. |

### 3699
### ARCHIE™

| | |
|---|---|
| Height: | 4 ½", 11.9 cm |
| Colour: | Brown bear; light blue waistcoat; red and white spotted handkerchief |
| Finish: | Gloss |
| Issued: | 1997 |
| Comm. by: | Compton & Woodhouse Ltd. |

| Beswick Number | U.K. £ | U.S. $ | Price Can. $ | Aust. $ |
|---|---|---|---|---|
| 3699 | 50. | 90. | 115. | 125. |

**3700**
**BERTIE**™

| | |
|---|---|
| Height: | 4 ½", 11.9 cm |
| Colour: | Dark brown bear; straw hat with red and purple band; yellow cane |
| Finish: | Gloss |
| Issued: | 1997 |
| Comm. by: | Compton & Woodhouse Ltd. |

| Beswick Number | U.K. £ | U.S. $ | Price Can. $ | Aust. $ |
|---|---|---|---|---|
| 3700 | 50. | 90. | 115. | 125. |

**3724**
**HENRY**™
**Style One**

| | |
|---|---|
| Height: | 4 ½", 11.9 cm |
| Colour: | Dark brown bear; purple tie, brown satchel |
| Finish: | Gloss |
| Issued: | 1998 |
| Comm. by: | Compton & Woodhouse Ltd. |

| Beswick Number | U.K. £ | U.S. $ | Price Can. $ | Aust. $ |
|---|---|---|---|---|
| 3724 | 50. | 90. | 115. | 125. |

**4130**
**HENRY**
**Style Two**

| | |
|---|---|
| Designer: | Robert Tabbenor |
| Height: | 5 ½", 14.0 cm |
| Colour: | Light brown |
| Issued: | 2001 in a limited edition of 2,500 |
| Finish: | Gloss |
| Comm. by: | Doulton-Direct |

| Beswick Number | | U.K. £ | U.S. $ | Price Can. $ | Aust. $ |
|---|---|---|---|---|---|
| 4130 | | 50. | 90. | 115. | 125. |

**4131**
**EDWARD**

| | |
|---|---|
| Designer: | Robert Tabbenor |
| Height: | 6", 15.0 cm |
| Colour: | Dark brown |
| Finish: | Gloss |
| Issued: | 2001 in a limited edition of 2,500 |
| Comm. by: | Doulton-Direct |

| Beswick Number | | U.K. £ | U.S. $ | Price Can. $ | Aust. $ |
|---|---|---|---|---|---|
| 4131 | | 50. | 90. | 115. | 125. |

**4132**
**GEORGE**

| | |
|---|---|
| Designer: | Robert Tabbenor |
| Height: | 6", 15.0 cm |
| Colour: | Golden brown |
| Finish: | Gloss |
| Issued: | 2001 in a limited edition of 2,500 |
| Comm. by: | Doulton-Direct |

| Beswick Number | U.K. £ | U.S. $ | Price Can. $ | Aust. $ |
|---|---|---|---|---|
| 4132 | 50. | 90. | 115. | 125. |

**4133**
**WILLIAM**

| | |
|---|---|
| Designer: | Robert Tabbenor |
| Height: | 6", 15.0 cm |
| Colour: | Light brown |
| Finish: | Gloss |
| Issued: | 2001 in a limited edition of 2,500 |
| Comm. by: | Doulton-Direct |

| Beswick Number | U.K. £ | U.S. $ | Price Can. $ | Aust. $ |
|---|---|---|---|---|
| 4133 | 50. | 90. | 115. | 125. |

# TOY SOLDIERS

## 1626
### TOY DRUMMER

| | |
|---|---|
| Designer: | J. Lawson |
| Height: | 2 ½", 6.4 cm |
| Colour: | 1. Red and white |
| | 2. Blue and white |
| Finish: | Gloss |
| Issued: | 1959 - 1966 |
| Set: | 1627, 1628 |

| Beswick Number | U.K. £ | U.S. $ | Price Can. $ | Aust. $ |
|---|---|---|---|---|
| 1626 | 50. | 90. | 115. | 125. |

## 1627
### TOY BUGLERS

| | |
|---|---|
| Designer: | J. Lawson |
| Height: | 1 ½", 5.0 cm |
| Colour: | 1. Red and white |
| | 2. Blue and white |
| Finish: | Gloss |
| Issued: | 1959 - 1966 |
| Set: | 1626, 1628 |

| Beswick Number | U.K. £ | U.S. $ | Price Can. $ | Aust. $ |
|---|---|---|---|---|
| 1627 | 40. | 75. | 95. | 100. |

## 1628
### TOY GUARDS

| | |
|---|---|
| Designer: | J. Lawson |
| Height: | 1 ½", 5.0 cm |
| Colour: | 1. Red and white |
| | 2. Blue and white |
| Finish: | Gloss |
| Issued: | 1959 - 1966 |
| Set: | 1626, 1627 |

| Beswick Number | U.K. £ | U.S. $ | Price Can. $ | Aust. $ |
|---|---|---|---|---|
| 1628 | 40. | 75. | 95. | 100. |

# SECTION FOUR

## ANIMAL FUN

Dog Playing Accordian,   Dog Asleep on Drum,   Dog with Glasses Reading a Book,   Dog with Toothache

# BUSH BABIES

### 1379
### BUSH BABY – WITH MIRROR

| | |
|---|---|
| Designer: | Mr. Orwell |
| Height: | 2", 5.0 cm |
| Colour: | Grey-brown |
| Finish: | Gloss |
| Issued: | 1955 - 1966 |
| Set: | 1380, 1381 |

| Beswick Number | U.K. £ | U.S. $ | Price Can. $ | Aust. $ |
|---|---|---|---|---|
| 1379 | 25. | 45. | 55. | 60. |

### 1380
### BUSH BABY – WITH CANDLESTICK

| | |
|---|---|
| Designer: | Mr. Orwell |
| Height: | 2", 5.0 cm |
| Colour: | Grey-brown |
| Finish: | Gloss |
| Issued: | 1955 - 1966 |
| Set: | 1379, 1381 |

| Beswick Number | U.K. £ | U.S. $ | Price Can. $ | Aust. $ |
|---|---|---|---|---|
| 1380 | 25. | 45. | 55. | 60. |

### 1381
### BUSH BABY – WITH BOOK

| | |
|---|---|
| Designer: | Mr. Orwell |
| Height: | 1 ½", 3.8 cm |
| Colour: | Grey-brown |
| Finish: | Gloss |
| Issued: | 1955 - 1966 |
| Set: | 1379, 1380 |

| Beswick Number | U.K. £ | U.S. $ | Price Can. $ | Aust. $ |
|---|---|---|---|---|
| 1381 | 25. | 45. | 55. | 60. |

# CATS' CHORUS

### CC1 (3762)
### PURRFECT PITCH™

| | |
|---|---|
| Modeller: | Shane Ridge |
| Height: | 4", 10.1 cm |
| Colour: | White cat; black dress and hair, red gloves and shoes |
| Finish: | Gloss |
| Issued: | 1998 - 2001 |

| Beswick Number | U.K. £ | U.S. $ | Price Can. $ | Aust. $ |
|---|---|---|---|---|
| CC1 (3762) | 30. | 50. | 60. | 65. |

### CC2 (3748)
### CALYPSO KITTEN™

| | |
|---|---|
| Modeller: | Shane Ridge |
| Height: | 4", 10.1 cm |
| Colour: | Black cat; patterned yellow, shirt, beige trousers, red and yellow drum |
| Finish: | Gloss |
| Issued: | 1998 - 2001 |

| Beswick Number | U.K. £ | U.S. $ | Price Can. $ | Aust. $ |
|---|---|---|---|---|
| CC2 (3748) | 25. | 45. | 55. | 60. |

### CC3 (3750)
### ONE COOL CAT™

| | |
|---|---|
| Modeller: | Shane Ridge |
| Height: | 4", 10.1 cm |
| Colour: | Ginger cat; blue suit with black trim, black shoes, yellow saxophone |
| Finish: | Gloss |
| Issued: | 1998 - 2001 |

| Beswick Number | U.K. £ | U.S. $ | Price Can. $ | Aust. $ |
|---|---|---|---|---|
| CC3 (3750) | 25. | 45. | 55. | 60. |

**CC4 (3754)**
**RATCATCHER BILK™**

| | |
|---|---|
| Modeller: | Shane Ridge |
| Height: | 4", 10.1 cm |
| Colour: | White cat; blue shirt and hat, yellow waistcoat, black trousers and clarinet |
| Finish: | Gloss |
| Issued: | 1998 - 2001 |

| Beswick Number | U.K. £ | U.S. $ | Price Can. $ | Aust. $ |
|---|---|---|---|---|
| CC4 (3754) | 25. | 45. | 55. | 60. |

**CC5 (3755)**
**TRAD JAZZ TOM™**

| | |
|---|---|
| Modeller: | Shane Ridge |
| Height: | 4", 10.1 cm |
| Colour: | Grey cat, trousers and waistcoat, lemon shirt, black hat, yellow trumpet |
| Finish: | Gloss |
| Issued: | 1998 - 2001 |

| Beswick Number | U.K. £ | U.S. $ | Price Can. $ | Aust. $ |
|---|---|---|---|---|
| CC5 (3755) | 25. | 45. | 55. | 60. |

**CC6 (3756)**
**CATWALKING BASS™**

| | |
|---|---|
| Modeller: | Shane Ridge |
| Height: | 4", 10.1 cm |
| Colour: | White cat; yellow jacket, green shirt, red trousers, black hat, tan bass |
| Finish: | Gloss |
| Issued: | 1998 - 2001 |

| Beswick Number | U.K. £ | U.S. $ | Price Can. $ | Aust. $ |
|---|---|---|---|---|
| CC6 (3756) | 25. | 45. | 55. | 60. |

**CC7 (3757)**
**FELINE FLAMENCO™**

| | |
|---|---|
| Modeller: | Shane Ridge |
| Height: | 4", 10.1 cm |
| Colour: | Ginger cat; lemon shirt, black trousers and waistcoat, red and white cumberbund, tan guitar |
| Finish: | Gloss |
| Issued: | 1998 - 2001 |

| Beswick Number | U.K. £ | U.S. $ | Price Can. $ | Aust. $ |
|---|---|---|---|---|
| CC7 (3757) | 25. | 45. | 55. | 60. |

**CC8 (3761)**
**BRAVURA BRASS™**

| | |
|---|---|
| Modeller: | Shane Ridge |
| Height: | 4", 10.1 cm |
| Colour: | Ginger cat; black suit and shoes, white shirt, yellow French horn |
| Finish: | Gloss |
| Issued: | 1998 - 2001 |

| Beswick Number | U.K. £ | U.S. $ | Price Can. $ | Aust. $ |
|---|---|---|---|---|
| CC8 (3761) | 25. | 45. | 55. | 60. |

## CC9 (3813)
### FAT CAT™

| | |
|---|---|
| Modeller: | Shane Ridge |
| Height: | 3 ¾", 9.5 cm |
| Colour: | Ginger cat, yellow shirt, grey trousers, red kerchief, black hat |
| Finish: | Gloss |
| Issued: | 1999 - 2001 |

| Beswick Number | U.K. £ | U.S. $ | Price Can. $ | Aust. $ |
|---|---|---|---|---|
| CC9 (3813) | 100. | 175. | 225. | 250. |

## CC10 (3833)
### GLAM GUITAR™

| | |
|---|---|
| Modeller: | Shane Ridge |
| Height: | 4 ¼", 10.8 cm |
| Colour: | Light brown cat, white coat, red boots |
| Finish: | Gloss |
| Issued: | 1999 - 2001 |

| Beswick Number | U.K. £ | U.S $ | Price Can. $ | Aust. $ |
|---|---|---|---|---|
| CC10 (3833) | 50. | 90. | 115. | 125. |

# CAT ORCHESTRA

### 1026
### CAT CONDUCTOR™

| | |
|---|---|
| Designer: | Arthur Gredington |
| Height: | 2", 5.0 cm |
| Colour: | Grey striped |
| Finish: | Gloss |
| Issued: | 1945 - 1973 |
| Set: | 1027, 1028, 1029 |

| Beswick Number | U.K. £ | U.S. $ | Price Can. $ | Aust. $ |
|---|---|---|---|---|
| 1026 | 35. | 60. | 75. | 80. |

### 1027
### CAT WITH CELLO™

| | |
|---|---|
| Designer: | Arthur Gredington |
| Height: | 2", 5.0 cm |
| Colour: | Grey striped |
| Finish: | Gloss |
| Issued: | 1945 - 1973 |
| Set: | 1026, 1028, 1029 |

| Beswick Number | U.K. £ | U.S. $ | Price Can. $ | Aust. $ |
|---|---|---|---|---|
| 1027 | 35. | 60. | 75. | 80. |

**1028**
## CAT WITH FIDDLE™

| | |
|---|---|
| Designer: | Arthur Gredington |
| Height: | 2", 5.0 cm |
| Colour: | Grey striped |
| Finish: | Gloss |
| Issued: | 1945 - 1973 |
| Set: | 1026, 1027, 1029 |

| Beswick Number | U.K. £ | U.S. $ | Price Can. $ | Aust. $ |
|---|---|---|---|---|
| 1028 | 35. | 60. | 75. | 80. |

**1029**
## CAT WITH SAXOPHONE™

| | |
|---|---|
| Designer: | Arthur Gredington |
| Height: | 2", 5.0 cm |
| Colour: | Grey striped |
| Finish: | Gloss |
| Issued: | 1945 - 1973 |
| Set: | 1026, 1027, 1028 |

| Beswick Number | U.K. £ | U.S. $ | Price Can. $ | Aust. $ |
|---|---|---|---|---|
| 1029 | 35. | 60. | 75. | 80. |

# CHIMPANZEE

**1049**
**CHIMPANZEE WITH PIPE**

Designer:     Arthur Gredington
Height:       4 ¾", 12.1 cm
Colour:       Light and dark brown chimpanzee; yellow and red pipe
Finish:       Gloss
Issued:       1946 - 1969

| Beswick Number | U.K. £ | U.S. $ | Price Can. $ | Aust. $ |
|---|---|---|---|---|
| 1049 | 75. | 135. | 175. | 185. |

# COUNTRY COUSINS

**PM 2101**
**SWEET SUZIE**™
**Thank You**

| | |
|---|---|
| Height: | 2 ¾", 7.0 cm |
| Colour: | Brown rabbit wearing a brown and yellow pinafore |
| Finish: | Resin |
| Issued: | 1994 - 1995 |

SWEET SUZIE "Thank you" PM 2101

| Beswick Number | U.K. £ | U.S. $ | Price Can. $ | Aust. $ |
|---|---|---|---|---|
| PM 2101 | 20. | 35. | 45. | 50. |

**PM 2102**
**PETER**™
**Once Upon A Time**

| | |
|---|---|
| Height: | 2 ½", 5.6 cm |
| Colour: | Brown hedgehog wearing a blue suit and a white bowtie |
| Finish: | Resin |
| Issued: | 1994 - 1995 |

PETER "Once upon a time" PM 2102

| Beswick Number | U.K. £ | U.S. $ | Price Can. $ | Aust. $ |
|---|---|---|---|---|
| PM 2102 | 20. | 35. | 45. | 50. |

**PM 2103**
**HARRY**™
**A New Home for Fred**

| | |
|---|---|
| Height: | 2", 5.0 cm |
| Colour: | Brown hedgehog wearing blue and white jumper and brown trousers |
| Finish: | Resin |
| Issued: | 1994 - 1995 |

HARRY "A new home for Fred" PM 2103

| Beswick Number | U.K. £ | U.S. $ | Price Can. $ | Aust. $ |
|---|---|---|---|---|
| PM 2103 | 20. | 35. | 45. | 50. |

**PM 2104**
**MICHAEL™**
**Happily Ever After**

| Height: | 2 ½", 6.4 cm |
| Colour: | Brown rabbit wearing a green jacket |
| Finish: | Resin |
| Issued: | 1994 - 1995 |

| Beswick Number | U.K. £ | U.S. $ | Price Can. $ | Aust. $ |
|---|---|---|---|---|
| PM 2104 | 20. | 35. | 45. | 50. |

**PM 2105**
**BERTRAM™**
**Ten Out of Ten**

| Height: | 3", 7.6 cm |
| Colour: | Brown owl; green and blue striped waistcoat, red bow tie, blue mortar board, red tassel |
| Finish: | Resin |
| Issued: | 1994 - 1995 |

| Beswick Number | U.K. £ | U.S. $ | Price Can. $ | Aust. $ |
|---|---|---|---|---|
| PM 2105 | 20. | 35. | 45. | 50. |

**PM 2106**
**LEONARDO™**
**Practice Makes Perfect**

| Height: | 2 ¾", 7.0 cm |
| Colour: | Brown owl wearing a brown hat; white palette and blue paintbrush |
| Finish: | Resin |
| Issued: | 1994 - 1995 |

| Beswick Number | U.K. £ | U.S. $ | Price Can. $ | Aust. $ |
|---|---|---|---|---|
| PM 2106 | 20. | 35. | 45. | 50. |

**PM 2107**
**LILY™**
**Flowers Picked Just for You**

| | |
|---|---|
| Height: | 3", 7.6 cm |
| Colour: | Brown hedgehog; pink dress with matching bonnet with white ribbon, yellow pinafore with white collar |
| Finish: | Resin |
| Issued: | 1994 - 1995 |

| Beswick Number | U.K. £ | U.S. $ | Price Can. $ | Aust. $ |
|---|---|---|---|---|
| PM 2107 | 20. | 35. | 45. | 50. |

**PM 2108**
**PATRICK™**
**This Way's Best**

| | |
|---|---|
| Height: | 3", 7.6 cm |
| Colour: | Brown owl wearing a blue and yellow checked waistcoat, white collar and blue bow tie, yellow hat with red band |
| Finish: | Resin |
| Issued: | 1994 - 1995 |

| Beswick Number | U.K. £ | U.S. $ | Price Can. $ | Aust. $ |
|---|---|---|---|---|
| PM 2108 | 20. | 35. | 45. | 50. |

**PM 2109**
**JAMIE™**
**Hurrying Home**

| | |
|---|---|
| Height: | 3", 7.6 cm |
| Colour: | Brown hedgehog; pink sailor top with white stripes, blue trousers |
| Finish: | Resin |
| Issued: | 1994 - 1995 |

| Beswick Number | U.K. £ | U.S. $ | Price Can. $ | Aust. $ |
|---|---|---|---|---|
| PM 2109 | 20. | 35. | 45. | 50. |

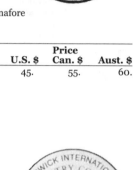

**PM 2111**
**MUM AND LIZZIE™**
**Let's Get Busy**

| | |
|---|---|
| Height: | 3 ¼", 8.3 cm |
| Colour: | Large brown rabbit wearing a blue dress and white pinafore |
| | Small brown rabbit wearing a white pinafore |
| Finish: | Resin |
| Issued: | 1994 - 1995 |

| Beswick Number | U.K. £ | U.S. $ | Price Can. $ | Aust. $ |
|---|---|---|---|---|
| PM 2111 | 25. | 45. | 55. | 60. |

**PM 2112**
**MOLLY AND TIMMY™**
**Picnic Time**

| | |
|---|---|
| Height: | 2 ¾", 7 cm |
| Colour: | Large brown mouse: pink dress, yellow bonnet and blue pinafore |
| | Small brown mouse: yellow dungarees, white top, blue hat |
| Finish: | Resin |
| Issued: | 1994 - 1995 |

| Beswick Number | U.K. £ | U.S. $ | Price Can. $ | Aust. $ |
|---|---|---|---|---|
| PM 2112 | 25. | 45. | 55. | 60. |

**PM 2113**
**POLLY AND SARAH™**
**Good News!**

| | |
|---|---|
| Height: | 3 ¼", 8.3 cm |
| Colour: | Brown rabbit wearing blue dress and pink apron |
| | Brown hedgehog wearing blue dress and scarf, green jacket, white pinafore |
| Finish: | Resin |
| Issued: | 1994 - 1995 |

| Beswick Number | U.K. £ | U.S. $ | Price Can. $ | Aust. $ |
|---|---|---|---|---|
| PM 2113 | 25. | 45. | 55. | 60. |

**PM 2114**
**BILL AND TED™**
**Working Together**

| | |
|---|---|
| Height: | 3 ¼", 8.3 cm |
| Colour: | Brown mouse in blue dungarees |
| | Brown hedgehog in green dungarees |
| Finish: | Resin |
| Issued: | 1994 - 1995 |

| Beswick Number | U.K. £ | U.S. $ | Price Can. $ | Aust. $ |
|---|---|---|---|---|
| PM 2114 | 20. | 35. | 45. | 50. |

**PM 2115**
**JACK AND DAISY™**
**How Does Your Garden Grow?**

| | |
|---|---|
| Height: | 2 ¾", 7 cm |
| Colour: | Male - brown mouse: white shirt, blue |
| | dungarees |
| | Female - brown mouse: pink and white |
| | striped dress, white pinafore |
| Finish: | Resin |
| Issued: | 1994 - 1995 |

| Beswick Number | U.K. £ | U.S. $ | Price Can. $ | Aust. $ |
|---|---|---|---|---|
| PM 2115 | 25. | 45. | 55. | 60. |

**PM 2116**
**ALISON AND DEBBIE™**
**Friendship is Fun**

| | |
|---|---|
| Height: | 2 ¾", 7 cm |
| Colour: | Rabbit - brown: pink dress, white pinafor( |
| | Squirrel - brown: blue dress pink apron |
| Finish: | Resin |
| Issued: | 1994 - 1995 |

| Beswick Number | U.K. £ | U.S. $ | Price Can. $ | Aust. $ |
|---|---|---|---|---|
| PM 2116 | 25. | 45. | 55. | 60. |

**PM 2119**
**ROBERT AND ROSIE™**
**Perfect Partners**

| | |
|---|---|
| Height: | 3 ¼", 8.3 cm |
| Colour: | Male - brown squirrel: blue dungarees, blue hat with red band |
| | Female - brown squirrel: pink dress with white collar, yellow hat |
| Finish: | Resin |
| Issued: | 1994 - 1995 |

| Beswick Number | U.K. £ | U.S. $ | Price Can. $ | Aust. $ |
|---|---|---|---|---|
| PM 2119 | 25. | 45. | 55. | 60. |

**PM 2120**
**SAMMY™**
**Treasure Hunting**

| | |
|---|---|
| Height: | 2 ¼", 5.7 cm |
| Colour: | Brown squirrel wearing a green shirt; blue sack |
| Finish: | Resin |
| Issued: | 1994 - 1995 |

| Beswick Number | U.K. £ | U.S. $ | Price Can. $ | Aust. $ |
|---|---|---|---|---|
| PM 2120 | 20. | 35. | 45. | 50. |

# DOGS

### 761
### DOG WITH TOOTHACHE

| | |
|---|---|
| Designer: | Mr. Watkin |
| Height: | 4 ¼", 10.8 cm |
| Colour: | 1. White dog; red kerchief |
| | 2. White dog; green kerchief |
| Finish: | Gloss |
| Issued: | 1939 - 1971 |
| Series: | Fun Models |

| Beswick Number | Colour | U.K. £ | U.S. $ | Price Can. $ | Aust. $ |
|---|---|---|---|---|---|
| 761 | Red | 50. | 90. | 115. | 125. |
| 761 | Green | 75. | 135. | 170. | 180. |

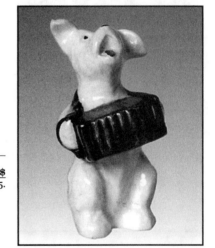

### 811
### DOG PLAYING ACCORDIAN

| | |
|---|---|
| Designer: | Mr. Watkin |
| Height: | 4", 10.1 cm |
| Colour: | White dog; green and brown accordion |
| Finish: | Gloss |
| Issued: | 1940 - 1970 |
| Series: | Fun Models |

| Beswick Number | U.K. £ | U.S. $ | Price Can. $ | Aust. $ |
|---|---|---|---|---|
| 811 | 50. | 90. | 115. | 125. |

### 812
### DOG ASLEEP ON DRUM

| | |
|---|---|
| Designer: | Mr. Watkin |
| Height: | 3", 7.6 cm |
| Colour: | White dog; yellow, blue and red drum |
| Finish: | Gloss |
| Issued: | 1940 - 1970 |
| Series: | Fun Models |

| Beswick Number | U.K. £ | U.S. $ | Price Can. $ | Aust. $ |
|---|---|---|---|---|
| 812 | 50. | 90. | 115. | 125. |

### 831
### DOG WITH GLASSES READING A BOOK

| | |
|---|---|
| Designer: | Arthur Gredington |
| Height: | 6 ¼", 15.9 cm |
| Colour: | White dog; yellow-red glasses; brown and white book |
| Finish: | Gloss |
| Issued: | 1940 - 1970 |
| Series: | Fun Models |

| Beswick Number | U.K. £ | U.S. $ | Price Can. $ | Aust. $ |
|---|---|---|---|---|
| 831 | 75. | 135. | 170. | 180. |

### 1054
### SPANIEL HOLDING "MY PLATE"

| | |
|---|---|
| Designer: | Arthur Gredington |
| Height: | 4 ¼", 12.1 cm |
| Colour: | White and brown |
| Finish: | Gloss |
| Issued: | 1947 - 1967 |
| Series: | Fun Models |

| Beswick Number | U.K. £ | U.S. $ | Price Can. $ | Aust. $ |
|---|---|---|---|---|
| 1054 | 60. | 110. | 135. | 150. |

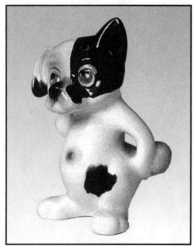

### 1738
### PUP WITH BONE

| | |
|---|---|
| Designer: | Harry Sales |
| Height: | 3 ¾", 9.5 cm |
| Colour: | White with black patches |
| Finish: | Gloss |
| Issued: | 1961 - 1967 |
| Series: | Fun Models |

| Beswick Number | U.K. £ | U.S. $ | Price Can. $ | Aust. $ |
|---|---|---|---|---|
| 1738 | 50. | 90. | 115. | 125. |

# ENGLISH COUNTRY FOLK

### ECF 1 (3418)
### HUNTSMAN FOX™

| | |
|---|---|
| Designer: | Amanda Hughes-Lubeck |
| Height: | 5 ¾", 14.6 cm |
| Colour: | Dark green jacket and cap, blue-grey trousers, green wellingtons |
| Finish: | Gloss |
| Issued: | 1993 - 1998 |

| Beswick Number | U.K. £ | U.S. $ | Price Can. $ | Aust. $ |
|---|---|---|---|---|
| ECF 1 (3418) | 50. | 90. | 115. | 125. |

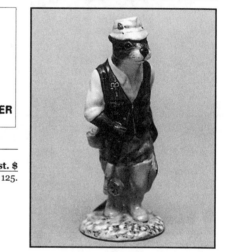

### ECF 2 (3419)
### FISHERMAN OTTER™

| | |
|---|---|
| Designer: | Warren Platt |
| Height: | 5 ¾", 14.6 cm |
| Colour: | Yellow shirt and hat, dark green waistcoat blue-grey trousers |
| Finish: | Gloss |
| Issued: | 1993 - 1998 |

| Beswick Number | U.K. £ | U.S. $ | Price Can. $ | Aust. $ |
|---|---|---|---|---|
| ECF 2 (3419) | 50. | 90. | 115. | 125. |

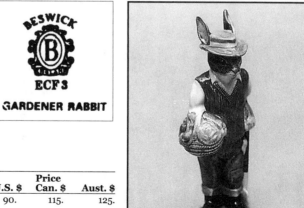

### ECF 3 (3420)
### GARDENER RABBIT™
### First Variation

| | |
|---|---|
| Designer: | Warren Platt |
| Height: | 6", 15.0 cm |
| Colour: | White shirt, red pullover, blue trousers, grey hat |
| Finish: | Gloss |
| Issued: | 1993 - 1999 |
| Varieties: | ECF 12 |

| Beswick Number | U.K. £ | U.S. $ | Price Can. $ | Aust. $ |
|---|---|---|---|---|
| ECF 3 (3420) | 50. | 90. | 115. | 125. |

**ECF 4 (3417)**
**GENTLEMAN PIG™**
**First Variation**

| | |
|---|---|
| Designer: | Amanda Hughes-Lubeck |
| Height: | 5 ¾", 14.6 cm |
| Colour: | Dark brown suit, yellow waistcoat |
| Finish: | Gloss |
| Issued: | 1993 - 1999 |
| Varieties: | ECF 10 |

| Beswick Number | U.K. $ | U.S. $ | Price Can. $ | Aust. $ |
|---|---|---|---|---|
| ECF 4 (3417) | 50. | 90. | 115. | 125. |

**ECF 5 (3422)**
**SHEPHERD SHEEPDOG™**

| | |
|---|---|
| Designer: | Warren Platt |
| Height: | 6 ¾", 17.2 cm |
| Colour: | Yellow smock |
| Finish: | Gloss |
| Issued: | 1993 - 1999 |

| Beswick Number | U.K. £ | U.S. $ | Price Can. $ | Aust. $ |
|---|---|---|---|---|
| ECF 5 (3422) | 50. | 90. | 115. | 125. |

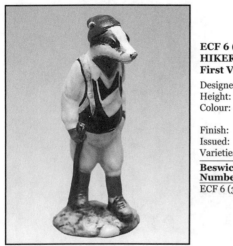

**ECF 6 (3421)**
**HIKER BADGER™**
**First Variation**

| | |
|---|---|
| Designer: | Warren Platt |
| Height: | 5 ¼", 13.3 cm |
| Colour: | Yellow shirt, blue waistcoat, red cap and socks |
| Finish: | Gloss |
| Issued: | 1993 - 1999 |
| Varieties: | ECF 9 |

| Beswick Number | U.K. £ | U.S. $ | Price Can. $ | Aust. $ |
|---|---|---|---|---|
| ECF 6 (3421) | 50. | 90. | 115. | 125. |

## ECF 7 (3447)
### MRS. RABBIT BAKING™
### First Variation

| | |
|---|---|
| Designer: | Martyn Alcock |
| Height: | 5 ½", 14.0 cm |
| Colour: | Mauve dress, white apron and cap |
| Finish: | Gloss |
| Issued: | 1994 - 1999 |
| Varieties: | ECF 13 |

ECF 7
MRS RABBIT BAKING

| Beswick Number | U.K. £ | U.S. $ | Price Can. $ | Aust. $ |
|---|---|---|---|---|
| ECF 7 (3447) | 50. | 90. | 115. | 125. |

## ECF 8 (3448)
### THE LADY PIG™
### First Variation

| | |
|---|---|
| Designer: | Amanda Hughes-Lubeck |
| Height: | 5 ½", 14.0 cm |
| Colour: | Green jacket, skirt and hat, brown umbrella |
| Finish: | Gloss |
| Issued: | 1994 - 1999 |
| Varieties: | ECF 11 |

ECF 8
THE LADY PIG

| Beswick Number | U.K. £ | U.S. $ | Price Can. $ | Aust. $ |
|---|---|---|---|---|
| ECF 8 (3448) | 50. | 90. | 115. | 125. |

## ECF 9 (3421)
### HIKER BADGER™
### Second Variation

| | |
|---|---|
| Designer: | Warren Platt |
| Height: | 5 ¼", 13.3 cm |
| Colour: | Green, red, black |
| Finish: | Gloss |
| Issued: | 1997 in a special edition of 1,000 |
| Varieties: | ECF 6 |
| Comm. by: | Sinclairs |

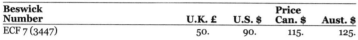

ECF 9
HIKER BADGER

Sinclairs
China, Crystal & Luxuries
NEW COLOURWAY 1997
PRODUCED EXCLUSIVELY FOR
20th CENTURY FAIRS JUNE 1997
IN A SPECIAL EDITION OF 1,000
85

| Beswick Number | U.K. £ | U.S. $ | Price Can. $ | Aust. $ |
|---|---|---|---|---|
| ECF 9 (3421) | 75. | 135. | 165. | 180. |

### ECF 10 (3417)
### GENTLEMAN PIG™
### Second Variation

| | |
|---|---|
| Designer: | Amanda Hughes-Lubeck |
| Height: | 5 ¾", 14.6 cm |
| Colour: | Light brown |
| Finish: | Gloss |
| Issued: | 1998 in a limited edition of 2,000 |
| Varieties: | ECF 4 |
| Comm. by: | Sinclairs |

| Beswick Number | U.K. £ | U.S. $ | Price Can. $ | Aust. $ |
|---|---|---|---|---|
| ECF 10 (3417) | 50. | 90. | 115. | 125. |

### ECF 11 (3448)
### THE LADY PIG™
### Second Variation

| | |
|---|---|
| Designer: | Amanda Hughes-Lubeck |
| Height: | 5 ½", 14.0 cm |
| Colour: | Browns |
| Finish: | Gloss |
| Issued: | 1998 in a limited edition of 2,000 |
| Varieties: | ECF 8 |
| Comm. by: | Sinclairs |

| Beswick Number | U.K. £ | U.S. $ | Price Can. $ | Aust. $ |
|---|---|---|---|---|
| ECF 11 (3448) | 50. | 90. | 115. | 125. |

## ECF 12 (3420)
## GARDENER RABBIT™
## Second Variation

| | |
|---|---|
| Designer: | Warren Platt |
| Height: | 6", 15.0 cm |
| Colour: | Black and slate |
| Finish: | Gloss |
| Issued: | 1998 in a limited edition of 2,000 |
| Varieties: | ECF 3 |
| Comm. by: | Sinclairs |

| Beswick Number | U.K. £ | U.S. $ | Price Can. $ | Aust. $ |
|---|---|---|---|---|
| ECF 12 (3420) | 50. | 90. | 115. | 125. |

## ECF 13 (3447)
## MRS. RABBIT BAKING™
## Second Variation

| | |
|---|---|
| Designer: | Martyn Alcock |
| Height: | 5 ½", 14.0 cm |
| Colour: | Grey, yellow, rust |
| Finish: | Gloss |
| Issued: | 1998 in a limited edition of 2,000 |
| Varieties: | ECF 7 |
| Comm. by: | Sinclairs |

| Beswick Number | U.K. £ | U.S. $ | Price Can. $ | Aust. $ |
|---|---|---|---|---|
| ECF 13 (3447) | 50. | 90. | 115. | 125. |

# FOOTBALLING FELINES

### FF 2 (3816)
### MEE-OUCH

| | |
|---|---|
| Designer: | Andy Moss |
| Height: | 3 ¼", 8.3 cm |
| Colour: | Blue shirt; white shorts; black boots |
| Finish: | Gloss |
| Issued: | 1998 in a special edition of 1,500 |
| Comm. by: | Sinclairs |

| Beswick Number | U.K. £ | U.S. $ | Price Can. $ | Aust. $ |
|---|---|---|---|---|
| FF 2 (3816) | 35. | 60. | 75. | 80. |

**Note:** FF1 not issued.

### FF 3 (3822)
### KITCAT

| | |
|---|---|
| Designer: | Andy Moss |
| Height: | 4 ¼", 10.8 cm |
| Colour: | Red shirt; white shorts; black boots |
| Finish: | Gloss |
| Issued: | 1998 in a special edition of 1,500 |
| Comm. by: | Sinclairs |

| Beswick Number | U.K. £ | U.S. $ | Price Can. $ | Aust. $ |
|---|---|---|---|---|
| FF 3 (3822) | 35. | 60. | 75. | 80. |

**FF 4 (3834)**
**DRIBBLE**

| Designer: | Andy Moss |
| Height: | 4 ¼", 10.8 cm |
| Colour: | White shirt; black shorts and boots |
| Finish: | Gloss |
| Issued: | 1999 in a special edition of 1,500 |
| Comm. by: | Sinclairs |

| Beswick Number | U.K. £ | U.S. $ | Price Can. $ | Aust. $ |
|---|---|---|---|---|
| FF 4 (3834) | 35. | 60. | 75. | 80. |

**FF 5 (3899)**
**THROW IN**

| Designer: | Andy Moss |
| Height: | 6", 15.0 cm |
| Colour: | Yellow shirt; white shorts; black boots |
| Finish: | Gloss |
| Issued: | 1999 in a special edition of 1,500 |
| Comm. by: | Sinclairs |

| Beswick Number | U.K. £ | U.S. $ | Price Can. $ | Aust. $ |
|---|---|---|---|---|
| FF 5 (3899) | 35. | 60. | 75. | 80. |

**FF 6 (3896)**
**REFEREE: RED CARD**

| Designer: | Andy Moss |
| Height: | 6 ¼", 15.9 cm |
| Colour: | Black uniform; black and white socks |
| Finish: | Gloss |
| Issued: | 2000 in a special edition of 1,500 |
| Comm. by: | Sinclairs |

| Beswick Number | U.K. £ | U.S. $ | Price Can. $ | Aust. $ |
|---|---|---|---|---|
| FF 6 (3896) | 75. | 135. | 165. | 180. |

# THE HERBS
## (Parsley and the Herbs)

This series was produced in the last couple of years before the Beswick factory closed its doors for the last time and all production ceased.

Originally it was the intention to produce a set of seven models but only four of these were put into production. No. 4211 *Mr. Onion*, No. 4212 *Mr. Basil* and No. 4224 *Lady Rosemary* were never produced. Due to the fact that these models were produced so late in Beswick's history will make them very hard to find.

### H 1 (4058)
### PARSLEY THE LION

Beswick No.: H 1 (4058)
Designer: Ivor Wood
Modeller: Shane Ridge
Height: 3 ¾", 9.5 cm
Colour: Greens, yellow and white
Finish: Gloss
Issued: 2001 in a limited edition of 2,500
Comm. by: Doulton-Direct

| Beswick Number | U.K. £ | U.S. $ | Price Can. $ | Aust. $ |
|---|---|---|---|---|
| H 1 (4058) | 75. | 135. | 170. | 180. |

### H 2 (4059)
### BAYLEAF THE GARDENER

Designer: Ivor Wood
Modeller: Shane Ridge
Height: 5 ¾", 14.6 cm
Colour: Red, white, grey, brown, cream and black
Finish: Gloss
Issued: 2001 in a limited edition of 2,500
Comm. by: Doulton-Direct

| Beswick Number | U.K. £ | U.S. $ | Price Can. $ | Aust. $ |
|---|---|---|---|---|
| H 2 (4059) | 75. | 135. | 170. | 180. |

## H 3 (4057)
### DILL THE DOG

| | |
|---|---|
| Designer: | Ivor Wood |
| Modeller: | Shane Ridge |
| Height: | 3 ½", 8.9 cm |
| Colour: | Brown, grey, yellow and cream |
| Finish: | Gloss |
| Issued: | 2001 in a limited edition of 2,500 |
| Comm. by: | Doulton-Direct |

| Beswick Number | U.K. £ | U.S. $ | Price Can. $ | Aust. $ |
|---|---|---|---|---|
| H 3 (4057) | 75. | 135. | 170. | 180. |

## H 4 (4056)
### SAGE THE OWL

| | |
|---|---|
| Designer: | Ivor Wood |
| Modeller | Shane Ridge |
| Height: | 3", 7.5 cm |
| Colour: | Green, brown, yellow and white |
| Finish: | Gloss |
| Issued: | 2001 in a limited edition of 2,500 |

| Beswick Number | U.K. £ | U.S. $ | Price Can. $ | Aust. $ |
|---|---|---|---|---|
| H 4 (4056) | 75. | 135. | 170. | 180. |

# HIPPOS ON HOLIDAY

### HH 1 (3513)
### GRANDMA™

| | | | |
|---|---|---|---|
| Modeller: | Amanda Hughes-Lubeck | | |
| Height: | 5", 12.7 cm | | |
| Colour: | Orange, grey, black and brown | | |
| Finish: | Gloss | | |
| Issued: | 1999 in a limited edition of 3,500 | | |

| Beswick Number | U.K. £ | U.S. $ | Price Can. $ | Aust. $ |
|---|---|---|---|---|
| HH 1 (3513) | 35. | 60. | 75. | 80. |

### HH 2 (3512)
### GRANDPA™

| | | | |
|---|---|---|---|
| Modeller: | Warren Platt | | |
| Height: | 5", 12.7 cm | | |
| Colour: | White jacket and cap, blue trousers | | |
| Finish: | Gloss | | |
| Issued: | 1999 in a limited edition of 3,500 | | |

| Beswick Number | U.K. £ | U.S. $ | Price Can. $ | Aust. $ |
|---|---|---|---|---|
| HH 2 (3512) | 35. | 60. | 75. | 80. |

### HH 3 (3489)
### MA™

| | | | |
|---|---|---|---|
| Modeller: | Amanda Hughes-Lubeck | | |
| Height: | 5", 12.7 cm | | |
| Colour: | Purple, grey, pink and yellow | | |
| Finish: | Gloss | | |
| Issued: | 1999 in a limited edition of 3,500 | | |

| Beswick Number | U.K. £ | U.S. $ | Price Can. $ | Aust. $ |
|---|---|---|---|---|
| HH 3 (3489) | 35. | 60. | 75. | 80. |

## HH 4 (3488)
### PA™

| | |
|---|---|
| Modeller: | Martyn Alcock |
| Height: | 5", 12.7 cm |
| Colour: | Yellow, green and grey |
| Finish: | Gloss |
| Issued: | 1999 in a limited edition of 3,500 |

| Beswick Number | U.K. £ | U.S. $ | Price Can. $ | Aust. $ |
|---|---|---|---|---|
| HH 4 (3488) | 35. | 60. | 75. | 80. |

## HH 5 (3491)
### HARRIET™

| | |
|---|---|
| Modeller: | Martyn Alcock |
| Height: | 5", 12.7 cm |
| Colour: | Pink and grey |
| Finish: | Gloss |
| Issued: | 1999 in a limited edition of 3,500 |

| Beswick Number | U.K. £ | U.S. $ | Price Can. $ | Aust. $ |
|---|---|---|---|---|
| HH 5 (3491) | 35. | 60. | 75. | 80. |

## HH 6 (3493)
### HUGO™

| | |
|---|---|
| Modeller: | Warren Platt |
| Height: | 4", 10.1 cm |
| Colour: | Grey, white, blue and yellow |
| Finish: | Gloss |
| Issued: | 1999 in a limited edition of 3,500 |

| Beswick Number | U.K. £ | U.S. $ | Price Can. $ | Aust. $ |
|---|---|---|---|---|
| HH 6 (3493) | 35. | 60. | 75. | 80. |

# KITTY MACBRIDE'S HAPPY MICE

**2526**
**A FAMILY MOUSE**™

| | |
|---|---|
| Designer: | Graham Tongue |
| Height: | 3 ½", 8.9 cm |
| Colour: | Brown, mauve, turquoise, light and dark green |
| Finish: | Gloss |
| Issued: | 1975 - 1983 |

| Beswick Number | U.K. £ | U.S. $ | Price Can. $ | Aust. $ |
|---|---|---|---|---|
| 2526 | 60. | 110. | 135. | 150. |

**2527**
**A DOUBLE ACT**™

| | |
|---|---|
| Designer: | Graham Tongue |
| Height: | 3 ½", 8.9 cm |
| Colour: | Yellow, orange, brown, green and blue |
| Finish: | Gloss |
| Issued: | 1975 - 1983 |

| Beswick Number | U.K. £ | U.S. $ | Price Can. $ | Aust. $ |
|---|---|---|---|---|
| 2527 | 60. | 110. | 135. | 150. |

## 2528
### THE RACEGOER™

| | |
|---|---|
| Designer: | David Lyttleton |
| Height: | 3 ½", 8.9 cm |
| Colour: | Brown, yellow and green |
| Finish: | Gloss |
| Issued: | 1975 - 1983 |

| Beswick Number | U.K. £ | U.S. $ | Price Can. $ | Aust. $ |
|---|---|---|---|---|
| 2528 | 60. | 110. | 135. | 150. |

## 2529
### A GOOD READ™

| | |
|---|---|
| Designer: | David Lyttleton |
| Height: | 2 ½", 6.4 cm |
| Colour: | Yellow, blue, brown and white |
| Finish: | Gloss |
| Issued: | 1975 - 1983 |

| Beswick Number | U.K. £ | U.S. $ | Price Can. $ | Aust. $ |
|---|---|---|---|---|
| 2529 | 125. | 225. | 275. | 300. |

## 2530
### LAZYBONES™

| | |
|---|---|
| Designer: | David Lyttleton |
| Size: | 1 ½" x 3 ½", 3.8 x 8.9 cm |
| Colour: | Blue, black, brown, green and white |
| Finish: | Gloss |
| Issued: | 1975-1983 |

| Beswick Number | U.K. £ | U.S. $ | Price Can. $ | Aust. $ |
|---|---|---|---|---|
| 2530 | 60. | 110. | 135. | 150. |

**2531**
**A SNACK™**

| | |
|---|---|
| Designer: | David Lyttleton |
| Height: | 3 ¼", 8.3 cm |
| Colour: | Brown, blue, yellow and green |
| Finish: | Gloss |
| Issued: | 1975 - 1983 |

| Beswick Number | U.K. £ | U.S. $ | Price Can. $ | Aust. $ |
|---|---|---|---|---|
| 2531 | 60. | 110. | 135. | 150. |

**2532**
**STRAINED RELATIONS™**

| | |
|---|---|
| Designer: | David Lyttleton |
| Height: | 3", 7.6 cm |
| Colour: | Brown, blue and green |
| Finish: | Gloss |
| Issued: | 1975 - 1983 |

| Beswick Number | U.K. £ | U.S. $ | Price Can. $ | Aust. $ |
|---|---|---|---|---|
| 2532 | 60. | 110. | 135. | 150. |

**2533**
**JUST GOOD FRIENDS™**

| | |
|---|---|
| Designer: | David Lyttleton |
| Height: | 3", 7.6 cm |
| Colour: | Brown, yellow, blue, red and green |
| Finish: | Gloss |
| Issued: | 1975 - 1983 |

| Beswick Number | U.K. £ | U.S. $ | Price Can. $ | Aust. $ |
|---|---|---|---|---|
| 2533 | 75. | 135. | 170. | 180. |

## 2565
### THE RING™

| Designer: | David Lyttleton |
| Height: | 3 ¼", 8.3 cm |
| Colour: | Brown, white, purple and yellow |
| Finish: | Gloss |
| Issued: | 1976 - 1983 |

| Beswick Number | U.K. £ | U.S. $ | Price Can. $ | Aust. $ |
| --- | --- | --- | --- | --- |
| 2565 | 150. | 275. | 325. | 375. |

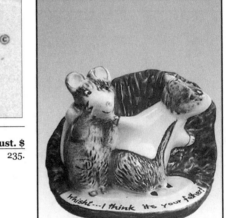

## 2566
### GUILTY SWEETHEARTS™

| Designer: | David Lyttleton |
| Height: | 2 ¼", 5.7 cm |
| Colour: | Brown, yellow, green and white |
| Finish: | Gloss |
| Issued: | 1976 - 1983 |

| Beswick Number | U.K. £ | U.S. $ | Price Can. $ | Aust. $ |
| --- | --- | --- | --- | --- |
| 2566 | 100. | 175. | 215. | 235. |

## 2589
### ALL I DO IS THINK OF YOU™

| Designer: | David Lyttleton |
| Height: | 2 ½", 6.4 cm |
| Colour: | Brown, yellow and white |
| Finish: | Gloss |
| Issued: | 1976 - 1983 |

| Beswick Number | U.K. £ | U.S. $ | Price Can. $ | Aust. $ |
| --- | --- | --- | --- | --- |
| 2589 | 275. | 500. | 625. | 675. |

# MONKEY BAND

## 1255
## MONKEY WITH DRUM

| Designer: | Jan Granoska |
|---|---|
| Height: | 2 ½", 6.4 cm |
| Colour: | Brown and green |
| Finish: | Gloss |
| Issued: | 1952 - 1963 |
| Set: | 1256, 1257, 1258, 1259, 1260 |

| Beswick Number | U.K. £ | U.S. $ | Price Can. $ | Aust. $ |
|---|---|---|---|---|
| 1255 | 150. | 275. | 350. | 375. |

## 1256
## MONKEY WITH TUBA

| Designer: | Jan Granoska |
|---|---|
| Height: | 2 ½", 6.4 cm |
| Colour: | Brown and green |
| Finish: | Gloss |
| Issued: | 1952 - 1963 |
| Set: | 1255, 1257, 1258, 1259, 1260 |

| Beswick Number | U.K. £ | U.S. $ | Price Can. $ | Aust. $ |
|---|---|---|---|---|
| 1256 | 150. | 275. | 350. | 375. |

## 1257
## MONKEY WITH FIDDLE

| Designer: | Jan Granoska |
|---|---|
| Height: | 2 ½", 6.4 cm |
| Colour: | Brown and green |
| Finish: | Gloss |
| Issued: | 1952 - 1963 |
| Set: | 1255, 1256, 1258, 1259, 1260 |

| Beswick Number | U.K. £ | U.S. $ | Price Can. $ | Aust. $ |
|---|---|---|---|---|
| 1257 | 150. | 275. | 350. | 375. |

## 1258
### MONKEY WITH SAXOPHONE

| | |
|---|---|
| Designer: | Jan Granoska |
| Height: | 2 ½", 6.4 cm |
| Colour: | Brown and green |
| Finish: | Gloss |
| Issued: | 1952 - 1963 |
| Set: | 1255, 1256, 1257, 1259, 1260 |

| Beswick Number | U.K. £ | U.S. $ | Price Can. $ | Aust. $ |
|---|---|---|---|---|
| 1258 | 150. | 275. | 350. | 375. |

## 1259
### MONKEY WITH GUITAR

| | |
|---|---|
| Designer: | Jan Granoska |
| Height: | 2 ½", 6.4 cm |
| Colour: | Brown and green |
| Finish: | Gloss |
| Issued: | 1952 - 1963 |
| Set: | 1255, 1256, 1257, 1258, 1260 |

| Beswick Number | U.K. £ | U.S. $ | Price Can. $ | Aust. $ |
|---|---|---|---|---|
| 1259 | 150. | 275. | 350. | 375. |

## 1260
### MONKEY WITH BANJO

| | |
|---|---|
| Designer: | Jan Granoska |
| Height: | 2 ½", 6.4 cm |
| Colour: | Brown and green |
| Finish: | Gloss |
| Issued: | 1952 - 1963 |
| Set: | 1255, 1256, 1257, 1258, 1259 |

| Beswick Number | U.K. £ | U.S. $ | Price Can. $ | Aust. $ |
|---|---|---|---|---|
| 1260 | 150. | 275. | 350. | 375. |

# PENGUIN FAMILY

**800**
**PENGUIN - CHICK**

| | |
|---|---|
| Designer: | Arthur Gredington |
| Height: | 2", 5.0 cm |
| Colour: | Black and white with yellow markings |
| Finish: | Gloss |
| Issued: | 1940 - 1973 |
| Set: | 801, 802, 803 |

| Beswick Number | U.K. £ | U.S. $ | Price Can. $ | Aust. $ |
|---|---|---|---|---|
| 800 | 15. | 25. | 30. | 35. |

**801**
**PENGUIN - CHICK**

| | |
|---|---|
| Designer: | Arthur Gredington |
| Height: | 2", 5.0 cm |
| Colour: | Black and white with yellow markings |
| Finish: | Gloss |
| Issued: | 1940 - 1973 |
| Set: | 800, 802, 803 |

| Beswick Number | U.K. £ | U.S. $ | Price Can. $ | Aust. $ |
|---|---|---|---|---|
| 801 | 15. | 25. | 30. | 35. |

**802**
**PENGUIN – WITH UMBRELLA**
Designer: Arthur Gredington
Height: 4 ¼", 10.8 cm
Colour: 1. Black and white; red umbrella
2. Black and white; green umbrella
Finish: Gloss
Issued: 1940 - 1973
Set: 800, 801, 803

| Beswick Number | Colourway | U.K. £ | U.S. $ | Price Can. $ | Aust. $ |
|---|---|---|---|---|---|
| 802 | Red | 25. | 45. | 55. | 60. |
| 802 | Green | 50. | 90. | 115. | 120. |

**803**
**PENGUIN - WITH WALKING STICK**
Designer: Arthur Gredington
Height: 3 ¾", 9.5 cm
Colour: Black and white; yellow markings; black walking stick
Finish: Gloss
Issued: 1940 - 1973
Set: 800, 801, 802

| Beswick Number | U.K. £ | U.S. $ | Price Can. $ | Aust. $ |
|---|---|---|---|---|
| 803 | 25. | 45. | 55. | 60. |

# THE PIG PROMENADE

**PP 1 (3446)**
**JOHN THE CONDUCTOR**™
**(Vietnamese Pot Bellied Pig)**

| | |
|---|---|
| Designer: | Martyn Alcock |
| Height: | 4 ¾", 12.1 cm |
| Colour: | Black jacket and bowtie |
| Finish: | Gloss |
| Issued: | 1993 - 1996 |

| Beswick Number | U.K. £ | U.S. $ | Price Can. $ | Aust. $ |
|---|---|---|---|---|
| PP 1 (3446) | 40. | 70. | 85. | 95. |

**PP 2 (3443)**
**MATTHEW THE TRUMPET PLAYER**™
**(Large White Pig)**

| | |
|---|---|
| Designer: | Amanda Hughes-Lubeck |
| Height: | 5", 12.7 cm |
| Colour: | Light red waistcoat and black bowtie |
| Finish: | Gloss |
| Issued: | 1993 - 1996 |

| Beswick Number | U.K. £ | U.S. $ | Price Can. $ | Aust. $ |
|---|---|---|---|---|
| PP 2 (3443) | 40. | 70. | 85. | 95. |

**PP 3 (3444)**
**DAVID THE FLUTE PLAYER**™
**(Tamworth Pig)**

| | |
|---|---|
| Designer: | Amanda Hughes-Lubeck |
| Height: | 5 ¼", 13.3 cm |
| Colour: | Dark green waistcoat and black bowtie |
| Finish: | Gloss |
| Issued: | 1993 - 1996 |

| Beswick Number | U.K. £ | U.S. $ | Price Can. $ | Aust. $ |
|---|---|---|---|---|
| PP 3 (3444) | 40. | 70. | 85. | 95. |

**PP 4 (3440)**
**ANDREW THE CYMBAL PLAYER**™
**(Gloucester Old Spotted Pig)**

| | |
|---|---|
| Designer: | Martyn Alcock |
| Height: | 4 ¾", 12.1 cm |
| Colour: | Blue waistcoat, black bowtie and yellow cymbals |
| Finish: | Gloss |
| Issued: | 1993 - 1996 |
| Varieties: | Also called George, PP10 |

| Beswick Number | U.K. £ | U.S. $ | Price Can. $ | Aust. $ |
|---|---|---|---|---|
| PP 4 (3440) | 40. | 70. | 85. | 95. |

**PP 5 (3453)**
**DANIEL THE VIOLINIST**™
**(Saddleback Pig)**

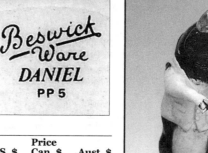

| | |
|---|---|
| Designer: | Amanda Hughes-Lubeck |
| Height: | 5 ¼", 13.3 cm |
| Colour: | Pale blue waistcoat and brown violin |
| Finish: | Gloss |
| Issued: | 1993 - 1996 |

| Beswick Number | U.K. £ | U.S. $ | Price Can. $ | Aust. $ |
|---|---|---|---|---|
| PP 5 (3453) | 45. | 80. | 100. | 110. |

**PP 6 (3454)**
**MICHAEL THE BASS DRUM PLAYER**™
**(Large Black Pig)**

| | |
|---|---|
| Designer: | Martyn Alcock |
| Height: | 4 ¾", 12.1 cm |
| Colour: | Yellow waistcoat, red and white drum |
| Finish: | Gloss |
| Issued: | 1993 - 1996 |

| Beswick Number | U.K. £ | U.S. $ | Price Can. $ | Aust. $ |
|---|---|---|---|---|
| PP 6 (3454) | 40. | 70. | 85. | 95. |

## PP 7 (3532)
## JAMES THE TRIANGLE PLAYER™
## (Tamworth Piglet)

| | |
|---|---|
| Designer: | Warren Platt |
| Height: | 4", 10.1 cm |
| Colour: | Purple waistcoat, black bowtie |
| Finish: | Gloss |
| Issued: | 1995 - 1996 |

| Beswick Number | U.K. £ | U.S. $ | Price Can. $ | Aust. $ |
|---|---|---|---|---|
| PP 7 (3532) | 40. | 70. | 85. | 95. |

## PP 8 (3564)
## RICHARD THE FRENCH HORN PLAYER™

| | |
|---|---|
| Designer: | Shane Ridge |
| Height: | 5", 12.7 cm |
| Colour: | Tan and beige waistcoat, black bowtie |
| Finish: | Gloss |
| Issued: | 1996 - 1996 |
| Varieties: | Also called Benjamin, PP12 |

| Beswick Number | U.K. £ | U.S. $ | Price Can. $ | Aust. $ |
|---|---|---|---|---|
| PP 8 (3564) | 35. | 60. | 75. | 80. |

## PP 9 (3562)
## CHRISTOPHER THE GUITAR PLAYER™

| | |
|---|---|
| Designer: | Warren Platt |
| Height: | 5 ½", 13.3 cm |
| Colour: | Yellow and cream waistcoat, black bowtie |
| Finish: | Gloss |
| Issued: | 1996 - 1996 |
| Varieties: | Also called Thomas, PP11 |

| Beswick Number | U.K. £ | U.S. $ | Price Can. $ | Aust. $ |
|---|---|---|---|---|
| PP 9 (3562) | 40. | 70. | 85. | 95. |

## PP 10 (3440)
### GEORGE™

| | |
|---|---|
| Designer: | Martyn Alcock |
| Height: | 4 ¾", 12.1 cm |
| Colour: | Dark green waistcoat, black bowtie, yellow cymbals |
| Finish: | Gloss |
| Issued: | 1996 in a limited edition of 2,000 |
| Varieties: | Also called Andrew, PP4 |
| Comm. by: | Sinclairs |

| Beswick Number | U.K. £ | U.S. $ | Price Can. $ | Aust. $ |
|---|---|---|---|---|
| PP 10 (3440) | 70. | 125. | 160. | 170. |

## PP 11 (3562)
### THOMAS™

| | |
|---|---|
| Designer: | Warren Platt |
| Height: | 5", 12.7 cm |
| Colour: | Green waistcoat, yellow bowtie, white guitar |
| Finish: | Gloss |
| Issued: | 1997 in a special edition of 2,000 |
| Varieties: | Also called Christopher the Guitar Player, PP9 |
| Comm. by: | Sinclairs |

| Beswick Number | U.K. £ | U.S. $ | Price Can. $ | Aust. $ |
|---|---|---|---|---|
| PP 11 (3562) | 70. | 125. | 160. | 175. |

## PP 12 (3564)
### BENJAMIN™

| | |
|---|---|
| Designer: | Shane Ridge |
| Height: | 5", 12.7 cm |
| Colour: | White, black, gold and orange |
| Finish: | Gloss |
| Issued: | 1997 in a special edition of 2,000 |
| Varieties: | Also called Richard the French Horn Player, PP8 |
| Comm. by: | Sinclairs |

| Beswick Number | U.K. £ | U.S. $ | Price Can. $ | Aust. $ |
|---|---|---|---|---|
| PP 12 (3564) | 70. | 125. | 160. | 175. |

# ROAD GANG

### 1766
### FOREMAN

| | |
|---|---|
| Designer: | Harry Sales |
| Height: | Unknown |
| Colour: | Unknown |
| Finish: | Gloss |
| Issued: | 1961 |
| Set: | 1767, 1768, 1769 |

| Beswick Number | | U.K. £ | U.S. $ | Price Can. $ | Aust. $ |
|---|---|---|---|---|---|
| 1766 | | | Possibly not put into production | | |

**Note:** Shape drawing only.

### 1767
### DIGGER

| | |
|---|---|
| Designer: | Harry Sales |
| Height: | Unknown |
| Colour: | Red jacket, blue cap |
| Finish: | Gloss |
| Issued: | 1961 |
| Set: | 1766, 1768, 1769 |

| Beswick Number | | U.K. £ | U.S. $ | Price Can. $ | Aust. $ |
|---|---|---|---|---|---|
| 1767 | | | Very rare | | |

**Note:** Sample model only.

## 1768
## DRILLER

| | |
|---|---|
| Designer: | Harry Sales |
| Height: | Unknown |
| Colour: | Red jacket, blue cap |
| Finish: | Gloss |
| Issued: | 1961 |
| Set: | 1766, 1767, 1769 |

| Beswick Number | U.K. £ | U.S. $ | Price Can. $ | Aust. $ |
|---|---|---|---|---|
| 1768 | | | Very rare | |

**Note:** Sample model only.

## 1769
## AT EASE

| | |
|---|---|
| Designer: | Harry Sales |
| Height: | Unknown |
| Colour: | Unknown |
| Finish: | Gloss |
| Issued: | 1961 |
| Set: | 1766, 1767, 1768 |

| Beswick Number | U.K. £ | U.S. $ | Price Can. $ | Aust. $ |
|---|---|---|---|---|
| 1769 | | Possibly not put into production | | |

**Note:** Shape drawing only.

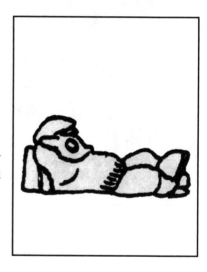

# SPORTING CAT

**3012**
**SPORTING CAT**

| | |
|---|---|
| Designer: | Warren Platt |
| Height: | 4 ¼", 10.8 cm |
| Colour: | 1. Cat dressed as a soccer player with striped jersey; black, blue, burgundy, red or yellow |
| | 2. Cat dressed as a soccer player with plain jersey; black, blue, burgundy, red or yellow |
| Modelled: | 1986 |
| Issued: | 1987 - 1987 |
| Series: | Fun Models |

| Colourways | Finish | U.K. £ | U.S. $ | Price Can. $ | Aust. $ |
|---|---|---|---|---|---|
| 1. Black stripe | Gloss | 50. | 90. | 115. | 125. |
| 2. Black | Gloss | 50. | 90. | 115. | 125. |
| 3. Blue stripe | Gloss | 50. | 90. | 115. | 125. |
| 4. Blue | Gloss | 50. | 90. | 115. | 125. |
| 5. Burgundy Stripe | Gloss | 50. | 90. | 115. | 125. |
| 6. Burgundy | Gloss | 50. | 90. | 115. | 125. |
| 7. Red stripe | Gloss | 50. | 90. | 115. | 125. |
| 8. Red | Gloss | 50. | 90. | 115. | 125. |
| 9. Yellow stripe | Gloss | 50. | 90. | 115. | 125. |
| 10. Yellow | Gloss | 50. | 90. | 115. | 125. |

**Note:** Introduced as a trial in August 1987, but not put into general production, although many sets were sold from the factory shop.

# SPORTING CHARACTERS

### SC 1 (3815)
### FLY FISHING

Designer:  Andy Moss
Height:    3 ¼", 8.3 cm
Colour:    Green, slate blue and black
Finish:    Gloss
Issued:    1998 in a special edition of 1,500
Comm. by:  Sinclairs

| Beswick Number | U.K. £ | U.S. $ | Price Can. $ | Aust. $ |
|---|---|---|---|---|
| SC 1 (3815) | 30. | 55. | 70. | 75. |

### SC 2 (3821)
### LAST LION OF DEFENCE

Designer:  Andy Moss
Height:    4 ¼", 10.8 cm
Colour:    Red and white
Finish:    Gloss
Issued:    1998 in a special edition of 1,500
Comm. by:  Sinclairs

| Beswick Number | U.K. £ | U.S. $ | Price Can. $ | Aust. $ |
|---|---|---|---|---|
| SC 2 (3821) | 35. | 60. | 75. | 80. |

### SC 3 (3832)
### IT'S A KNOCKOUT

Designer:  Andy Moss
Height:    4 ¼", 10.8 cm
Colour:    Red, white and black
Finish:    Gloss
Issued:    1998 in a special edition of 1,500
Comm. by:  Sinclairs

| Beswick Number | U.K. £ | U.S. $ | Price Can. $ | Aust. $ |
|---|---|---|---|---|
| SC 3 (3832) | 30. | 55. | 70. | 75. |

### SC 4 (3895)
### SLOPING OFF

| | |
|---|---|
| Designer: | Andy Moss |
| Height: | 5 ¼", 13.3 cm |
| Colour: | White, black and yellow |
| Finish: | Gloss |
| Issued: | 1999 in a special edition of 1,500 |
| Comm. by: | Sinclairs |

| Beswick Number | U.K. £ | U.S. $ | Price Can. $ | Aust. $ |
|---|---|---|---|---|
| SC 4 (3895) | 30. | 55. | 70. | 75. |

### SC 5 (3905)
### A ROUND WITH FOXY

| | |
|---|---|
| Designer: | Andy Moss |
| Height: | 6", 15.0 cm |
| Colour: | Green, yellow and brown |
| Finish: | Gloss |
| Issued: | 2000 in a special edition of 1,500 |
| Comm. by: | Sinclairs |

| Beswick Number | U.K. £ | U.S. $ | Price Can. $ | Aust. $ |
|---|---|---|---|---|
| SC 5 (3905) | 50. | 90. | 115. | 120. |

### SC 6 (3911)
### OUT FOR A DUCK

| | |
|---|---|
| Designer: | Andy Moss |
| Height: | 5 ½", 14.0 cm |
| Colour: | Cream |
| Finish: | Gloss |
| Issued: | 2000 in a special edition of 1,500 |
| Comm. by: | Sinclairs |

| Beswick Number | U.K. £ | U.S. $ | Price Can. $ | Aust. $ |
|---|---|---|---|---|
| SC 6 (3911) | 40. | 70. | 85. | 95. |

# SQUIRREL FAMILY

## 1007
### SQUIRREL - STANDING

| | |
|---|---|
| Designer: | Arthur Gredington |
| Height: | 2 ¼", 5.7 cm |
| Colour: | Tan |
| Finish: | Gloss |
| Issued: | 1944 - c.1963 |
| Set: | 1008, 1009 |
| Series: | Fun Models |

| Beswick Number | U.K. £ | U.S. $ | Price Can. $ | Aust. $ |
|---|---|---|---|---|
| 1007 | 20. | 35. | 45. | 50. |

## 1008
### SQUIRREL - LYING

| | |
|---|---|
| Designer: | Arthur Gredington |
| Height: | 1 ¾", 4.5 cm |
| Colour: | Tan |
| Finish: | Gloss |
| Issued: | 1944 - c.1963 |
| Set: | 1007, 1009 |
| Series: | Fun Models |

| Beswick Number | U.K. £ | U.S. $ | Price Can. $ | Aust. $ |
|---|---|---|---|---|
| 1008 | 20. | 35. | 45. | 50. |

## 1009
### SQUIRREL – WITH NUT CRACKER

| | |
|---|---|
| Designer: | Arthur Gredington |
| Height: | 4 ½", 11.9 cm |
| Colour: | Tan |
| Finish: | Gloss |
| Issued: | 1944 - c.1963 |
| Set: | 1007, 1008 |
| Series: | Fun Models |

| Beswick Number | U.K. £ | U.S. $ | Price Can. $ | Aust. $ |
|---|---|---|---|---|
| 1009 | 50. | 90. | 115. | 120. |

# TORTOISE FAMILY

### 1335
### TORTOISE MOTHER WITH HAT

| | |
|---|---|
| Designer: | Jan Granoska |
| Length: | 2 ¾", 7.0 cm |
| Colour: | Brown |
| Finish: | Gloss |
| Issued: | 1954 - 1973 |
| Set: | 1336, 1337 |
| Series: | Fun Models |

| Beswick Number | U.K. £ | U.S. $ | Price Can. $ | Aust. $ |
|---|---|---|---|---|
| 1335 | 40. | 70. | 85. | 95. |

### 1336
### TORTOISE GIRL WITH BONNET

| | |
|---|---|
| Designer: | Jan Granoska |
| Length: | 1 ¾", 4.5 cm |
| Colour: | Brown |
| Finish: | Gloss |
| Issued: | 1954 - 1973 |
| Set: | 1335, 1337 |
| Series: | Fun Models |

| Beswick Number | U.K. £ | U.S. $ | Price Can. $ | Aust. $ |
|---|---|---|---|---|
| 1336 | 30. | 55. | 70. | 75. |

### 1337
### TORTOISE BOY WITH CAP

| | |
|---|---|
| Designer: | Jan Granoska |
| Length: | 1 ¾", 4.5 cm |
| Colour: | Brown |
| Finish: | Gloss |
| Issued: | 1954 - 1973 |
| Set: | 1335, 1336 |
| Series: | Fun Models |

| Beswick Number | U.K. £ | U.S. $ | Price Can. $ | Aust. $ |
|---|---|---|---|---|
| 1337 | 30. | 55. | 70. | 75. |

# SECTION FIVE

## FIGURES

Polish Girl with Hen, Model No. 1222

**303**
**POLICEMAN**

| Designer: | Mr. Symcox |
|---|---|
| Height: | Unknown |
| Colour: | Unknown |
| Finish: | Gloss |
| Issued: | 1935 - 1954 |

| Beswick Number | U.K. £ | U.S. $ | Price Can. $ | Aust. $ |
|---|---|---|---|---|
| 303 | | | Very rare | |

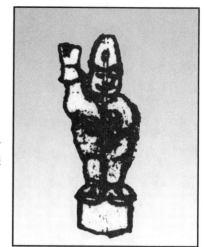

**374**
**GIRL WITH POT OF HONEY**

| Designer: | Miss Greaves |
|---|---|
| Height: | 5", 12.7 cm |
| Colour: | 1. All blue |
| | 2. Green coat, pink dress |
| | 3. Pink spotted coat, green dress |
| Finish: | Gloss |
| Issued: | 1936 - 1954 |

| Beswick Number | U.K. £ | U.S. $ | Price Can. $ | Aust. $ |
|---|---|---|---|---|
| 374 | 150. | 275. | 325. | 375. |

**375**
**BOY (ON BASE)**

| Designer: | Miss Greaves |
|---|---|
| Height: | Unknown |
| Colour: | Unknown |
| Finish: | Gloss |
| Issued: | 1936 - 1954 |

| Beswick Number | U.K. £ | U.S. $ | Price Can. $ | Aust. $ |
|---|---|---|---|---|
| 375 | | | Very rare | |

## 388
## GIRL WITH FINGER IN MOUTH

| | |
|---|---|
| Designer: | Miss Greaves |
| Height: | 5 ¾", 14.6 cm |
| Colour: | Unknown |
| Finish: | Gloss |
| Issued: | 1936 - 1954 |

| Beswick Number | U.K. £ | U.S. $ | Price Can. $ | Aust. $ |
|---|---|---|---|---|
| 388 | | | Very rare | |

## 389
## MAN ON ROCK

| | |
|---|---|
| Designer: | Miss Greaves |
| Height: | Unknown |
| Colour: | Unknown |
| Finish: | Gloss |
| Issued: | 1936 - 1954 |

| Beswick Number | U.K. £ | U.S. $ | Price Can. $ | Aust. $ |
|---|---|---|---|---|
| 389 | | | Very rare | |

## 390
## GIRL IN BREEZE

| | |
|---|---|
| Designer: | Miss Greaves |
| Height: | 5 ½", 14.0 cm |
| Colour: | Pink |
| Finish: | Gloss |
| Issued: | 1936 - 1954 |

| Beswick Number | U.K. £ | U.S. $ | Price Can. $ | Aust. $ |
|---|---|---|---|---|
| 390 | 200. | 350. | 425. | 475. |

**391**
**GIRL WITH HANDS IN MUFF**

| Designer: | Miss Greaves |
|---|---|
| Height: | 7 ¼", 18.4 cm |
| Colour: | Blue and pink |
| Finish: | Gloss |
| Issued: | 1936 - 1954 |

| Beswick Number | U.K. £ | U.S. $ | Price Can. $ | Aust. $ |
|---|---|---|---|---|
| 391 | 200. | 350. | 425. | 475. |

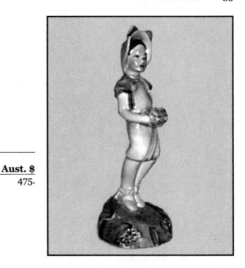

**392**
**CHILD LYING DOWN**

| Designer: | Miss Greaves |
|---|---|
| Height: | Unknown |
| Colour: | Unknown |
| Finish: | Gloss |
| Issued: | 1936 - 1954 |

| Beswick Number | U.K. £ | U.S. $ | Price Can. $ | Aust. $ |
|---|---|---|---|---|
| 392 | 200. | 350. | 425. | 475. |

**437**
**GIRL WITH FLARED DRESS**

| Designer: | Miss Greaves |
|---|---|
| Height: | 4 ¾", 12.1 cm |
| Colour: | 1. Blue striped dress |
| | 2. Yellow and pink dress |
| Finish: | Gloss |
| Issued: | 1936 - 1954 |

| Beswick Number | U.K. £ | U.S. $ | Price Can. $ | Aust. $ |
|---|---|---|---|---|
| 437 | 300. | 525. | 650. | 700. |

Photograph not
available
at press time

### 438
### GIRL WITH FRILLED DRESS

| Designer: | Miss Greaves |
|---|---|
| Height: | Unknown |
| Colour: | Unknown |
| Finish: | Gloss |
| Issued: | 1936 - 1954 |

| Beswick Number | U.K. £ | U.S. $ | Price Can. $ | Aust. $ |
|---|---|---|---|---|
| 438 | | | Very rare | |

### 441
### LADY STANDING ON BASE

| Designer: | Miss Greaves |
|---|---|
| Height: | 8", 20.3 cm |
| Colour: | Blue |
| Finish: | Gloss |
| Issued: | 1936 - 1954 |

| Beswick Number | U.K. £ | U.S. $ | Price Can. $ | Aust. $ |
|---|---|---|---|---|
| 441 | | | Very rare | |

### 442
### BOY STANDING ON BASE

| Designer: | Miss Greaves |
|---|---|
| Height: | 8", 20.3 cm |
| Colour: | Blue |
| Finish: | Gloss |
| Issued: | 1936 - 1954 |

| Beswick Number | U.K. £ | U.S. $ | Price Can. $ | Aust. $ |
|---|---|---|---|---|
| 442 | 200. | 350. | 425. | 475. |

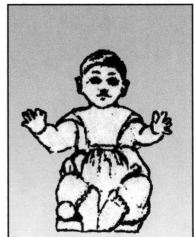

**443**
**CHILD SITTING**

| Designer: | Miss Greaves |
|---|---|
| Height: | Unknown |
| Colour: | Unknown |
| Finish: | Gloss |
| Issued: | 1936 - 1954 |

| Beswick Number | U.K. £ | U.S. $ | Price Can. $ | Aust. $ |
|---|---|---|---|---|
| 443 | | | Very rare | |

**501**
**CLOWN**

| Designer: | Mr. Watkin |
|---|---|
| Height: | Unknown |
| Colour: | Unknown |
| Finish: | Gloss |
| Issued: | 1937 - 1954 |

| Beswick Number | U.K. £ | U.S. $ | Price Can. $ | Aust. $ |
|---|---|---|---|---|
| 501 | | | Very rare | |

Photograph not
available
at press time

**622**
**MR. CHAMBERLAIN**

| Designer: | Mr. Owen |
|---|---|
| Height: | Unknown |
| Colour: | Unknown |
| Finish: | Gloss |
| Issued: | 1938 - 1940 |

| Beswick Number | U.K. £ | U.S. $ | Price Can. $ | Aust. $ |
|---|---|---|---|---|
| 622 | | | Very rare | |

Photograph not
available
at press time

### 903
### TRUMPET BOY

| Designer: | Arthur Gredington |
|---|---|
| Height: | 4 ½", 11.9 cm |
| Colour: | Green and black |
| Finish: | Gloss |
| Issued: | 1940 - 1948 |
| Series: | Kindergarten |

| Beswick Number | | U.K. £ | U.S. $ | Price Can. $ | Aust. $ |
|---|---|---|---|---|---|
| 903 | | 125. | 225. | 275. | 300. |

### 904
### BOOK WORM

| Designer: | Arthur Gredington |
|---|---|
| Height: | 5 ½", 14.0 cm |
| Colour: | Green and browns |
| Finish: | Gloss |
| Issued: | 1940 - 1948 |
| Series: | Kindergarten |

| Beswick Number | | U.K. £ | U.S. $ | Price Can. $ | Aust. $ |
|---|---|---|---|---|---|
| 904 | | 175. | 300. | 375. | 400. |

### 905
### GOOSE GIRL

| Designer: | Arthur Gredington |
|---|---|
| Height: | 6", 15.0 cm |
| Colour: | Yellow, black and white |
| Finish: | Gloss |
| Issued: | 1940 - 1948 |
| Series: | Kindergarten |

| Beswick Number | | U.K. £ | U.S. $ | Price Can. $ | Aust. $ |
|---|---|---|---|---|---|
| 905 | | 150. | 275. | 350. | 375. |

## 906
## STROLLING ALONG

| Designer: | Arthur Gredington |
|---|---|
| Height: | 4 ¾", 12.1 cm |
| Colour: | Browns and green |
| Finish: | Gloss |
| Issued: | 1941 - 1948 |
| Series: | Kindergarten |

| Beswick Number | U.K. £ | U.S. $ | Price Can. $ | Aust. $ |
|---|---|---|---|---|
| 906 | 150. | 275. | 350. | 375. |

**Note:** Dog available separately as No. 1242, see the *Beswick Animals*: A Charlton Standard Catalogue.

## 908
## STORMY WEATHER

| Designer: | Arthur Gredington |
|---|---|
| Height: | 6", 15.0 cm |
| Colour: | Green, brown and yellow |
| Finish: | Gloss |
| Issued: | 1941 - 1948 |
| Series: | Kindergarten |

| Beswick Number | U.K. £ | U.S. $ | Price Can. $ | Aust. $ |
|---|---|---|---|---|
| 908 | 175. | 300. | 375. | 400. |

## 909
## PUPPY LOVE

| Designer: | Arthur Gredington |
|---|---|
| Height: | 5 ½", 14.0 cm |
| Colour: | Brown and green |
| Finish: | Gloss |
| Issued: | 1941 - 1948 |
| Series: | Kindergarten |

| Beswick Number | U.K. £ | U.S. $ | Price Can. $ | Aust. $ |
|---|---|---|---|---|
| 909 | 150. | 275. | 350. | 375. |

**Note:** Dog available separately as No. 1241 see the *Beswick Animals*: A Charlton Standard Catalogue.

### 910
### MEDITATION

| Designer: | Arthur Gredington |
|---|---|
| Height: | 5", 12.7 cm |
| Colour: | Browns and white |
| Finish: | Gloss |
| Issued: | 1941 - 1948 |
| Series: | Kindergarten |

| Beswick Number | | U.K. £ | U.S. $ | Price Can. $ | Aust. $ |
|---|---|---|---|---|---|
| 910 | | 150. | 275. | 350. | 375. |

### 911
### MAX & MORITZ

| Designer: | Arthur Gredington |
|---|---|
| Height: | 5 ½", 14.0 cm |
| Colour: | Green, black and brown |
| Finish: | Gloss |
| Issued: | 1941 - 1948 |
| Series: | Kindergarten |

| Beswick Number | | U.K. £ | U.S. $ | Price Can. $ | Aust. $ |
|---|---|---|---|---|---|
| 911 | | 150. | 275. | 350. | 375. |

### 912
### FARM BOY

| Designer: | Arthur Gredington |
|---|---|
| Height: | 5 ¾", 14.6 cm |
| Colour: | Green, brown and black |
| Finish: | Gloss |
| Issued: | 1941 - 1948 |
| Series: | Kindergarten |

| Beswick Number | | U.K. £ | U.S. $ | Price Can. $ | Aust. $ |
|---|---|---|---|---|---|
| 912 | | 150. | 275. | 350. | 375. |

**913**
**GLOBE TROTTER**

| Designer: | Arthur Gredington |
|---|---|
| Height: | 5 ¼", 13.3 cm |
| Colour: | Browns, green and yellow |
| Finish: | Gloss |
| Issued: | 1941 - 1948 |
| Series: | Kindergarten |

| Beswick Number | U.K. £ | U.S. $ | Price Can. $ | Aust. $ |
|---|---|---|---|---|
| 913 | 150. | 275. | 350. | 375. |

**914**
**SHEPHERD'S BOY**

| Designer: | Arthur Gredington |
|---|---|
| Height: | 5 ½", 14.0 cm |
| Colour: | Browns, green and white |
| Finish: | Gloss |
| Issued: | 1941 - 1948 |
| Series: | Kindergarten |

| Beswick Number | U.K. £ | U.S. $ | Price Can. $ | Aust. $ |
|---|---|---|---|---|
| 914 | 200. | 350. | 425. | 475. |

**924**
**WINSTON CHURCHILL**

| Designer: | Unknown |
|---|---|
| Height: | 6", 15.0 cm |
| Colour: | Black |
| Finish: | Gloss |
| Issued: | 1941 - 1954 |

| Beswick Number | U.K. £ | U.S. $ | Price Can. $ | Aust. $ |
|---|---|---|---|---|
| 924 | 350. | 600. | 750. | 800. |

### 990
### HAPPINESS

| | |
|---|---|
| Designer: | Arthur Gredington |
| Height: | 5", 12.7 cm |
| Colour: | Brown |
| Finish: | Gloss |
| Issued: | 1942 |
| Series: | Kindergarten |

| Beswick Number | U.K. £ | U.S. $ | Price Can. $ | Aust. $ |
|---|---|---|---|---|
| 990 | 150. | 275. | 350. | 375. |

### 1020
### MADONNA

| | |
|---|---|
| Designer: | Arthur Gredington |
| Height: | 14", 35.5 cm |
| Colour: | 1. Maroon and yellow cloak, blue dress |
| | 2. All cream |
| Finish: | Gloss |
| Issued: | 1945 - 1954 |

| Beswick Number | U.K. £ | U.S. $ | Price Can. $ | Aust. $ |
|---|---|---|---|---|
| 1020 | | | Rare | |

### 1086
### CLOWN AND DOG

| | |
|---|---|
| Designer: | Arthur Gredington |
| Height: | 7 ¼", 18.4 cm |
| Colour: | Pink, blue, red, yellow and white |
| Finish: | Gloss |
| Issued: | 1947 - 1958 |

| Beswick Number | U.K. £ | U.S. $ | Price Can. $ | Aust. $ |
|---|---|---|---|---|
| 1086 | 300. | 525. | 650. | 700. |

**Note:** Dog available separately as No. 1239 see the *Beswick Animals*: A Charlton Standard Catalogue.

## 1087
### JESTER SITTING

| | |
|---|---|
| Designer: | Arthur Gredington |
| Height: | 5", 12.7 cm |
| Colour: | Burgundy, pale green and blue |
| Finish: | Gloss |
| Issued: | 1947 - 1958 |

| Beswick Number | U.K. £ | U.S. $ | Prie Can. $ | Aust. $ |
|---|---|---|---|---|
| 1087 | 300. | 525. | 650. | 700. |

## 1091
### GYPSY GIRL

| | |
|---|---|
| Designer: | Arthur Gredington |
| Height: | 7 ¼", 18.4 cm |
| Colour: | Blue bodice, blue and yellow striped skirt |
| Finish: | Gloss |
| Issued: | 1947 - 1958 |

| Beswick Number | U.K. £ | U.S. $ | Price Can. $ | Aust. $ |
|---|---|---|---|---|
| 1091 | 200. | 350. | 425. | 475. |

## 1093
### BOY HIKER

| | |
|---|---|
| Designer: | Arthur Gredington |
| Height: | 6", 15.0 cm |
| Colour: | Pale green shirt, dark green shorts |
| Finish: | Gloss |
| Issued: | 1947 - 1954 |

| Beswick Number | U.K. £ | U.S. $ | Price Can. $ | Aust. $ |
|---|---|---|---|---|
| 1093 | 200. | 350. | 425. | 475. |

**1094**
**GIRL HIKER**

| | |
|---|---|
| Designer: | Arthur Gredington |
| Height: | 6", 15.0 cm |
| Colour: | Unknown |
| Finish: | Gloss |
| Issued: | 1947 - 1954 |

| Beswick Number | U.K. £ | U.S. $ | Price Can. $ | Aust. $ |
|---|---|---|---|---|
| 1094 | | | Rare | |

**1096**
**SPORTSMAN AND DOG**

| | |
|---|---|
| Designer: | Arthur Gredington |
| Height: | 6 ¾", 17.2 cm |
| Colour: | Green, tan and blue |
| Finish: | Gloss |
| Issued: | 1947 - 1958 |

| Beswick Number | U.K. £ | U.S. $ | Price Can. $ | Aust. $ |
|---|---|---|---|---|
| 1096 | 200. | 350. | 425. | 475. |

**Note:** Dog available separately as No. 1240 see the *Beswick Animals:* A Charlton Standard Catalogue.

**1097**
**FRUIT SELLER (Peddler)**

| | |
|---|---|
| Designer: | Arthur Gredington |
| Height: | 6 ½", 16.5 cm |
| Colour: | Green jacket and hat, yellow waistcoat, pink and white apron, blue trousers, basket of oranges |
| Finish: | Gloss |
| Issued: | 1947 - 1958 |

| Beswick Number | U.K. £ | U.S. $ | Price Can. $ | Aust. $ |
|---|---|---|---|---|
| 1097 | 200. | 350. | 425. | 475. |

## 1122
### BUTCHER BOY

Designer:   Arthur Gredington
Height:     5 ¼", 13.3 cm
Colour:     Yellow shirt, green short trousers, red cap, blue
            and white striped apron
Finish:     Gloss
Issued:     1948 - 1958

| Beswick Number | U.K. £ | U.S. $ | Price Can. $ | Aust. $ |
|---|---|---|---|---|
| 1122 | 200. | 350. | 425. | 475. |

## 1123
### GARDENER

Designer:   Arthur Gredington
Height:     6 ¼", 15.9 cm
Colour:     Yellow pullover and hat, light blue shirt, darker blue trousers
Finish:     Gloss
Issued:     1948 - 1954

| Beswick Number | U.K. £ | U.S. $ | Price Can. $ | Aust. $ |
|---|---|---|---|---|
| 1123 | 200. | 350. | 425. | 475. |

## 1124
### SHEPHERD BOY

Designer:   Arthur Gredington
Height:     6 ¼", 15.9 cm
Colour:     Pale blue jacket, light brown trousers
Finish:     Gloss
Issued:     1948 - 1956

| Beswick Number | U.K. £ | U.S. $ | Price Can. $ | Aust. $ |
|---|---|---|---|---|
| 1124 | 200. | 350. | 425. | 475. |

### 1125
### SCOTSMAN

Designer: Arthur Gredington
Height: 6 ¼", 15.9 cm
Colour: Blue jacket, green kilt
Finish: Gloss
Issued: 1948 - 1954

| Beswick Number | U.K. £ | U.S. $ | Price Can. $ | Aust. $ |
|---|---|---|---|---|
| 1125 | 300. | 550. | 700. | 800. |

### 1221
### HUNGARIAN GIRL WITH TURKEY

Designer: Jan Granoska
Height: 7 ¼", 18.4 cm
Colour: Maroon bodice, green skirt
Finish: Gloss
Issued: 1951 - 1962
Set: 1222, 1227, 1230, 1247

| Beswick Number | U.K. £ | U.S. $ | Price Can. $ | Aust. $ |
|---|---|---|---|---|
| 1221 | 200. | 350. | 425. | 475. |

### 1222
### POLISH GIRL WITH HEN

Designer: Jan Granoska
Height: 7", 17.8 cm
Colour: Green and yellow bodice, light and dark green skirts
Finish: Gloss
Issued: 1951 - 1962
Set: 1221, 1227, 1230, 1247

| Beswick Number | U.K. £ | U.S. $ | Price Can. $ | Aust. $ |
|---|---|---|---|---|
| 1222 | 200. | 350. | 425. | 475. |

**1223**
## SPANIARD PULLING DONKEY

| | |
|---|---|
| Designer: | Jan Granoska |
| Height: | 4 ½", 11.9 cm |
| Colour: | Cream shirt and dark blue trousers |
| Finish: | Gloss |
| Issued: | 1951 - 1962 |

| Beswick Number | U.K. £ | U.S. $ | Price Can. $ | Aust. $ |
|---|---|---|---|---|
| 1223 | 250. | 450. | 550. | 600. |

**Note:** Pair with 1224.

**1224**
## SPANIARD PUSHING DONKEY

| | |
|---|---|
| Designer: | Jan Granoska |
| Height: | 4 ½", 11.9 cm |
| Colour: | Cream shirt and pale brown trousers |
| Finish: | Gloss |
| Issued: | 1951 - 1962 |

| Beswick Number | U.K. £ | U.S. $ | Price Can. $ | Aust. $ |
|---|---|---|---|---|
| 1224 | 250. | 450. | 550. | 600. |

**Note:** Pair with 1223.

**1227**
## SWEDISH GIRL WITH COCKEREL

| | |
|---|---|
| Designer: | Jan Granoska |
| Height: | 7 ", 17.8 cm |
| Colour: | Dark purple, green, red and white |
| Finish: | Gloss |
| Issued: | 1952 - 1962 |
| Set: | 1221, 1222, 1230, 1247 |

| Beswick Number | U.K. £ | U.S. $ | Price Can. $ | Aust. $ |
|---|---|---|---|---|
| 1227 | 200. | 350. | 425. | 475. |

### 1230
### DANISH GIRL WITH PIG

| | |
|---|---|
| Designer: | Jan Granoska |
| Height: | 5 ¾", 14.6 cm |
| Colour: | Dark purple bodice, green skirt and white apron |
| Finish: | Gloss |
| Issued: | 1952 - 1962 |
| Set: | 1221, 1222, 1227, 1247 |

| Beswick Number | U.K. £ | U.S. $ | Price Can. $ | Aust. $ |
|---|---|---|---|---|
| 1230 | 200. | 350. | 425. | 475. |

### 1234
### ITALIAN GIRL LEADING GOAT

| | |
|---|---|
| Designer: | Jan Granoska |
| Height: | 5 ½", 14.0 cm |
| Colour: | White, dark purple, yellow and green |
| Finish: | Gloss |
| Issued: | 1952 - 1962 |

| Beswick Number | U.K. £ | U.S. $ | Price Can. $ | Aust. $ |
|---|---|---|---|---|
| 1234 | 250. | 450. | 550. | 600. |

**Note:** Pair with 1238

### 1238
### ITALIAN GIRL WITH GOAT EATING HAT

| | |
|---|---|
| Designer: | Jan Granoska |
| Height: | 6", 15.0 cm |
| Colour: | Dark purple bodice, decorated skirt and blouse |
| Finish: | Gloss |
| Issued: | 1952 - 1962 |

| Beswick Number | U.K. £ | U.S. $ | Price Can. $ | Aust. $ |
|---|---|---|---|---|
| 1238 | 250. | 450. | 550. | 600. |

**Note:** Pair with 1234

**1244**
### SPANISH GIRL ON DONKEY

| | |
|---|---|
| Designer: | Jan Granoska |
| Height: | 5 ½", 14.0 cm |
| Colour: | Green dress with pink and dark purple |
| Finish: | Gloss |
| Issued: | 1952 - 1962 |

| Beswick Number | U.K. £ | U.S. $ | Price Can. $ | Aust. $ |
|---|---|---|---|---|
| 1244 | 250. | 450. | 550. | 600. |

**Note:** Pair with 1245.

**1245**
### SPANISH CHILDREN ON DONKEY

| | |
|---|---|
| Designer: | Jan Granoska |
| Height: | 4 ½", 11.9 cm |
| Colour: | Yellow dress with dark purple and green |
| Finish: | Gloss |
| Issued: | 1952 - 1962 |

| Beswick Number | U.K. £ | U.S. $ | Price Can. $ | Aust. $ |
|---|---|---|---|---|
| 1245 | 250. | 450. | 550. | 600. |

**Note:** Pair with 1244.

**1247**
### FINNISH GIRL WITH DUCK

| | |
|---|---|
| Designer: | Jan Granoska |
| Height: | 7 ", 17.8 cm |
| Colour: | Two shades of green, white and dark purple |
| Finish: | Gloss |
| Issued: | 1952 - 1962 |
| Set: | 1221, 1222 , 1227, 1230 |

| Beswick Number | U.K. £ | U.S. $ | Price Can. $ | Aust. $ |
|---|---|---|---|---|
| 1247 | 200. | 350. | 425. | 475. |

### 1262
### BALINESE DANCER

| Designer: | Jan Granoska |
|---|---|
| Height: | 3 ½", 8.9 cm |
| Colour: | Unknown |
| Finish: | Gloss |
| Issued: | 1952 - 1962 |
| Set: | 1263, 1320, 1321, 1333, 1334 |

| Beswick Number | U.K. £ | U.S. $ | Price Can. $ | Aust. $ |
|---|---|---|---|---|
| 1262 | 125. | 225. | 275. | 300. |

### 1263
### INDIAN DANCER

| Designer: | Jan Granoska |
|---|---|
| Height: | 3 ½", 8.9 cm |
| Colour: | Pink and green dress, beige trousers |
| Finish: | Gloss |
| Issued: | 1952 - 1962 |
| Set: | 1262, 1320, 1321, 1333, 1334 |

| Beswick Number | U.K. £ | U.S. $ | Price Can. $ | Aust. $ |
|---|---|---|---|---|
| 1263 | 125. | 225. | 275. | 300. |

### 1320
### SIAMESE DANCER

| Designer: | Jan Granoska |
|---|---|
| Height: | 3 ½", 8.9 cm |
| Colour: | Green and pink dress, blue cape |
| Finish: | Gloss |
| Issued: | 1953 - 1962 |
| Set: | 1262, 1263, 1321, 1333, 1334 |

| Beswick Number | U.K. £ | U.S. $ | Price Can. $ | Aust. $ |
|---|---|---|---|---|
| 1320 | 125. | 225. | 275. | 300. |

## 1321
## JAVANESE DANCER

| | |
|---|---|
| Designer: | Jan Granoska |
| Height: | 3 ½", 8.9 cm |
| Colour: | Pink skirt, green bodice, dark blue trim |
| Finish: | Gloss |
| Issued: | 1953 - 1962 |
| Set: | 1262, 1263, 1320, 1333, 1334 |

| Beswick Number | U.K. £ | U.S. $ | Price Can. $ | Aust. $ |
|---|---|---|---|---|
| 1321 | 125. | 225. | 275. | 300. |

## 1333
## CHINESE DANCER

| | |
|---|---|
| Designer: | Jan Granoska and J. Haywood |
| Height: | 3 ½", 8.9 cm |
| Colour: | Dark blue and beige |
| Finish: | Gloss |
| Issued: | 1953 - 1962 |
| Set: | 1262, 1263, 1320, 1321, 1334 |

| Beswick Number | U.K. £ | U.S. $ | Price Can. $ | Aust. $ |
|---|---|---|---|---|
| 1333 | 125. | 225. | 275. | 300. |

## 1334
## HAWAIIAN DANCER

| | |
|---|---|
| Designer: | Jan Granoska |
| Height: | Unknown |
| Colour: | Unknown |
| Finish: | Gloss |
| Issued: | 1954 |
| Set: | 1262, 1263, 1320, 1321, 1333 |

| Beswick Number | U.K. £ | U.S. $ | Price Can. $ | Aust. $ |
|---|---|---|---|---|
| 1334 | Possibly not put into production | | | |

### 1347
### SUSIE JAMAICA

| | |
|---|---|
| Designer: | Mr. Orwell |
| Height: | 7", 17.8 cm |
| Colour: | Yellow blouse and skirt with red trim |
| Finish: | Gloss |
| Issued: | 1954 - 1975 |

| Beswick Number | U.K. £ | U.S. $ | Price Can. $ | Aust. $ |
|---|---|---|---|---|
| 1347 | 150. | 275. | 350. | 375. |

### 1737
### COUPLE SITTING

| | |
|---|---|
| Designer: | Mr. Brumbie |
| Height: | 8 ½", 21.6 cm |
| Colour: | White and brown |
| Finish: | Gloss |
| Issued: | 1961 - 1963 |

| Beswick Number | U.K. £ | U.S. $ | Price Can. $ | Aust. $ |
|---|---|---|---|---|
| 1737 | 250. | 450. | 550. | 600. |

### 1878
### WELSH LADY

| | |
|---|---|
| Designer: | Albert Hallam |
| Height: | 5", 12.7 cm |
| Colour: | 1. Black and red shawl |
| | 2 Black and white shawl |
| Finish: | Gloss |
| Issued: | 1963 - 1969 |

| Beswick Number | U.K. £ | U.S. $ | Price Can. $ | Aust. $ |
|---|---|---|---|---|
| 1878 | 75. | 125. | 160. | 170. |

**1993**
**LADY WITH FAN**

| Designer: | Unknown |
|---|---|
| Height: | 7 ½", 19.1 cm |
| Colour: | Unknown |
| Finish: | Gloss |
| Issued: | 1964 - 1965 |

| Beswick Number | U.K. £ | U.S. $ | Price Can. $ | Aust. $ |
|---|---|---|---|---|
| 1993 | | | Rare | |

**1994**
**LADY WITH HAT**

| Designer: | Unknown |
|---|---|
| Height: | 7 ½", 19.1 cm |
| Colour: | Unknown |
| Finish: | Gloss |
| Issued: | 1964 - 1965 |

| Beswick Number | U.K. £ | U.S. $ | Price Can. $ | Aust. $ |
|---|---|---|---|---|
| 1994 | | | Rare | |

**1995**
**LADY IN BALL GOWN**

| Designer: | Unknown |
|---|---|
| Height: | 7", 17.8 cm |
| Colour: | Blue and white |
| Finish: | Gloss |
| Issued: | 1964 - 1965 |

| Beswick Number | U.K. £ | U.S. $ | Price Can. $ | Aust. $ |
|---|---|---|---|---|
| 1995 | 200. | 350. | 425. | 475. |

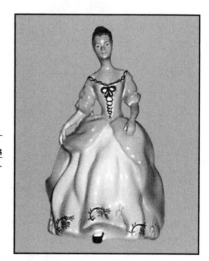

**2181**
**KNIGHT OF ST. JOHN**

Designer:     Albert Hallam
Height:       6 ¾", 17.2 cm
Colour:       Black and grey
Finish:       Gloss
Issued:       1968 in a limited edition of 500

| Beswick Number | U.K. £ | U.S. $ | Price Can. $ | Aust. $ |
|---|---|---|---|---|
| 2181 | 200. | 350. | 425. | 475. |

**Note:** Issued to commemorate Golden Jubilee year of the Priory for Wales.

# FIGURES
## Kindergarten Series

Shepherd's Boy

Stormy Weather

Farm Boy

Book Worm

Globe Trotter

Max & Moritz

Goose Girl

# FIGURES

Spanish Girl with Cockerel

Finnish Girl with Duck

Polish Girl with Hen

Hungarian Girl with Turkey

Danish Girl with Pig

# FIGURES

Italian Girl Leading Goat

Spanish Children on Donkey

Spanish Girl on Donkey

Italian Girl With Goat Eating Hat

# FIGURES

Siamese Dancer

Girl in Breeze

Indian Dancer

Chinese Dancer

Girl with Flared Dress

Javanese Dancer

Girl with Pot of Honey
(Green coat)

Girl with Pot of Honey
(Pink spotted coat)

# FIGURES

Shepherd Boy

Butcher Boy

Scotsman

Gardener

Boy Hiker

Fruit Seller (Peddler)

# DICKENS WARE

Peggoty — Teapot

Sairey Gamp — Teapot

Micawber — Cream

Micawber — Salt

Sairey Gamp — Pepper

Pecksniff — Sugar

# DICKENS WARE
## Character Jugs

Tony Weller

Sairey Gamp

Scrooge

Captain Cuttle

Barnaby Rudge

Martin Chuzzlewit

Little Nell's Grandfather

Betsy Trotwood

Mr. Bumble the Beadle

# CHARACTER AND TOBY JUGS

Toby Philpot

P. G. W. Colonel

Midshipman Toby

Falstaff

Henry VIII

# SECTION SIX

## DICKENS WARE

Micawber, Character Jug; Model No. 310

Style One, Variation Three                    Style Two

**274**
**TONY WELLER – WALL PLAQUE**

Designer:      Mr. Watkin
Height:        7 ½", 19.1 cm
Colour:        1.  Yellow-green jacket, orange cravat, orange
                   and cream hat with black band
               2.  Green-blue jacket
               3.  Dark green jacket
Finish:        Gloss
Issued:        1935 - 1943

| Beswick Number | U.K. £ | U.S. $ | Price Can. $ | Aust. $ |
|---|---|---|---|---|
| 274 | 75. | 125. | 150. | 175. |

**280**
**MR. MICAWBER – WALL PLAQUE**

Designer:      Mr. Watkin
Height:        9", 22.9 cm
Colour:        White shirt with high collar, black cravat and hat
Finish:        Gloss
Issued:        1935 - 1943

| Beswick Number | U.K. £ | U.S. $ | Price Can. $ | Aust. $ |
|---|---|---|---|---|
| 280 | 75. | 125. | 150. | 175. |

**281**
**TONY WELLER – CHARACTER JUG**
**Style One, Variation One**

   Whip touches ear; closed mouth smile; note position of band on the whip
handle.

Designer:      Mr. Watkin
Height:        7", 17.8 cm
Colour:        Black coat, white shirt with high collar, yellow cravat with
               horseshoe pin, yellow hat with black band
Handle:        Whip
Finish:        Gloss
Issued:        1935 - 1943

| Beswick Number | U.K. £ | U.S. $ | Price Can. $ | Aust. $ |
|---|---|---|---|---|
| 281 | 50. | 90. | 115. | 125. |

**281**
**TONY WELLER – CHARACTER JUG**
**Style One, Variation Two**

Whip touches ear; closed mouth smile; note position of band on the whip handle.

| | |
|---|---|
| Designer: | Mr. Watkin |
| Height: | 7", 17.8 cm |
| Colour: | Blue coat with light green collar, white shirt with high collar, brown cravat with gold horsehoe pin, beige hat with dark blue band |
| Handle: | Whip |
| Finish: | Matt |
| Issued: | Unknown |

| Beswick Number | U.K. £ | U.S. $ | Price Can. $ | Aust. $ |
|---|---|---|---|---|
| 281 | 50. | 90. | 115. | 125. |

**281**
**TONY WELLER – CHARACTER JUG**
**Style One, Variation Three**

Whip touches ear; smile showing teeth; note position of band on whip handle.

| | |
|---|---|
| Designer: | Mr. Watkin |
| Height: | 7", 17.8 cm |
| Colour: | Tan coat, white shirt with high collar, green and yellow cravat with horseshoe pin, green hat |
| Handle: | Whip |
| Finish: | Gloss |
| Issued: | 1945 - 1970 |

| Beswick Number | U.K. £ | U.S. $ | Price Can. $ | Aust. $ |
|---|---|---|---|---|
| 281 | 50. | 90. | 115. | 125. |

**281**
**TONY WELLER – CHARACTER JUG**
**Style Two**

Whip touches hat; closed mouth smile; note curly wisp of hair.

| | |
|---|---|
| Designer: | Mr. Watkin |
| Remodelled: | Mr. Tongue |
| Height: | 7", 17.8 cm |
| Colour: | Red-brown coat, green patterned cravat, green hat |
| Handle: | Whip |
| Finish: | Gloss |
| Issued: | 1970 - 1973 |

| Beswick Number | U.K. £ | U.S. $ | Price Can. $ | Aust. $ |
|---|---|---|---|---|
| 281 | 50. | 90. | 115. | 125. |

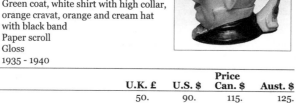

### 310
### MICAWBER – CHARACTER JUG
**Style One, Variation One**

| | |
|---|---|
| Designer: | Mr. Watkin |
| Height: | 9", 22.9 cm |
| Colour: | Green coat, white shirt with high collar, orange cravat, orange and cream hat with black band |
| Handle: | Paper scroll |
| Finish: | Gloss |
| Issued: | 1935 - 1940 |

| Beswick Number | U.K. £ | U.S. $ | Price Can. $ | Aust. $ |
|---|---|---|---|---|
| 310 | 50. | 90. | 115. | 125. |

### 310
### MICAWBER – CHARACTER JUG
**Style One, Variation Two**

| | |
|---|---|
| Designer: | Mr. Watkin |
| Height: | 9", 22.9 cm |
| Colour: | Black coat and hat, white shirt with high collar, white cravat |
| Handle: | Paper scroll reading "Title Deeds" |
| Finish: | Gloss |
| Issued: | 1940 - 1943 |

| Beswick Number | U.K. £ | U.S. $ | Price Can. $ | Aust. $ |
|---|---|---|---|---|
| 310 | 50. | 90. | 115. | 125. |

### 310
### MICAWBER – CHARACTER JUG
**Style One, Variation Three**

| | |
|---|---|
| Designer: | Mr. Watkin |
| Height: | 9", 22.9 cm |
| Colour: | Green coat and hat, white shirt with high collar, red cravat with white spots |
| Handle: | Paper scroll reads "Title Deeds" |
| Finish: | Gloss |
| Issued: | 1943 - 1970 |

| Beswick Number | U.K. £ | U.S. $ | Price Can. $ | Aust. $ |
|---|---|---|---|---|
| 310 | 50. | 90. | 115. | 125. |

### 310
### MICAWBER – CHARACTER JUG
### Style Two (Eyes looking to the right)

| | |
|---|---|
| Designer: | Mr. Watkin |
| Remodelled: | Graham Tongue |
| Height: | 9", 22.9 cm |
| Colour: | Dark maroon coat, dark green hat, white shirt with high collar, maroon cravat |
| Handle: | Paper scroll reading "Title Deeds" |
| Finish: | Gloss |
| Issued: | 1970 - 1973 |

| Beswick Number | U.K. £ | U.S. $ | Price Can. $ | Aust. $ |
|---|---|---|---|---|
| 310 | 50. | 90. | 115. | 125. |

### 371
### SAIREY GAMP – CHARACTER JUG

| | |
|---|---|
| Designer: | Mr. Watkin |
| Height: | 6 ¾", 17.2 cm |
| Colour: | Maroon coat, green hat with cream polka dots, maroon umbrella with brown handle |
| Handle: | Umbrella |
| Finish: | Gloss |
| Issued: | 1936 - 1973 |

| Beswick Number | U.K. £ | U.S. $ | Price Can. $ | Aust. $ |
|---|---|---|---|---|
| 371 | 40. | 70. | 85. | 95. |

### 372
### SCROOGE – CHARACTER JUG

| | |
|---|---|
| Designer: | Mr. Watkin |
| Height: | 7", 17.8 cm |
| Colour: | Maroon coat and scarf, white shirt with high collar, green hat with white dots |
| Handle: | Part of the hat with tassle |
| Finish: | Gloss |
| Issued: | 1936 - 1973 |

| Beswick Number | U.K. £ | U.S. $ | Price Can. $ | Aust. $ |
|---|---|---|---|---|
| 372 | 40. | 70. | 85. | 95. |

**673**
**TONY WELLER - SUGAR**

| | |
|---|---|
| Designer: | Mr. Watkin |
| Height: | 2 ¾", 7.0 cm |
| Colour: | Green hat, brown coat, green and cream scarf |
| Finish: | Gloss |
| Issued: | 1939 - 1967 |

| Beswick Number | U.K. £ | U.S. $ | Price Can. $ | Aust. $ |
|---|---|---|---|---|
| 673 | 15. | 25. | 30. | 35. |

**674**
**MICAWBER - CREAM**

| | |
|---|---|
| Designer: | Mr. Watkin |
| Height: | 3 ¼", 8.3 cm |
| Colour: | 1. Brown coat, green hat |
| | 2. Dark brown coat, grey hat |
| Handle: | 1. Walking cane with yellow handle |
| | 2. Walking cane with orange handle |
| Finish: | Gloss |
| Issued: | 1939 - 1973 |

| Beswick Number | U.K. £ | U.S. $ | Price Can. $ | Aust. $ |
|---|---|---|---|---|
| 674 | 15. | 25. | 30. | 35. |

**689**
**SAIREY GAMP - PEPPER**

| | |
|---|---|
| Designer: | Mr. Watkin |
| Height: | 2 ½", 6.4 cm |
| Colour: | Brown coat, green bonnet, green and pink scarf |
| Finish: | Gloss |
| Issued: | 1939 - 1967 |

| Beswick Number | U.K. £ | U.S. $ | Price Can. $ | Aust. $ |
|---|---|---|---|---|
| 689 | 15. | 25. | 30. | 35. |

**Note:** Sold as a pair with Micawber salt.

**690**
**MICAWBER - SALT**

| | |
|---|---|
| Designer: | Mr. Watkin |
| Height: | 3 ½", 8.9 cm |
| Colour: | Brown coat, green hat |
| Finish: | Gloss |
| Issued: | 1939 - 1967 |

| Beswick Number | U.K. £ | U.S. $ | Price Can. $ | Aust. $ |
|---|---|---|---|---|
| 690 | 15. | 25. | 30. | 35. |

**Note:** Sold as a pair with Sairey Gamp pepper.

**691**
**SAIREY GAMP - TEAPOT**

| | |
|---|---|
| Designer: | Mr. Watkin |
| Height: | 5 ½", 14.0 cm |
| Colour: | Brown coat, green bonnet, green scarf with white spots |
| Handle: | Umbrella |
| Finish: | Gloss |
| Issued: | 1939 - 1973 |

| Beswick Number | U.K. £ | U.S. $ | Price Can. $ | Aust. $ |
|---|---|---|---|---|
| 691 | 25. | 50. | 65. | 70. |

**1116**
**PEGGOTY - TEAPOT**

| | |
|---|---|
| Designer: | Arthur Gredington |
| Height: | 6", 15.0 cm |
| Colour: | Black coat and hat, light blue cravat, grey spout |
| Handle: | Rope |
| Finish: | Gloss |
| Issued: | 1948 - 1973 |

| Beswick Number | U.K. £ | U.S. $ | Price Can. $ | Aust. $ |
|---|---|---|---|---|
| 1116 | 75. | 125. | 150. | 170. |

**1117**
**PECKSNIFF - CREAM**

| | |
|---|---|
| Designer: | Arthur Gredington |
| Height: | 3 ½", 8.9 cm |
| Colour: | Reddish-brown coat with black trim; light blue shirt; light brown handle |
| Handle: | Plain |
| Finish: | Gloss |
| Issued: | 1948 - 1973 |

| Beswick Number | U.K. £ | U.S. $ | Price Can. $ | Aust. $ |
|---|---|---|---|---|
| 1117 | 20. | 35. | 45. | 50. |

**Note:** Pair with Model No. 1129.

**1118**
**PICKWICK – SUGAR**

| | |
|---|---|
| Designer: | Arthur Gredington |
| Height: | 3", 7.6 cm |
| Colour: | Grey hat, reddish-brown coat, green shirt, blue bow-tie, yellow glasses |
| Finish: | Gloss |
| Issued: | 1948 - 1973 |

| Beswick Number | U.K. £ | U.S. $ | Price Can. $ | Aust. $ |
|---|---|---|---|---|
| 1118 | 15. | 25. | 30. | 35. |

**Note:** Available with or without a cover. Pair with Model No. 1119.

**1119**
**PICKWICK – CREAM**

| | |
|---|---|
| Designer: | Arthur Gredington |
| Height: | 3 ¼", 8.3 cm |
| Colour: | Grey hat, reddish-brown coat, green shirt, blue bow-tie, yellow glasses |
| Handle: | Cane |
| Finish: | Gloss |
| Issued: | 1948 - 1973 |

| Beswick Number | U.K. £ | U.S. $ | Price Can. $ | Aust. $ |
|---|---|---|---|---|
| 1119 | 15. | 25. | 30. | 35. |

**Note:** Pair with Model No. 1118.

### 1120
### CAPTAIN CUTTLE – CHARACTER JUG

| | |
|---|---|
| Designer: | Arthur Gredington |
| Height: | 4 ½", 11.9 cm |
| Colour: | Black coat and hat, light blue cravat, white shirt with high collar |
| Handle: | Hook |
| Finish: | Gloss |
| Issued: | 1948 - 1973 |

| Beswick Number | U.K. £ | U.S. $ | Price Can. $ | Aust. $ |
|---|---|---|---|---|
| 1120 | 25. | 50. | 65. | 70. |

### 1121
### BARNABY RUDGE – CHARACTER JUG

| | |
|---|---|
| Designer: | Arthur Gredington |
| Height: | 4 ½", 11.9 cm |
| Colour: | Reddish-brown coat, blue shirt, grey hat |
| Handle: | Black bird with yellow beak |
| Finish: | Gloss |
| Issued: | 1948 - 1970 |

| Beswick Number | U.K. £ | U.S. $ | Price Can. $ | Aust. $ |
|---|---|---|---|---|
| 1121 | 35. | 60. | 75. | 80. |

### 1129
### PECKSNIFF - SUGAR

| | |
|---|---|
| Designer: | Arthur Gredington |
| Height: | 3 ½", 8.9 cm |
| Colour: | Brown coat, white shirt with high collar, blue cravat |
| Finish: | Gloss |
| Issued: | 1948 - 1967 |

| Beswick Number | U.K. £ | U.S. $ | Price Can. $ | Aust. $ |
|---|---|---|---|---|
| 1129 | 15. | 25. | 30. | 35. |

**Note:** Pair with Model No. 1117.

**1203**
**DOLLY VARDEN - TEAPOT**

| | |
|---|---|
| Designer: | Arthur Gredington |
| Height: | 6 ¼", 15.9 cm |
| Colour: | Yellow hat, blue bow with dark blue polka dots |
| Handle: | Feather |
| Finish: | Gloss |
| Issued: | 1950 - 1973 |

| Beswick Number | U.K. £ | U.S. $ | Price Can. $ | Aust. $ |
|---|---|---|---|---|
| 1203 | 35. | 60. | 75. | 80. |

**1204**
**MR. VARDEN - CREAM**

| | |
|---|---|
| Designer: | Arthur Gredington |
| Height: | 3 ¼", 8.3 cm |
| Colour: | Purple coat, green hat, yellow cravat |
| Handle: | Yellow key |
| Finish: | Gloss |
| Issued: | 1950 - 1973 |

| Beswick Number | U.K. £ | U.S. $ | Price Can. $ | Aust. $ |
|---|---|---|---|---|
| 1204 | 15. | 25. | 30. | 35. |

**Note:** Pair with Model No. 1205.

**1205**
**MRS. VARDEN – SUGAR**

| | |
|---|---|
| Designer: | Arthur Gredington |
| Height: | 3", 7.6 cm |
| Colour: | Green coat, blue bow, pink and blue hat |
| Finish: | Gloss |
| Issued: | 1950 - 1967 |

| Beswick Number | U.K. £ | U.S. $ | Price Can. $ | Aust. $ |
|---|---|---|---|---|
| 1205 | 15. | 25. | 30. | 35. |

**Note:** Pair with Model No. 1204.

**1206**
**SAIREY GAMP – PRESERVE WITH LID**

Designer:   Arthur Gredington
Height:     3", 7.6 cm
Colour:     1. Green hat, brown coat, bow with green and yellow spots
            2. Red hat, black coat, bow with red and yellow spots
Finish:     Gloss
Issued:     1950 - 1967

| Beswick Number | U.K. £ | U.S. $ | Price Can. $ | Aust. $ |
|---|---|---|---|---|
| 1206 | 15. | 25. | 30. | 35. |

**1207**
**TONY WELLER – PRESERVE WITH LID**

Designer:   Arthur Gredington
Height:     3 ½", 8.9 cm
Colour:     Brown coat, green hat, green and cream scarf
Finish:     Gloss
Issued:     1950 - 1967

| Beswick Number | U.K. £ | U.S. $ | Price Can. $ | Aust. $ |
|---|---|---|---|---|
| 1207 | 15. | 25. | 30. | 35. |

**1369**
**SAM WELLER - TEAPOT**

Designer:   Arthur Gredington
Height:     6 ¼", 15.9 cm
Colour:     Light brown coat, brown hat, light orange cravat
Handle:     Umbrella
Finish:     Gloss
Issued:     1955 - 1973

| Beswick Number | U.K. £ | U.S. $ | Price Can. $ | Aust. $ |
|---|---|---|---|---|
| 1369 | 40. | 70. | 90. | 95. |

## 2030
## MARTIN CHUZZLEWIT – CHARACTER JUG

| Designer: | Albert Hallam |
| Height: | 4 ¾", 12.1 cm |
| Colour: | Green coat, white shirt, brown hat |
| Handle: | "Last will and testimony Martin Chuzzlewit" |
| Finish: | Gloss |
| Issued: | 1965 - 1973 |

| Beswick Number | U.K. £ | U.S. $ | Price Can. $ | Aust. $ |
|---|---|---|---|---|
| 2030 | 20. | 35. | 45. | 50. |

## 2031
## LITTLE NELL'S GRANDFATHER – CHARACTER JUG

| Designer: | Albert Hallam |
| Height: | 5 ½", 14.0 cm |
| Colour: | Grey-green coat and hat, red shirt |
| Handle: | Candle snuffer |
| Finish: | Gloss |
| Issued: | 1965 - 1973 |

| Beswick Number | U.K. £ | U.S. $ | Price Can. $ | Aust. $ |
|---|---|---|---|---|
| 2031 | 20. | 35. | 45. | 50. |

## 2032
## MR. BUMBLE THE BEADLE – CHARACTER JUG

| Designer: | Albert Hallam |
| Height: | 5", 12.7 cm |
| Colour: | Black with yellow trim hat, light green cravat |
| Handle: | Walking cane |
| Finish: | Gloss |
| Issued: | 1965 - 1973 |

| Beswick Number | U.K. £ | U.S. $ | Price Can. $ | Aust. $ |
|---|---|---|---|---|
| 2032 | 20. | 35. | 45. | 50. |

**2075**
**BETSY TROTWOOD – CHARACTER JUG**

| | |
|---|---|
| Designer: | Albert Hallam |
| Height: | 5", 12.7 cm |
| Colour: | Dark green and mauve dress, light blue and pink mobcap, yellow wool, light brown needles |
| Handle: | Knitting needles and wool |
| Finish: | Gloss |
| Issued: | 1966 - 1973 |

| Beswick Number | U.K. £ | U.S. $ | Price Can. $ | Aust. $ |
|---|---|---|---|---|
| 2075 | 30. | 55. | 65. | 75. |

# SECTION SEVEN

## CHARACTER AND TOBY JUGS

Falstaff, Model No. 2095

**931**
**WINSTON CHURCHILL**

| | |
|---|---|
| Designer: | Mr. Watkin |
| Height: | 7", 17.8 cm |
| Colour: | Navy jacket and trousers, blue bow tie, Union Jack |
| Handle: | Yellow lion |
| Finish: | Gloss |
| Issued: | 1941 - 1954 |

| Beswick Number | U.K. £ | U.S. $ | Price Can. $ | Aust. $ |
|---|---|---|---|---|
| 931 | 250. | 450. | 575. | 600. |

**Note:** The inscription reads "We shall fight them on the beaches, the landing grounds in the fields, in the streets, and on the hills, we shall never surrender" Churchill 1940. This model has been seen with a non-original lid – see photo.

**1110**
**TOBY PHILLPOT**
**Style One — Holding Jug**

| | |
|---|---|
| Designer: | Arthur Gredington |
| Height: | 8", 20.3 cm |
| Colour: | Green and maroon coat, brown hat, trousers and jug, blue cravat and socks |
| Handle: | Plain |
| Finish: | Gloss |
| Issued: | 1948 -by 1973 |

| Beswick Number | U.K. £ | U.S. $ | Price Can. $ | Aust. $ |
|---|---|---|---|---|
| 1110 | 60. | 110. | 135. | 150. |

**1111**
**TOBY PHILLPOT**
**Style Two — Holding Glass and Jug**

| | |
|---|---|
| Designer: | Arthur Gredington |
| Height: | 6 ½", 16.5 cm |
| Colour: | 1. Maroon and yellow coat, purple trousers and hat, green waistcoat, blue cravat and socks |
| | 2. Maroon coat, yellow trousers and cravat, pale green waistcoat, black hat, blue socks |
| Handle: | Plain |
| Finish: | Gloss |
| Issued: | 1948 -by 1973 |

| Beswick Number | U.K. £ | U.S. $ | Price Can. $ | Aust. $ |
|---|---|---|---|---|
| 1111 | 60. | 110. | 135. | 150. |

**1112**
**MIDSHIPMAN TOBY**

| | |
|---|---|
| Designer: | Arthur Gredington |
| Height: | 1. Medium 5 ¼", 13.3 cm |
| | 2. Small 3 ½", 8.9 cm |
| Colour: | Purple coat, blue shirt and socks, green and yellow waistcoat, red trousers and dark blue hat |
| Handle: | Plain |
| Finish: | Gloss |
| Issued: | 1. Medium 1948 - 1973 |
| | 2. Small 1948 - 1966 |

| Beswick Number | Description | U.K. £ | U.S. $ | Price Can. $ | Aust. $ |
|---|---|---|---|---|---|
| 1112 | Medium | 125. | 225. | 275. | 300. |
| — | Small | 100. | 175. | 225. | 250. |

**1113**
**MARTHA GUNN**

| | |
|---|---|
| Designer: | Arthur Gredington |
| Height: | 3 ½", 8.9 cm |
| Colour: | 1. Lilac and turquoise dress, red and yellow hat, red shoes, yellow base |
| | 2. Purple and green dress, red and yellow hat, green shoes, beige base |
| Handle: | Plain |
| Finish: | Gloss |
| Issued: | 1948 - 1962 |

| Beswick Number | U.K. £ | U.S. $ | Price Can. $ | Aust. $ |
|---|---|---|---|---|
| 1113 | 100. | 175. | 220. | 240. |

**1114**
**TOBY PHILLPOT**
**Style Three**

| | |
|---|---|
| Designer: | Arthur Gredington |
| Height: | 3 ½", 8.9 cm |
| Colour: | Maroon coat with brown cuffs, yellow trousers and hat, light blue cravat and socks, white waistcoat |
| Finish: | Gloss |
| Issued: | 1948 - 1962 |

| Beswick Number | U.K. £ | U.S. $ | Price Can. $ | Aust. $ |
|---|---|---|---|---|
| 1114 | 40. | 70. | 90. | 95. |

**2092**
**P. G. W. COLONEL**

| | |
|---|---|
| Designer: | Graham Tongue |
| Height: | 5", 12.7 cm |
| Colour: | Black, white and red |
| Handle: | Plain "Peters Griffen Woodward Inc" |
| Finish: | Gloss |
| Issued: | 1967 - 1967 |

| Beswick Number | U.K. £ | U.S. $ | Price Can. $ | Aust. $ |
|---|---|---|---|---|
| 2092 | 25. | 45. | 55. | 60. |

**Note:** This jug was produced by Beswick for the 35th anniversary of Peters, Griffin, Woodward, Inc. (U.S.A. Department Store).

**2095**
**FALSTAFF**

| | |
|---|---|
| Designer: | Albert Hallam |
| Height: | 6 ¾", 15.9 cm |
| Colour: | Green coat with gold trim, red hat |
| Handle: | Feather from hat |
| Finish: | Gloss |
| Issued: | 1967 - 1963 |

| Beswick Number | U.K. £ | U.S. $ | Price Can. $ | Aust. $ |
|---|---|---|---|---|
| 2095 | 30. | 55. | 70. | 75. |

**2099**
**HENRY VIII**

| | |
|---|---|
| Designer: | Albert Hallam |
| Height: | 7", 17.8 cm |
| Colour: | Brown coat, black hat with white feather, light brown shirt |
| Handle: | Garter |
| Finish: | Gloss |
| Issued: | 1967 - 1973 |

| Beswick Number | U.K. £ | U.S. $ | Price Can. $ | Aust. $ |
|---|---|---|---|---|
| 2099 | 35. | 65. | 80. | 90. |

Midshipman Toby, Model No. 1112

# INDICES

# Alphabetical Index

# Model Number Index

| | | |
|---|---|---|
| 1207 | Tony Weller - Preserve with Lid | 284 |
| 1221 | Hungarian Girl With Turkey | 264 |
| 1222 | Polish Girl With Hen | 264 |
| 1223 | Spaniard Pulling Donkey | 265 |
| 1224 | Spaniard Pushing Donkey | 265 |
| 1227 | Swedish Girl with Cockerel | 265 |
| 1230 | Danish Girl With Pig | 266 |
| 1234 | Italian Girl Leading Goat | 266 |
| 1238 | Italian Girl With Goat Eating Hat | 266 |
| 1244 | Spanish Girl on Donkey | 267 |
| 1245 | Spanish Children on Donkey | 267 |
| 1247 | Finnish Girl With Duck | 267 |
| 1255 | Monkey with Drum | 234 |
| 1256 | Monkey with Tuba | 234 |
| 1257 | Monkey with Fiddle | 234 |
| 1258 | Monkey with Saxophone | 235 |
| 1259 | Monkey with Guitar | 235 |
| 1260 | Monkey with Banjo | 235 |
| 1262 | Balinese Dancer | 268 |
| 1263 | Indian Dancer | 268 |
| 1274 | Flopsy, Mopsy and Cottontail, Style One | 59 |
| 1275 | Miss Moppet | 71 |
| 1276 | Johnny Town-Mouse | 68 |
| 1277 | Foxy Whiskered Gentleman, Small Size | 60 |
| 1278 | Mickey Mouse | 137 |
| 1279 | Jiminy Cricket | 137 |
| 1280 | Pluto | 138 |
| 1281 | Goofy | 138 |
| 1282 | Pinocchio | 138 |
| 1283 | Donald Duck | 139 |
| 1289 | Minnie Mouse | 139 |
| 1291 | Thumper | 139 |
| 1301 | Nana | 125 |
| 1302 | Smee | 125 |
| 1307 | Peter Pan | 126 |
| 1312 | Tinker Bell | 126 |
| 1320 | Siamese Dancer | 268 |
| 1321 | Javanese Dancer | 269 |
| 1325 | Dopey | 140 |
| 1326 | Happy | 140 |
| 1327 | Bashful | 141 |
| 1328 | Sneezy | 141 |
| 1329 | Doc | 141 |
| 1330 | Grumpy | 142 |
| 1331 | Sleepy | 142 |
| 1332 | Snow White | 142 |
| 1333 | Chinese Dancer | 269 |
| 1334 | Hawaiian Dancer | 269 |
| 1335 | Tortoise Mother with Hat | 248 |
| 1336 | Tortoise Girl with Bonnet | 248 |
| 1337 | Tortoise Boy with Cap | 248 |
| 1347 | Susie Jamaica | 270 |
| 1348 | Tommy Brock | 105 |
| 1355 | Duchess, Style One (Holding Flowers) | 56 |
| 1365 | Pigling Bland | 91 |
| 1369 | Sam Weller - Teapot | 284 |
| 1379 | Bush Baby - With Mirror | 203 |
| 1380 | Bush Baby - With Candlestick | 203 |
| 1381 | Bush Baby - With Book | 203 |
| 1531 | Tree Lamp Base | 119 |
| 1545 | The Old Woman Who Lived in a Shoe | 100 |
| 1626 | Toy Drummer | 200 |
| 1627 | Toy Buglers | 200 |
| 1628 | Toy Guards | 200 |
| 1675 | Goody Tiptoes | 62 |
| 1676 | Tabitha Twitchit | 97 |
| 1737 | Couple Sitting | 270 |
| 1738 | Pup With Bone | 218 |
| 1766 | Foreman | 242 |
| 1767 | Digger | 242 |
| 1768 | Driller | 243 |
| 1769 | At Ease | 243 |
| 1796 | Old Mr. Brown | 84 |
| 1801 | Pianist | 173 |
| 1802 | Piano | 173 |
| 1803 | Cat - Singing | 174 |
| 1804 | Boy Without Spectacles | 174 |
| 1805 | Boy With Spectacles | 174 |
| 1824 | Dog - Singing | 175 |
| 1825 | Boy With Guitar | 175 |
| 1826 | Girl With Harp | 175 |
| 1851 | Anna Maria | 50 |
| 1878 | Welsh Lady | 270 |
| 1940 | Mr. Benjamin Bunny | 73 |
| 1941 | Cecily Parsley | 54 |
| 1942 | Mrs. Flopsy Bunny | 77 |
| 1993 | Lady With Fan | 271 |
| 1994 | Lady With Hat | 271 |
| 1995 | Lady In Ball Gown | 271 |
| 2030 | Martin Chuzzlewit - Character Jug | 285 |
| 2031 | Little Nell's Grandfather - Character Jug | 285 |
| 2032 | Mr. Bumble the Beadle - Character Jug | 285 |
| 2061 | Amiable Guinea-Pig, Style One | 49 |
| 2075 | Betsy Trotwood - Character Jug | 286 |
| 2082 | Jemima Puddle-Duck Plaque | 116 |
| 2083 | Peter Rabbit Plaque, First Version | 117 |
| 2085 | Tom Kitten Plaque | 118 |
| 2092 | P. G. W. Colonel | 292 |
| 2095 | Falstaff | 292 |
| 2099 | Henry VIII | 291 |
| 2181 | Knight of St. John | 272 |
| 2193 | Winnie the Pooh | 132 |
| 2196 | Eeyore | 132 |
| 2214 | Piglet | 133 |
| 2215 | Rabbit | 133 |
| 2216 | Owl | 133 |
| 2217 | Kanga | 134 |
| 2272 | Anglund Boy | 123 |
| 2276 | Aunt Pettitoes | 51 |
| 2284 | Cousin Ribby | 56 |
| 2293 | Anglund Girl With Doll | 123 |
| 2295 | Display Stand | 119 |
| 2317 | Anglund Girl With Flowers | 123 |
| 2333 | Appley Dapply | 50 |
| 2334 | Pickles | 91 |
| 2381 | Pig-Wig | 92 |
| 2394 | Tigger | 134 |
| 2395 | Christopher Robin | 134 |
| 2424 | Mr. Alderman Ptolemy | 72 |
| 2425 | Sir Isaac Newton | 95 |
| 2452 | Sally Henny Penny | 94 |
| 2453 | Mr. Jackson | 74 |
| 2476 | Alice, Style One | 3 |
| 2477 | White Rabbit | 3 |

# Royal Doulton Stores

## DOULTON AND COMPANY STORES - UK

*Doulton and Company is the new name for Royal Doulton on high street, offering the very best of our three brands plus selected collectables and giftware and homewares from a range of specialist brands.*

**Doulton and Company Dudley**
Unit 52, Merry Hill,
Brierley Hill, Dudley
West Midlands
DY5 1SR

**Doulton and Company Outlet
Superstore Etruria**
Forge Lane, Etrura, Stoke-on-Trent
Staffordshire
ST1 5NN

**Doulton and Company Hanley**
The Potteries Centre
Hanley, Stoke-on-Trent
Staffordshire
ST1 1PS

**Doulton and Company Hereford**
19-21 Maylords Street,
Maylord Shopping Centre
Hereford, Herefordshire
HR1 2DS

**Doulton and Company HOME**
Central 12 Shopping Park
Southport
PR9 0TQ

**Doulton and Company Swindon**
McArthur Glen Designer Outlet
Great Western, Kemble Drive
Swindon, Wilts
SN2 2DY

## LAWLEYS/CHINACAVES - UK

**Lawleys Blackpool**
Unit 37, Houndshill Shopping Centre,
Fylde, Blackpool
Lancashire
FY1 4HU

**Lawleys Carisle**
63 Castle Street
Carlisle, Cumbria
CA3 8SL

**Lawleys Chelmsford**
42 High Chelmer
Chelmsford, Essex
CM1 1XU

**Lawleys Derby
Edwards**
71 St. Peters Street
Derby, Derbyshire
DE1 2AB

**Lawleys Peterborough**
7 Bridge Street
Peterborough, Cambridgeshire
PE1 1HJ

**Lawleys Reading**
21 Queen Victoria Street
Reading, Berkshire
RG1 1SY

**Lawleys Torquay**
38 Fleet Street
Torquay, Devon
TQ2 5DJ

**Chinacave Llandudno**
94 Mostyn Street
Llandudno, Gwynedd
LL30 2SB

**Chinacave Macclesfield**
Unit 1, 25 Castle Street Mall
Macclesfield, Cheshire
SK11 6AF

## FACTORY SHOPS AND OUTLETS - UK

**Factory Shop Burslem**
Nile Street, Burslem
Stoke-on-Trent, Staffordshire
ST6 2AJ

**Factory Shop Fenton**
Disribution Centre, Victoria Road
Fenton, Stoke-on-Trent
Staffordshire, ST4 2PJ

**Factory Shop Regent**
Regent Works, Lawley Street
Longton, Stoke-on-Trent
Staffordshire, ST3 1LZ

**Factory Shop Stourbridge**
Crystal Glass Centre, Churton House
Audnam, Stourbridge
West Midlands, DY8 4AJ

**Factory Outlet Bridgend**
Unit 66, Welsh Designer Outlet
Village, Bridgend, Shropshire
CF32 9SU

*FOR YOUR NEAREST ROYAL
DOULTON DEPARTMENT, PLEASE
CALL ROYAL DOULTON CONSUMER
ENQUIRIES ON 01782 404041*

**Factory Outlet Colne**
Boundary Mill Stores, Burnley Road
Colne, Lancashire
BB8 8LS

**Factory Outlet Dover**
De Bradelei Wharf
Cambridge Road
Dover, Kent, CT17 9BY

**Factory Outlet
Ellesmere Port**
Unit 106, Cheshire Oaks
Kinsey Road, Ellesmere Port
Cheshire, L65 9LA

### Visit our website at:

## ROYAL DOULTON  www.royaldoulton.com

# Royal Doulton Stores

## ROYAL DOULTON STORES – CANADA

**Calgary**
Market Mall
C2 - 3625 Shaganappi Trail
NW, Calgary, AB T3A 0E2

**Cookstown**
Cookstown Manufacturers
Outlet, RR1, Cookstown,
ON L0L 1L0

**Dartmouth**
Micmac Mall, 21 Micmac
Dartmouth, NS B3A 4K7

**Edmonton**
West Edmonton Mall
8882 - 170th Street
Edmonton, AB T5T 3J7

**Fredericton**
Regent Mall
1381 Regent Street,
Fredericton, NB
E3C 1A2

**London**
White Oaks Mall
1105 Wellington Road
London, ON
N6E 1V4

**Markham**
Markville Shopping Centre
5000 Highway #7
Markham, ON
L3R 4M9

**Pickering**
Pickering Town Centre
1355 Kingston Road
Pickering, ON
L1V 1B8

**Surrey**
Guildford Town Centre
Surrey, BC
V3R 7C1

**Toronto**
Fairview Mall
1800 Sheppard Avenue East
Willowdale, ON
M2J 5A7

**Vaughan**
Vaughan Mills
Royal Doulton Home
1 Bass Pro Mills Drive
Vaughan, On
L4K 5W4

**Waterloo**
St. Jacobs Factory Outlet
Mall, 25 Benjamin Road
Waterloo, ON N2V 2G8

**Winnipeg**
Polo Park Shopping Centre
1485 Portage Ave.
Winnipeg, MA
R3G 0W4

## ROYAL DOULTON STORES – UNITED STATES

**Belz Factory Outlet World
(Mall 1)**
Orlando Shopping Center
Space #47-A
5401 West Oak Ridge Road
Orlando, Florida 32819

**Burlington**
Prime Outlets – Burlington
288 Fashion Way, Store #5
Burlington, WA 98233

**Calhoun**
Prime Outlets - Colhoun
455 Belwood Rd., Suite 20
Calhoun, GA 30701

**Camarillo**
Camarillo Premium Outlets
740 Ventura Blvd,     Suite
530
Camarillo, CA 93010

**Central Valley**
Woodbury Common
Premium Outlets
234 Red Apple Court
Central Valley, NY 10917

**Ellenton**
Gulf Coast Factory Store
5501 Factory Shops Blvd.
Ellenton, Fl 34222

**Estero**
Miromar Outlets
10801 Corkscrew Rd.
Suite 366, Estero, Fl 33928

**Flemington**
Liberty Village
Premium Outlets
34 Liberty Village
Flemington, NJ08822

**Gilroy**
Premium Outlets – Gilroy
681 Leavesley Road
Suite C290
Gilroy, CA 95020

**Jeffersonville**
Ohio Factory Shops
8150 Factory Shops Blvd.
Jeffersonville, OH 43128

**Kittery**
Kittery Outlet Center
Route 1
Kittery, ME 03904-2505

**Las Vegas**
Belz Factory Outlet World
7400 Las Vegas Blvd.
South Suite 244
Las Vegas, NV 89123

**Pigeon Forge**
Belz Factory Outlet
2655 Teaster Lane
Suite 26
Pigeon Forge TN 37683

**Prince William**
Potomac Mills
2700 Potomac Mills Circle
Suite 976
Prince William, VA 22192

**San Marcos**
Tanger Factory Outlet Centre
4015 Interstate 35 South
Suite 402
San Marcos, TX 78666

**St. Augustine**
Belz Factory Outlet World
500 Belz Outlet Blvd
Suite 80
St. Augustine, Fl 32084

**Vacaville**
Factory Stores at Vacaville
352 Nut Tree Rd.
Vacaville CA 95687

## Visit our website at:
## www.royaldoulton.com

# ROYAL DOULTON